Journeys
(with a cancer)

Jenny Cole

Published by Pawprints PO Box 6934 London N8 9BB ©1995
Printed and bound in Great Britain by BPC Paperbacks Ltd
A member of The British Printing Company Ltd

This book is dedicated to
Frances Hale
and
Conrad Kaplan

ACKNOWLEDGEMENTS

To everyone who helped me through the more difficult parts of my journey (and were still around when I expressed my rage and fear) but especially to Jo, Nina, Anita, Del, my sister Wendy, Su, who pointed me in the right direction, Frances, who despite her own pain helped me when I needed her.

To Erl, for his support, dinners and battles with officialdom, Charles, for his belief in me to succeed, Will, for his constant phonecalls, John for his many listening lunches, Charlie, Hugh and Conrad.

To those who I could not have done without when I took my body to them to 'do something with it': Paola, Lily, Robert, Iro, Harry, and Trish (and animals) who was always there.

To the staff of the Middlesex/UCH hospital . . . Glen, Professor Taylor, Dr Omar, Dorothy and Rebecca and all the Chemotherapy nurses, Phlebotomists and Radiographers. I do appreciate what you did for me.

Thanks to all who have helped with the book . . . especially Martin, John and Terry, Del, Peter (Canon), Hugo, Elizabeth, Stan, Gary and my sister Wendy.

And . . . to Waffles, who drove me crazy but kept my sanity.

Thank you to those who 'volunteered' their comments. They all helped to convince me that what I was trying to do wasn't totally insane.

". . . She sent a copy of a rough manuscript recording her fight, which arrived on the day I entered hospital to prepare for surgery. As Ann and I read the script we began to realise that this was the beginning of our journey and that we had to become very single-minded in concentrating on my recovery. It was extremely helpful to understand that the fears, the confusion, the hurt were not exclusive and could be combated by positive thinking; a message which is a recurring theme of Jenny's story. Her experiences became a starting point for my journey, reinforcing my determination to beat the unwanted invader and providing a focus for Ann to link into, and bond with, my healing.

My journey was not easy, but looking back Jenny's book was invaluable in preparing me for the fight and her support during my treatment reassuring and inspirational.

Thank you Jenny"

Charlie Fehrs (Nottingham)

"Jenny's book is a deeply moving experience of one woman's ability to cope and grow with a diagnosis of cancer. For those of you who are in a similar experience and don't know what to do, read Jenny's book and things will become clearer! She takes away the fear!"

Elizabeth Hamer (London)

"Jenny's book has proved compelling reading. I recommend it to anyone who has cancer themselves, or who is a carer or relative. Her fight throughout continuing adversity was remarkable and her sense of humour makes the book entertaining as well as informative. I'm sure as I did, readers will find Jenny's descriptions of her use of so many forms of complementary therapies of great help."

Val Miles (Saffron Walden)

"Being a sufferer of Lupus erythematosis I found her book a magnificently touching and inspiring read, proving that there is light at the end of the tunnel."

Meera (London)

Foreword

When faced with a life-threatening disease some people accept it, turn their faces to the wall and wait to die; others refuse to accept it and carry on (sadly, not for very long) as if nothing had happened; but luckily there are some brave souls who do neither. They fully accept what is happening to them but instead of running away they turn towards it and face it head on with everything they've got. In the absence of the promise of a cure such people stubbornly seek out their own cures, willing to explore everything and anything that might help them. They embark upon a journey that inevitably leads them beyond their physical problems, drawing them into mental, spiritual and emotional realms that are full of mystery and possibility. Jenny Cole is one of these remarkable people. In this wise and witty book she shares some of her experiences on the road towards her own healing. This can sometimes be a very rough and bumpy road involving a fair amount of questioning and confrontation but—as an exasperated consultant once admitted to me—'difficult patients do best'. Each one of us has to find our own way towards our own unique healing potential but Jenny's story will encourage and inspire anyone who feels the urge to start searching.

Penny Brohn
(*Co-founder of the Bristol Cancer Help Centre*)

Preface

Immediately after diagnosis in January 1993 I kept a diary of the events that consumed my every waking minute, and much of the night. It was my way of trying to understand the situation that had been spiralling out of control for over a year. The account is chronological and mainly written while under the influence of Radiation and Chemotherapy; it has not been embellished at a later date. The flashbacks occurred when they seemed relevant to my questions. The anger, rage, despair and humour occurred when they seemed the only answer.

One point I have to emphasise: the treatment I describe and the medical states I experienced are only relevant to me, Jenny Cole, with the type of cancer I had (have) at the stage it had progressed to, with the Orthodox treatments from the hospital I attended in 1993 . . . and with the Complementary therapies that I chose to absorb.

The rest was up to me.

I do not aim to condemn nor condone outright any specific treatment . . . it is how I perceived them. Neither do I wish to influence nor prevent anyone from following an Orthodox hospital regime, or any other regime, if that is what they feel is right for them. However, I do hope that the energy and commitment I offer my body every day is something that even the hardest sceptic may wish to follow.

I have 'enjoyed' most of my journeys . . . and hope to have many more . . . I know I have not finished my travels.

Jenny Cole
January 1995

21st January 1993

"Mrs Cole, do sit down."

(*Why does everyone assume I'm married?*)

"As you know blah, blah, blah, blahblah, blah and we were hoping to find blah, blah, blah, blahblah, blah. However, blah, blah, blah, white cells (*Are they the Goodies or the Baddies? Are they the Goodies or the Baddies? Are they the Goodies or the Baddies?*) So, I'll leave you in the capable hands of Dorothy who will be able to explain anything you might want to know."

"Have you fully understood what has just been said to you?" asked Dorothy.

"Not a word . . . but I take it I've got cancer?"

"Yes."

"Why didn't he say so then."

"They don't like to use that word because most people find it too frightening."

"Well I'm not 'most people'."

Courtesy of the NHS the small room was stiflingly hot. My face was rapidly becoming the colour of my crimson top, so I asked:

"Is it hot in here or am I having one of my Hot Flushes?"

"It's hot."

"Could I have a window opened?"

"Certainly."

"What happens now?"

Dorothy talked of Chemotherapy, Visualisation, Counselling. At least I think she did. My brain was not functioning too well, though not through fear or disbelief: it was just *so* hot.

"I suppose you are going through the stage of 'Why me?'"

"No, on the contrary, Why *not* me?"

It was just something else to be flung at me by life, so in a way I was not surprised.

This did not mean that I'd given any thought to cancer and the possibility of my getting it. Months later a friend asked me if I'd ever thought I would get cancer. No more than I'd given a thought to whether I'd be knocked down (or up) or own a mansion in the country.

How strange a day can become. It had begun with my normal routine of administering love and affection, and food (in that order) to Waffles, my cat. She knew, had known, all along that something was not right. She had slept as close to me as she could on the adjacent pillow and had approached me for her obligatory cuddle either from the right side or from the foot of the bed.

I was fairly pleased that my appointment was on a Thursday, thus missing another disquieting day at the prison where I worked. It had been becoming a problem to haul myself into that atmosphere.

But hadn't everything become a problem recently?

On the tube journey down to University College Hospital, I remember cradling my left breast protectively against every jerk and jolt of the Underground system. Even walking down stairs had become an unpleasant experience, so the fault lay with my body, not the antiquated rolling stock of the capital's transport system.

By the end of the day they would have discovered the cause of my discomfort and all would be well.

Simple.

UCH fourth floor: Breast Clinic. Small room, small white gown.

Hotness.

Two obligatory students entered the room with the doctor, and stood in silence as my left breast, which had not allowed me to touch it, was swiftly and expertly prodded and poked.

Both students approached when it was their turn to inflict pain and discomfort and gingerly, lightly, fingered the offending protuberance. In protest at this assault it had become hot, and pain was shooting backwards and forwards, as if seeking a way out.

"I'd like you to have a needle expiration."
"When?"
"Now."

I was shown into another room where a technician asked for the exact location of the lump.

Lump?

There had never been a lump.

"It's just sort of painful all over," I offered, feeling guilty that perhaps I had made his job more difficult.

He stuck a long needle into the most tender part . . . and the pain darted around the breast, in fury.

"How long do the results take to come through?" I queried, thinking that like all other biopsies I'd had, it would be at least four weeks.

(Six on the NHS?)

"A few minutes," he answered.

Was I talking too much? If so, does he think I'm nervous? Verbal diarrhoea, as it is sometimes called, is supposed to be a sign of acute nervousness. Isn't it?

3

With me, however, I seem to talk more in direct correlation to others 'not saying anything'. And this guy was non-communicative to perfection.

Speak to ME!!!!

My thirst for information has always been alive and present and now, with part of me under attack and unable to speak for itself, I felt I had the right to act like an over-possessive parent.

Tell ME!!!!

I sat in the smaller inner waiting room having purchased a Klix cup of liquid, euphemistically, called tea. My thoughts, if I had any, were for the hope that something could be done for the pain. It had never occurred to me that something major might be wrong with my breast.

It was painful. Everyone knew that Breast cancer was *not* painful, didn't they. Didn't they?

Fast rewind to November-ish 1992. Days of Activity, Action and Aerobics.

I became aware that my left breast was 'unhappy'. This is the only way I can describe the tender sensation that was slowly creeping up on me.

I asked my friends who had produced children and perhaps had also breast fed, what Mastitis was like.

Tender.

That's it, I had Mastitis.

As an Aromatherapist I slapped (gently) essential Oil of Rose all over my breast and waited to see what would happen.

I smelt of roses.

Or to be exact, I smelt expensively of roses, as it is one of the most costly flowers to process.

I persevered only for about a week and a half. I believe in Aromatherapy, but appreciate that it cannot cure everything . . . just as allopathic medicine also cannot cure everything.

9th December 1992 I took myself back to the Well Women clinic in Wood Green where, the previous March, I had been prescribed Hormone Replacement Therapy (HRT)
 "It's not happy, is it?" observed the female doctor.
 Her view was that perhaps the HRT had over stimulated a gland, or blocked something.
 "Come off HRT and pop along to the UCH which is the best breast clinic in the country. It will probably take some time to get an appointment and you may well find that the breast will calm down in the meantime. But, even if it does, you should still go, because you can't be too careful at your age."

"At your age"! Throughout my numerous visits to clinics, hospitals and advice centres, this had been a standard adage.
 Females constantly draw the short straw, since they seem to be permanently at 'that' age, whether at fifteen or fifty.

It's not fair!
 (*This statement to be accompanied by the noise of stamping feet à la five year old.*)

She wrote a letter on out-of-date headed note paper belonging to the clinic. Don't mock; it's a miracle the clinic had survived as long as it had, considering everything else in Haringey had been shut down.
 "Take this letter down personally," I was advised.

Apparently hospitals are notorious at misdirecting mail away from itself, so this fe-mail ensured she directed herself and the letter to the reception desk. It would be useful to sus out the venue.

I was really pleased it was UCH and not the Middlesex Hospital I was to attend. Whilst I was not opposed to the Middlesex it had been the scene of many Operations and I was naturally reluctant to make its acquaintance again.

Life's a Bitch.

The breast remained 'not happy' for the next four weeks. After that it was positively 'depressed'. Should I make an earlier appointment? No, it's only another couple of weeks and an NHS hospital doesn't usually have any spare appointments, except for emergencies, and I knew this wasn't an emergency, only painful.

Very painful.

So. Cancer.
   The only questions I could think to ask were: 'Why was it painful?' and 'I thought Breast cancer was a quiet and peaceful lump?'

Yes ... but I have Inflammatory Breast cancer, which is painful and doesn't develop as a lump.
   Well, ask a simple question and you get a simple answer.

Clutching various appointment cards and a cotton wool brain I exited into the Warren Street area and, sod the expense, hailed a taxi.
   I can't remember the exact world problem the taxi driver started to talk about, but I do remember offering my own views on the subject. He soon noticed that any responses to

his never ending soliloquy had dried up, and glancing in his mirror, seemed to realise that what I wanted more than anything was for my tears to dry up.

"Blimey love, what's up?"

"I've just been told I've got cancer, but I'm all right, really." I was then treated to a history of all the members of his family who had had cancer and survived, how wonderful the Health Service was these days, that new cures were being discovered every day and that I mustn't worry 'cause that was the worst thing to do.

My God, I found myself totally agreeing with a taxi driver!

Wherever you are, thank you for just 'acting normally' with me.

I was soon to divide people, friends, colleagues and family into those who could cope with 'cancer', and those who could not. My Christmas card list (if I kept one) would be shortened and lengthened within the first few months.

I pressed the automatic button on the phone to reach Ellis's office. He had said he wanted to know of any news.

"It's cancer".

Silence for a split second, as his brain tries not only to compute the information but to think of an appropriate response.

"How do you feel?" he said.

"Fine." And I wasn't lying . . . honest.

Next person to ring was my sister. A Mother-Earth-okay-I-will-put-everything-right-for-you sorterouter but emotional sister.

7

Be firm.

"I don't want you to make any reaction AT ALL, but it's cancer." A muffled set of 'I'm desperate not to make any emotional reaction at all' noises could just be made out.

Well done, Sis.

The rest of the evening was filled with incoming and outgoing phone calls, as North London Tom-Toms (okay, telephones) began working overtime.

My friends were great as opposed to many!

Most offered support and help as and if required, but appreciated that I was not the sort of person to be fussed over in an over-protective way.

I'd survived too many problems in my life single-handedly to fully relinquish my independent, tenacious bloody-mindedness.

This was up to me . . . with a little help from my friends.

I was exhausted.

I think I tried to eat.

I think I drank some wine.

I had to cuddle Waffles. I had to.

I needed to be hugged. To be told that everything would be alright. That help and compassion were near.

Did I dare go to Ellis's bedroom and ask if he would hold me, just hold me?

I stood at the bottom of the stairs leading up to his room. I could see that, like me, he had been unable to sleep, as his light was on.

I stood rooted to the spot unable to move forward to ask for his help. Could I do it? No, I was not brave enough. I could not risk any more rejection.

It was a lonely, frightening night . . . but Waffles was

there. She clung to me all night, occasionally licking the salty tears that slowly and quietly rolled down my cheeks.

22nd January. UCH Oncology department and Glen.

Or to be formal, Dr Glen Blackman.

Dorothy had arranged to be with me on that morning as I hadn't wanted anyone to come with me.

(*Told you I was Independent.*)

Glen examined me again then decided against starting me on Chemotherapy until the Cytology report became available, which would not be until the following Monday.

"Don't want to pump you full of chemicals if it's not really necessary, even though there's only a 1% chance that it's not cancer." He assured me that with the amount of Chemotherapy used by UCH I would not feel nauseous or lose my hair.

"Any questions?" he asked.

"What do you think of Complementary therapies?"

"Fine, providing they don't promise the earth and cost the earth."

"Great." (I'm actually surprised but delighted.)

"May I ask *you* a question," he said.

"Yes, sure."

"What do you think of Orthodox medicine?"

"It has its place," I said, slightly tongue in cheek, "Why do you ask?"

"I wouldn't want to carry on with treatment if you were totally opposed to Orthodox medicine. You would be fighting it the whole time."

I was impressed.

I have another session with Dorothy and we make a date for my first taste of Visualisation.

9

"Visualisation? What exactly is that?"

"It's wonderful," she said, which was enough for me, as by this time I had realised that this free, NHS Cancer Counsellor Gem, called Dorothy, was just what the Doctor ordered.

I had some homework to do. Find a book called 'Love, Medicine and Miracles' by Bernie Siegal, and buy some travel sickness bands to help the nausea.

(*I thought someone had told me I wouldn't feel sick?*)

January 25th: I return to the hospital to start Chemotherapy. Jo, a friend, volunteered to come with me and, as she hadn't demanded to do so, I agreed.

Glen informed me that the test had, in fact, shown up cancer. I think I would almost have been let down if it *hadn't* been cancer—I'd invested too much energy in its acceptance.

"I won't ever be able to donate blood again, will I?"

"No."

I was only one pint short of my Silver badge! As an AB+, my blood was relatively rare—told you I wasn't like 'most people'—and it was by becoming a blood donor that I had received positive proof that my father was not, in fact, my father.

Explanation?

Mr Cole, who had doted on me, even though he knew I wasn't his child, had encouraged me to become a donor, especially as I had faithfully accompanied him to his sessions (to eat the biscuits).

He had always boasted of being a Universal Donor, that is, an O Rh negative.

At that time, three years after his death, and the day after my mother's death, I was studying physiological aspects of psychology and 1+1 didn't make 2. Or, was I not reading the data correctly? I had arranged to meet my sister, Wendy, for lunch to discuss the death of our mother. It was during that lunchtime meeting she informed me of dad's death-bed confession to her that he had not been my biological father ... He had made her promise not to tell me until after our mother's death, and that he had not wanted the truth to die with him.

Investigations pointed the finger at a dark, swarthy, Basque Separatist Lodger, called Pedro.

A lodger?

Called Pedro?

Good Grief!

Where was I?

Glen handed me a prescription.

"What's this for?" I asked.

"Anti-nausea tablets."

"But you told me I wouldn't feel nauseous."

"You won't . . . because of these tablets."

(*In that case, where's my wig?*)

I was advised not to read any books about Breast cancer, as they would probably not refer to my particular type of cancer. They may confuse, or worse, frighten me.

(*Just how rare is it?*)

I cross the corridor and meet Rebecca, my Chemotherapy nurse. She explains what is going to happen.

I had already asked Glen to write down exactly what chemicals would be zapping around my body, but Rebecca then handed me a neat legible (non-doctor's handwriting) card containing the required information.

Cyclophosphamide, Methotrexate and Fluorouracil (CMF for short.)

A vein in my wrist refused to stand out despite both thumps and encouragement, from Rebecca.

"There's only one thing for it," she announced to another nurse. The Bowl.

The Bowl turned out to be not a piece of high-tech equipment, but simply a bowl containing hot(-ish) water. A few minutes with my hand, and my life, in hot water produced the necessary vein.

An intravenous drip is set up and saline starts circulating in my blood.

The first chemical is bright yellow.

"This will make you glow in the dark," says Rebecca casually.

I look up in astonishment.

"Only joking," said Rebecca. "Just testing your reactions."

The second chemical from a huge horse syringe was a clear liquid. For 'dessert' another bag of clear liquid was hooked up along with the saline drip.

The whole process took an hour.

Jo was allowed to sit with me and tea was brought in on a tray! Very civilised.

How do I feel?

Not sure. It was rather like trying out a new cocktail and not knowing exactly what was in it.

Only time would tell.

I was given some extra-strong nausea tablets and another six tablets, to work as an antidote to the chemicals. These I had to take exactly 24 hours after treatment; and thereafter every six hours.

Rebecca said she'd ring me at home in the morning, just to make sure I was alright. In the meantime, if I was at all worried about anything, I had been given various phone numbers which could connect me to professional advisers on a 24 hour basis.

Jo and I left by taxi.

"How are you feeling now?" she enquired.

"Fine"

But I noticed she was keeping her distance and looked at me strangely, as if I were suddenly going to explode or go berserk.

Or was this the chemicals?

I felt . . . I felt . . . I felt . . . as if I'd been filled up with chemicals.

"I think I'll go to bed."

I decided the effect was rather like having drunk several cases of cheap, red wine . . . very quickly . . . on an empty stomach.

Not that I've actually experienced that, but I used my imagination.

Or is this the effect of the chemicals?

The phone rang.

"1514," I oozed chemically.

"Guess who?" said a deep male voice.

"Now look! I'm never in the mood for this sort of prank, especially after being filled up with chemicals; unless you tell me who you are within five seconds I'm going to put the phone down."

"Peter," said a rushed deep voice.

"Peter? Peter who?"

"Peter, your brother."

Does it seem strange that I did not recognise my own brother's voice? This, however was *not* the fault of the chemicals. My family has always reminded me of that classic film 'The Anniversary' with Bette Davis in the star role of my (our) mother.

More explanation are due:

The last time (and the only one I could remember) when the five of us children had been together as siblings had been at our mother's funeral. My oldest brother described us as a 'group of middle-aged orphans'.

That was over twenty years ago in 1974. I had not seen my brothers since then, despite two of them living in the London area.

I had apparently 'offended' Peter when I was an 18-year-old rebel . . . It had taken him twenty-five years, and cancer, to 'forgive'.

"Sorry I haven't been in touch sooner" he muttered.

"Oh, that's alright" I heard myself saying.

What's in these chemicals!!!!!!!!?

What indeed. I did not feel ill, but I did feel strange, as if my nose had grown, was growing, into a funnel. Worst of all, Waffles refused to come near me, perhaps because my skin was beginning to smell ever so slightly of . . . chemicals.

The next morning I waited in for Rebecca to call to check on my chemical 'corrosion'. I wanted to be out by noon yet didn't want her to be worried if she rang and there was no reply.

So, I phoned her.

"Hallo, my I speak to Rebecca, please?"

A male voice said he would go and get her and asked who was speaking.

"Jenny"

"Oh, hi, Jenny. It's Glen."

"Glen?"

"Dr Blackman."

Good Heavens! What is happening in the National Health Service? A *doctor* answers the phone and gets a nurse for me.

The following day I went to work.

My car decided to come out in sympathy and refused to start. The A.A. man told me I needed a new battery.

Me, or the car?

I drove 28 miles to work but don't remember what I did after I got there.

I drove the 28 miles home and slept ten hours.

Perhaps this Chemotherapy is stronger than I thought?

It is.

Friday was going to be a busy day at the hospital.

Glen had arranged various X-rays and a Mammogram.

The Mammographist (?) took one look at my sore, tender, enlarged breast and doubted it would be possible.

"Well, let's give it a try," I offered helpfully, never having undergone a Mammogram before.

Ignorance is not bliss: it means you have to be educated.

The right breast, at least, could oblige?

Two things come to mind following this the 'London Dungeon Torture Chamber' practical demonstration.

One: the process of squashing a breast almost flat, being asked if it was bearable, then squashing it even more, convinced me that I could not (and would not) allow the machine anywhere near my left breast.

Two: you just knew it had been invented by a man!!! What sort of machine would be invented if men had cancer of the penis as often as women had cancer of the breast.

AAaarrrggghhhhh!!!!!

Now nursing two painful breasts (!), I went in search of Dorothy. She was delighted and impressed by my attitude and acceptance of the cancer.

"Doesn't everyone stand and fight, then?"

Apparently not.

15

She put me through the paces of learning to relax and mentally rid my body of the cancer.

I was taught to imagine 'floating' on a peaceful lake with the sun beaming down on me. And then basically to imagine the cancer cells leaving my body and falling into the water. However, so as not to pollute the lake the cells had to become something that would be of benefit to the lake.

· I began by allowing the cells to become food for the fish. The problem was, how to extract the cells from the breast?

To have them gushing from the nipple may have been the most natural method; but I could not accept this on medical grounds. It would have appeared as a discharge, which is not conducive to thoughts of recovery.

What did my cancer feel like? It was hot and stingy and active . . . very much like a beehive.

I found that, as I relaxed, my imagination took over and very soon it became an MGM epic, starring Waffles. She swam over to me and, as she dried out in the sun the radiation rays concentrating on my left breast stupefied the bees until they became dozy and lethargic. As they emerged from their hive Waffles swatted them into the water. She gave me a running commentary as she watched them sink to the bottom of the lake; only to reappear as huge, purple and pink flowers, which surrounded my body.

After a while the activity in my breast calmed down and so did Waffles. We both slept peacefully and drifted back to the shore. We continued this activity until the hot stingy sensation began to diminish with only an occasional swatting needed.

We still visit that lake, although it was superseded by another Visualisation whereby every time I breathed in I imagined my breast filling with chemicals. Then, as I breathed out it slowly began to erode a perfect egg-shaped lump, bit by bit, until nothing remained.

"Hi, Jenny, It's Warren," said a familiar voice.

I hadn't seen Warren since Christmas. We were part of the 'Odds and Sods' of North London, catered for at a user-friendly Greek restaurant, with its user-friendly name of Wild Track.

Warren had last seen me flying around in a mad haze of exuberant health! . . . otherwise known as Greek Dancing.

"How are you, Warren?" I asked, genuinely interested.

"Terrible."

"Terrible?"

"Well I hate January; it's cold and miserable and boring. I'm still paying for Christmas and New Year; I hate my job; I hate computers; I've got a cold, which I can't shake off; I don't like London; I hate . . ."

Okay, I know it was a bit naughty of me to let him carry on like this, but I did . . .

"How are you?" he finally enquired.

"Oh, fine, but I've got cancer."

"Aargh!! Why did you let me prattle on like that?" he exploded.

"Because you probably are feeling worse than me"

(*If he didn't then, he did now.*)

The reason for his call was that Mac, another 'Sod' (or maybe 'Odd') was having a birthday drink at the Wild Track and everyone was invited. Everyone usually turns up anyway, but it's always nice to be asked.

Mac, a dry Lancastrian Wit, was expecting a lively evening; I was merely pleased that I'd kept awake long enough to attend.

"This is nice," said Mac, settling in for the night. "And, later on Jen will liven things up with a spot of dancing," he beamed.

I turn to Warren.

"Haven't you told him?" I enquired.

17

"No, I didn't know if you wanted to keep it quiet."

Quiet? How could I remain in a Greek restaurant all evening and not dance, and hope to keep it quiet?

"Told me what?" demanded Mac.

"I've got cancer."

"Well," he said. "That's put the kibosh on any Brilliant Birthday Banter from me. How can anyone top that? Thank you very much. We might as well all go home now."

Delivered in his dry manner, this statement sounded funny, but this Wordprocessor hasn't a regional accent, so doesn't.

His concern and his support flowed out, which is more than could be said for the wine.

The idea of consuming alcohol when I already had a lethal cocktail circulating in my blood was both mentally and physically abhorrent. The effort of eating, talking or even sitting was also rapidly becoming 'not a good idea'.

I left.

The day before my cancer had been confirmed I had received a letter inviting me to attend an interview for a Senior Lecturer's post at a local Further Education College.

I rang to say I would attend.

I talked this over with Dorothy. Should I cancel? How could I accept? (such ego!) Perhaps if the starting date wasn't until May, I might be well enough?

The questions bounced out one after another and flew around the room.

"Calm down," said Dorothy. "One thing at a time. Go to the interview, and take it from there".

I went.

At least . . . my body went, and even that started to deflate throughout the day.

I couldn't remember my NVQ (National Vocational Qualification) from my BTec (Business Technology).

Later that day . . .

"1514"

"Miss Cole?"

"Speaking."

"I'm phoning to say that, I'm sorry but we've offered the job to . . . "

. . . "Thank goodness for that," I butted in.

The realisation that the requirements of The Successful Candidate were to be in charge of Staffing, Time-tables, Curriculum, Health and Safety, Holiday Rotas, Finance etc etc (there were many etceteras) as well as 18 hours teaching a week, was too much for my energy level . . . it was rapidly draining away through my hands.

This is one of the current problems in education. They not only want your body and soul but your blood as well . . . and mine, at present, is full of CMF.

Back to the drawing board, or in my case, clay. Throughout the early days (daze?) of Chemotherapy I continued to teach at a Category C prison.

How would the men react to my cancer?

One young man, noted for his belief in honesty, no matter what chaos it caused, asked if I knew when I was going to d . . . d . . .

" 'Die' is the word you're looking for Sam and I can assure you that it is the last thing on my mind."

Others took a more friendly approach. One student, (I've always refused to call them inmates) on hearing of my plight, sent off to a Catholic Order for a tin medallion, purported to have healing powers.

"I told them you were a nice lady and that you had cancer. So, they've blessed it. You don't have to wear it but I thought it might give you some comfort?" he muttered shyly, as he handed me the tiny disc on a piece of blue string.

19

I was nearly in tears.

"Thank you, David; thank you."

At a staff meeting later that morning, under Any Other Business, I decided to mention my gift.

"At the risk of sounding 'American', I would like to share with you this lovely token given to me by David."

Murmurs of "how sweet" could be heard.

"How did he know you had cancer? We haven't said anything to the men."

"I told them."

"Have any of the others made any comments?"

"Well, apart from Sam asking me when I was going to die, the rest have been most helpful."

"Helpful?"

"Yes, I've had that many offers of 'can I kiss it better'," I purred, waiting for the reaction.

Silence, apart from the embarrassed shuffling of papers.

(*She jokes about it, and sexual jokes at that!*)

"I told them, thank you, but it's too painful ... but you can kiss the other one in sympathy, if you like."

More silence. You could have heard my medallion drop.

Individual reactions and my reaction to these individuals gave me many hours of pleasure (?). No, perhaps an insight into the fear that cancer still holds over most people.

Very few could bring themselves to say the actual word 'cancer'.

The fact that the consultant in the hospital couldn't say it to my face gives an indication of the taboo surrounding this condition.

Most refer to it as an 'illness' or 'problem', that I was 'poorly' or 'unwell'. Providing they don't mind me correcting them, I don't mind them finding it a problem in the first place.

Others had read too many gloom and doom articles on the subject and automatically assumed not only the worst, but had me dead and buried within the year.

One student, in particular, was lucky to leave the class alive after saying: "We all love and admire your courage, but we'll miss you when you've gone."

"Gone?"

On a sadder note several friends couldn't cope at all.

When I informed one friend of my cancer she remarked that I was taking it very philosophically.

"I'm approaching it from the point of view that it's an experience, which I have to get the best from. After all, not that many people can say they've had Chemotherapy."

"*Experienced* Chemotherapy!!! Experienced *Chemotherapy*!!! You haven't even begun to know what Chemotherapy can be like," she thundered. "I have one friend whose hair has fallen out and is vomiting all over the place, another who's had a Mastectomy and another friend has just died ... and you tell me you're 'experiencing' cancer and Chemotherapy?"

(*Pardon me for living!*)

She also condemned me for my attitude to two other aspects of my life, one of them being my continued concern for Ellis; and demanded explanations.

I don't need this, I thought; but didn't say.

I won't be phoning you again, I thought; but didn't say.

Others never replied to my letters.

21

That's their problem. I refuse to make it mine.

My hunt for suitable Complementary therapists had begun. Now I had a reason to try things like Colour Healing and Crystal Therapy, whereas before I would have felt voyeuristic to just ask for a session. Luckily, because of my Massage and Aromatherapy connections, I was able to ask for personal recommendations.

I got them.

My greatest concern with having Chemotherapy and Radiotherapy was that, at the end of the treatment, I didn't want to be a depleted and sickly specimen. I knew that the Aura surrounding each person (I like to think of it as a personal ozone layer and we all know what happens when that is damaged) is filled with energy patterns. If these are blocked then disease can occur.

I had been recommended Lily, so gave her a ring.
    "Hallo, I would like some Colour Healing please."
    "Yes dear. What seems to be the problem?"
    "I'm having treatment for cancer, but I'm worried about my Aura. Can you help?"
    (*Can you prevent me from getting the Greenhouse effect?*)
    "Certainly, and we can work directly on your cancer as well."

I arrived at a conventional suburban house having no idea what and how Healing took place, let alone Colour Healing.
    Lily's 'hand-maidens' showed me upstairs to her room.
    The classic image of 'everyone's grandmother' greeted me warmly and we sat together and talked for nearly an hour.

For cancer treatment (one is not allowed to say 'cure' as the medical profession gets very angry . . . very angry) Lily uses Spring Green, Brilliant White and Amethyst.

I still didn't know what was happening.

I soon learnt that colour is energy, and very powerful. Colour vibrates, so will have an effect on the body, especially on damaged areas which need to be re-tuned to the correct vibration.
   (*But how does the colour get inside?*)
   She rang for assistance and one of the hand-maidens appeared looking as though she'd rushed into the nearest Oxfam shop and put on the first garments she'd seen.
   We transferred to another room, where I was asked to lie down. Lily and her helper proceeded to place their hands on strategic areas of my body occasionally muttering a few inaudible words.

"Do you speak to your Guardian Angel?" Lily enquired.
   "Guardian Angel? If I had believed in a Guardian Angel I would have told him, or her, to naff off years ago as a disappointment to his, or her, trade."
   "You should talk to your Guardian Angel," Lily insisted.

   (*What is going on?*)

As Lily progressed down my body I was given a mini-history of my war torn flesh.

"And what has been going on here?" she demanded, as her hands rested on my abdomen."

"Well". I then reeled off the numerous Operations I had participated in during my gynaecological period (period?) finalising in a Hysterectomy at the age of thirty-two. The post mortem on the offending uterus proved it to be 'normal', implying that it was me who was at fault (!)

A few years later when my bladder began to pack up, the same look came across the faces of the doctors. "She's at it again," I could hear them saying.

Was I really systematically destroying parts of my body?

This time I proved them wrong. (Naa na naa naa na.)

My insides were described by the consultant as 'frayed lace', as my bladder had disintegrated releasing the acidic urine to rot through the more delicate internal tissues.

"Do you want the good news or the bad news?" the doctor enquired.

"The bad news."

"There are only two hospitals in the country who do this operation."

"What's the good news, then?"

"This is one of them."

(*Don't ever say that doctors have no sense of humour.*)

Lily absorbed the information.

"But you have another little problem there as well, haven't you?"

This was a reference to the Total Blockage I had been enduring since the Chemotherapy, which by now had back-logged up to my ears.

"It will be alright in the morning," she soothed.

I hope she's right.

When I left the house and drove back across North London towards home I began to develop a headache and feel nauseous . . . and my breast began to throb.

By the time I arrived home I felt terrible.

The headache had spread across my forehead like a tight band, indicating a 'digestive' problem. (Tell me about it!)

Normally I would reach for Peppermint essential oil, but I was worried because my training had told me not to use essential oils on active cancer patients; and although not very active at this precise moment, I knew what they meant.

I reached for the paracetamol.

One hour later the pain had intensified. I was now beginning to get worried. Ellis was out, and although I hate to cause unnecessary fuss, I considered ringing the hospital. I instinctively reached for the Peppermint oil.

I woke ten hours later.

No headache.

No blockage.

Lily (and Peppermint) thank you.

All this time I continued to teach pottery, both at the prison and in a small informal class at a Community Centre. It's tiring at the best of times but I soon realised that my energy level sank perilously close to rock (or clay) bottom.

I knew that I needed energy to fight the cancer and that if I depleted my reserves too much then I was asking for trouble.

But, I continued to ask for trouble.

I started sleeping badly, imagining problems that weren't there, had vivid, strange dreams and generally chipped away at those precious reserves.

What was I doing????

Ten days after Chemotherapy I was to have a nadir blood test and report back to the Oncology department. Rebecca translated the computer feed-out, and was impressed.

The important components of my blood were not only standing up well to Chemotherapy but were positively blooming, especially my red blood count, which was still 12.5.

"So, you mean I could feel worse?"

Advice is free . . . so freely given.

At the Community Centre I bumped into Anita, who I'd worked with on an informal basis, for six years.

She'd heard of my cancer and asked what I was doing about it.

I told her.

She knew of, and had trained with, Lily and stated that I was honoured to be receiving healing directly from her and not one of her students.

"You must also go to this amazing Homeopath I've found," she said, rapidly scribbling down his Bethnal Green phone number.

"Bethnal Green," I moaned.
"Go," she ordered.

I weighed up my decision only to visit alternative therapists who had been personally recommended to me, with my tiredness of contemplating Bethnal Green, Bethnal Green won.

I had made the mistake of booking an afternoon appointment for a day when I had been teaching. By the time I arrived in this, for me, unfamiliar part of town, I was already knackered.

I knew the theory behind Homeopathy; that the total person is considered not just the symptom but, by the end of the two hour session I felt as though I'd enrolled, studied and graduated from a ten-year course on metaphysics.

The conversation between us was reminiscent of a sword fight with thrusts and parries, and with Robert carrying the sharper sword plus several replacements.

It just wasn't fair.

"So, what do you think I can do for you?" was his opening gambit.

"I don't expect you to cure my cancer, but I'd like you to help my body keep in as good a shape as possible to fight it."

"I'm glad you don't expect me to cure you because I'm not allowed to say that I can."

"What can you do?"

"Lots of things."

"Such as?"

"Lots of things."

"Are you always as communicative as this?"

"Yes."

Despite the problem of trying to extract information from him (information he was not prepared to give) it was one of the most stimulating intellectual encounters I'd had for many a year.

Cancer, he said, was the body giving up when the mind would not be persuaded that something was impossible.

I thought of 1992 ... and shuddered. What a year!

The questionnaire I'd been asked to complete delved into family medical history (father, unknown) and a tiny space for my medical history (not unknown).

There was just not enough space.

What food did I like; what kind of environment did I like to live in; what made me lose my temper; what ... what ... what etc.
　　"Had anyone told me that I'd had gonorrhoea?"
　　"Gonorrhoea? When, what, how, who, eehh?"
　　The speed of his throw-away questions, barely waiting for a fully considered answer, made me sink further and further into the chair.

Until.

"Have you a five-year plan?" he asked wearily.
　　"Five year plan!!!!! How can ANYONE have a five-year plan with a shitty government like ours," I exploded.

　　(*Who rattled her cage?*)

Part of the gloom that had overtaken me in 1992 was the almost self-satisfied manner in which my country's greatest assets such as education, health and community were being ripped apart.

I felt powerless.

I thought of 1992 ... and shuddered.

28

"You must have a five-year plan. It's imperative for someone with cancer; otherwise they may as well give up now."

Silence . . . as I seethed and pondered.

"And, you must avoid negativity at all cost; that's also imperative."

"Anything else?" I asked sarcastically.

"Yes, track down some Spruce Flower essence."

"You mean like the Bach Flower Remedies?"

"Good heavens, no. That would be like asking Poirot to investigate the mass murder of the Royal family. Very old-hat."

"What then?"

"You may be able to get some from Freshlands at the East West centre. Do you know it?"

I certainly did. That was where I had taken a course on Shiatsu at the height of my misery in '92. At the end of the course I had not wanted to leave the building, as it was the only place I'd felt safe and cared for.

It was an enormous effort to return to that Nothingness, but I had a furry friend waiting for, and needing, me.

I was given several packets of anonymous white tablets with precise instructions written on the sides. 'Now', 'Morning', and 'Evening'.

"Don't be surprised if you find yourself saying something that you've wanted to say for a long time. Just let it out."

"What sort of thing?" I asked naively.

"You'll see," he said, with a smile.

I left Bethnal Green, and Robert, and returned home to the negativity I'd been told to avoid.

The Day, and Robert, had proved too much; I crawled into bed.

A few days later, Ellis phones from work.

"1514"

"Are you all right?"

"Yes."

"You seem to have something on your mind?"

"No more than usual."

"Do you want to talk about it?"

If I had been a cartoon character it would have looked as if I were vomiting words. I couldn't stop them.

Weeks, if not months of hurt and sadness, poured out in an unstoppable flow.

"I won't reward the cancer by putting my arm round you," he had said.

Meaning?

Meaning that his deep down inability to show even the smallest amount of affection would not change just because I had cancer.

I felt like a Romanian orphan: all the medical help had arrived but there was no one to hug me.

"Would you like me to come home?"

"No!"

I rang Freshlands to see if they had any Spruce. I didn't know what I was buying so didn't know what to expect. They hadn't any in stock but as soon as I told them what I needed it for, suggested that I rang the Flower and Gem people direct.

They were also very helpful and immediately posted two bottles to me.

Bottles?

When two 30ml bottles arrived there were no instructions, so I rang Robert for advice.

Robert was out but his business partner was only too glad to help.

"I've got some Spruce, but how do I take it?"

"I don't know," he apologised.

"Ok, then. Second question. Is it true that some essential oils can antidote Homeopathic medicine?"

"Yes."

"Such as?"

"Nothing has been categorically proved, but it has been noted that essential oils such as Peppermint, Tea Tree, Eucalyptus and Camphor 'can' or 'may' negate Homeopathy; it depends on the individual. Substances like Vic and Olbas oil, which contain Eucalyptus etc may also have a negative effect on the treatment.

Horrors! Let's hope I don't have the need for Peppermint again. If I do I hope there's a God of Blockages (or lack of them).

He remarked that I seemed very positive about everything, but, how was I coping with all the treatment?

"I'm coping with the cancer completely, and Chemotherapy isn't too bad but, Robert . . . "

"Eh?"

"Well I know I can survive cancer, but can I survive Robert . . .?" A muffled laugh could be heard from the other end of the phone. I was alarmed that he might think that I was criticising Robert and his treatment and fumbled over an explanation to ameliorate the situation.

"I don't mean anything derogatory but I'm not sure if I'm well enough to cope with him."

"You'll cope, you're an exceptional person."

Exceptional? That was the word that Bernie Siegal used to describe the type of person who stood the best chance of overcoming cancer.

His book 'Love, Medicine and Miracles' recommended to me by Dorothy was read and absorbed within a few days of its purchase. Scribbles and underlinings (it's my book) pin-pointed phrases that reached right into my need to under-stand the cause and relevance of cancer to me.

I wasn't going through a 'Why me' stage, but, 'Why me? Was there a reason to all this?'

I was on shaky ground.

Already Robert had said that it was the body's way of getting the brain to accept something.

In 'Love, Medicine and Miracles' it states:

"The immune system, then, is controlled by the brain either indirectly through the hormones in the bloodstream, or, directly through the nerves and neurochemicals. One of the most widely accepted explanations of cancer, the 'surveillance' theory, states that cancer cells are developing in our bodies all the time but are normally destroyed by white blood cells before they can become dangerous tumours. Cancer appears when the immune system becomes suppressed and can no longer deal with this routine threat. It follows that whatever upsets the brain's control of the immune system will foster malignancy."

I thought of 1992 . . . and shuddered.

Lawrence LeShan, an experimental psychologist, carried out an in-depth study on 71 of his most seriously ill patients and found 'despair', as opposed to depression, was a condition pre-dating the cancer in 68 out of the 71 patients.

Bernie Siegal's book is full of investigative data, like the LeShan findings, and goes on to list other 'passive emotions' such as grief, feelings of failure, and suppression of anger as being possible precursors to the development of cancer.

Did I feel that bad in 1992?

If I was that susceptible to the influence of my renegade hormones, how did I become an ECaP?

An ECaP?

An ECaP is Bernie Siegal's name for people who take charge of their own cancer. It stands for Exceptional Cancer Patient, and to him this is a far more powerful tool to recovery (or prolongation of life) than any drug. Without the individual's desire and determination to survive, the medical profession is trying to win an uphill battle.

I like my battles downhill: it's easier.

His profile of an ECaP is that of a survivor. 'They are generally successful at careers they like, and they remain employed during illness, or return soon after. They are receptive and creative, but sometimes hostile (*Grr*), having strong egos and a sense of their own adequacy. They have a high degree of self-esteem and self-love. They are rarely docile (*Grr*). They retain control of their lives. They are intelligent with a strong sense of reality. They are self reliant: they don't need to be included among others, although they value interaction with others. Although concerned with their own welfare, they are also tolerant and concerned with others. They tend to be non-conformists with a permissive morality—they are unprejudiced, and they appreciate diversity among other people.'

Well . . . so far, if I count up my score I have 4 points for negativity and 22 for being a 'jolly good chap-ess'.

I'm winning!!!!

What's this bit about 'strong egos and a high degree of self esteem'?

'The truth is that compulsively proper and generous people predominate among cancer patients because they put the needs of others ahead of their own. Cancer may be called the disease of 'Nice'.

33

(Well, Bernie thinks so, anyway!)

One thing for certain, it can really concentrate the mind. On hearing that I had cancer I mentally pulled a plug from the wall marked 'work, money, fear, loneliness, anger, assault, house, councils, squatters, men, man' and picked up another marked 'ME' and firmly plugged it into the National Grid.

Everything else became irrelevant . . . almost.

'Love, Medicine and Miracles' is a very thought-provoking book, despite its over-the-top American style, where everyone is a wonderful, warm, kind and generous person.

Scoop away the cream and you find real people who are successfully empowering those with cancer to take control.

Because of this we make terrible patients.

But it works.

Just as Visualisation can be a powerful healing experience, so too can any form of creativity. In my work as a Potter and Craft teacher I know only too well the changes that can be brought about by an individual who has discovered a hidden talent.

By using the hands in what most people still think of as being a bit of useless fun, the brain is freed to roam into hitherto forgotten channels and repressed alley-ways.

Some individuals have shunned and avoided 'art' on the pretext that it is solely for children, students and weirdos but basically many of them are too afraid of what they may be disturbing: they'd rather not know.

I am a Potter, or at least a teacher of pottery, and one who doesn't readily pick up a paintbrush. However I've found over the years that at times of need or 'crisis' it is a paintbrush I've reached for and not a lump of clay.

After the initial readjustment to life with cancer I had a need to paint, an urge to paint.

But, what?

Slowly and without any conscious composition I began to chart the reasons (allegedly) for my cancer and the various treatments and approaches I had been introduced to, or were being subjected to.

My painting showed me carrying a net shopping basket which contained all the elements of 1992, which had given me so much turmoil.

A big lion (Leo) had captured a prize lamb (Aries), but in the process had mortally wounded it. Attached to the lion's tail is the key to the house, where we lived. The house went with the male. A green bottle is broken in two: the label read 'Chateaued Peace'. Two jugs (slang for prison), one with a wire round its neck, look on. Cards and money (thirty pieces of silver?) stand in important piles. Two poems—one sonnet by Shakespeare entitled 'Being your slave', which the lion used to recite to me; one poem by Cole entitled 'It's only me'.

Luckily the handle had broken and I had released the contents. (Is it that easy? No!)

With my other hand I was carrying a big 'C' like a magnet and I was zapping myself better in the middle of the painting, while I visualised and received Chemotherapy. I'm surrounded by items representing the various therapies that I had tried, or, the treatments that I was undergoing: Shiatsu, Crystals, Colour Healing, Aromatherapy, Homeopathy, Indian Medicine Cards and Satsumas.

Satsumas? I needed them, I craved for them for days after the Chemotherapy, even though I had never been that fond of citric fruits. Frances, a long term friend also with cancer, craved for pink grapefruit. In Aromatherapy the acid in lemon turns to alkaline in the stomach. Could it be then that the citric fruit counteracts the acidity of the Chemotherapy?

The reactions to my 'painting' were mixed; some gave me a look of sympathy and suspected that the cancer had reached my brain.

(*Cheek!*)

Others felt it was a bit scattered.

I'll go along with that. After all, you don't feel totally together for the first two weeks, and if that had been communicated, then so be it.

Most did not understand my style of figures. These ghost-like creatures were a manifestation of my bored brain more than twenty years ago when I was having one of my many gyneacological Operations. Not having anything to interest me, or to be more precise, anything simple enough for me to cope with, I started to doodle on some writing paper. To begin with the nurses said 'That's nice dear' but as they (the doodles) got wilder and wilder I could see them (the nurses) considering a tranquilliser dart.

Gradually the swirls of biro took shape . . . dinosaurs? monsters? Don't give up your day job.

Creatures evolved into people, who took on a life of their own. A raised shoulder evoked surprise, two raised shoulders confusion. For the next twenty years these amorphous beings appeared in all my visual solving daubs . . . To counter artistic criticism I called them merely my psychological doodlings.

We knew better.

I'd never been an out of control fan or groupie, even in the heady days of the Beatles. I didn't even scream when I met the Rolling Stones and talked to them for half an hour, while friends went berserk outside the theatre.

Such composure and control!

However I surprised myself when I realised I was inspired

36

and thankful enough to Bernie Siegal to send him a colour photocopy of this painting, as he had spoken of the power of painting away your cancer.

(*I wonder if he got it?*)

I continued to work at the prison for my contractual two and a half days a week, but the pressure was beginning to mount as the effect of Competitive Tendering started to bite ... we were all in danger. My employers, West Herts College, had just been informed that they had lost the bid. Had they been successful, our jobs would have been safe. As it was, another local college, with an appalling reputation, was to take over not only us but several other prisons.

But, keep an open mind. After all, Thames Television couldn't lay the blame at Carlton's door for having lost the franchise. Perhaps the new college would be alright?

But, then again, perhaps not.

A meeting was arranged for the various top bods to come and see us and hopefully to allay our fears.

They increased tenfold.

Not only did the new-to-be Prison Education Management Officer know nothing about prisons, as he'd never worked in one (and believe me theory is nothing like practice when it comes to prisons) but, the Principal, who leaned back in his chair in a manner more fitting to a Football Manager (with apologies to Football Managers) really stunned us.

Most of the Lecturers were local and therefore au fait with the problems of the college. It had been stated in the local paper that the Principal was leaving.

"Are you the incoming or the outgoing Principal?" we enquired politely.

"Oh, I'm off," he announced. "You won't see me for dust.

37

I've been offered another £20,000 a year to be Principal of a large college."

There was an audible gasp, and even some of his colleagues had the grace to look uncomfortable. *Another £20,000!!!* And there we were not knowing who, if any of us, would be employed after August. As far as we were concerned the Home Office and this college were about to throw us to the lions . . . and I already had mine at home. I can do without this, I thought, and went home to bed.

The next day, after a fitful night's sleep in which I dreamt of long never-ending corridors in an education establishment, I had my second Chemotherapy.

Glen was not available, as he was organising the move of the Oncology department of University College Hospital to . . . the Middlesex Hospital!

I had my pre-Chemotherapy check with another doctor, who commented that my breast was still very hot.

"Yes, I had hoped it would be much better than this but I suppose the Chemotherapy has a lot of work to do," I offered.

What did I know???

"Has the pain decreased?" she asked.

The pain was in retreat but not before mounting a rear guard action courtesy of Robert. One of his questions had been whether or not I had pain. It had by then calmed down considerably but, as he handed me the anonymous tablets he informed me it would return.

The pain would return. Why?

The mysterious workings of Homeopathy causes temporary reinstatement of any effect of the body's ill health; but it soon calms down.

I felt reassured by this, because if I hadn't been told, I would have been worried; more worried.

However, Homeopathy apart, the breast wasn't as soothed as I had hoped.

But, it will be so.

I stepped across boxes and files to reach the tiny room where Rebecca and Clare were waiting for me.

I felt safe, and said so.

"It won't be as cosy as this at the Middlesex," they muttered apologetically.

"Meaning? I will still be seeing both of you, won't I?" I asked, as I looked from one to the other trying to read their expressions. "No, we've been put on the reception desk in the clinic." You could read their thoughts at twenty paces.

My next visit would be different for many reasons.

At the UCH my blood was tested in the outpatients and I was handed an envelope with the results. I liked this system because as an ECaP I could open the letter and investigate. It didn't matter that I wouldn't be able to understand the print out; it was *my* print out. At the Middlesex I would also have my blood taken in out-patients department but the results would then be phoned through to the Chemotherapy ward.

But I want to be able to not understand my results!

The tea system would alter as well . . . shock, horror. The UCH presented you with a tray on which stood a teapot (remember those?), a milk jug, a proper spoon, and, slightly letting the side down, a polystyrene cup. I had it on good authority that it would be back to the Klix cup of liquid, which you could call anything you like: tea, coffee, soup.

"Bring your own tea bag," they suggested.

There may be more of a delay as well at the Middlesex,

because the Chemotherapy had to be ordered from the pharmacy, instead of being made up by the nurses.

I absorbed all the information, but as the chemicals were beginning to work their way into synaptic junctions I didn't know I had, I decided to cross these bridges when I got to them.

My diary observed: Feel worse than last time because I was dreading it last time and I felt alright-ish. So this time I was expecting to feel good, and didn't. I knew what I meant, even if it was Chemo-babble.

The next day was a faint memory of constant headache, constant sinus pain, constant thirst and constant non-bowel movement.

The Great Blockage had returned.

I slept most of the day and night, surfacing only for water, loo trips (as opposed to runs!), satsumas and vague attempts to fight off Waffles, who couldn't understand why I was ignoring her.

"I feel lousy Puddytat, go away."

"Wah, prrp, prrrp, prow."

A warm, wet welcoming nose nuzzled against my cheek and started to furiously lick my face, as if her life depended on it.

Somewhere in my brain I registered the sensations of headache, thirst, stomach ache, a face now roughened by wet sandpaper, and a breathing problem.

Breathing problem?

Waffles had settled down for the night on what was, for her, a comfortable bed, albeit one that attempted to rise and fall in an endeavour to keep oxygen circulating in my lungs.

Waffles!!!!

I slept.

I woke feeling fantastic.

No headache, no sinus pain, no nausea, no imminent unblocking sensation and only a slight sense of unreality.

I donned my Boot's Travel Bands to go to work. These were not to aid my twenty-eight mile journey but to ward off any extremes of nausea. They work by exerting carefully controlled pressure on the acupressure point of both wrists, called the Nei-Kuan point. The point is easy to locate by placing the three middle fingers on the inside of the wrist making sure that the edge of the third finger is against the wrist crease. It lies just under the edge of the index finger and centralised between the two tendons.

This is a handy acupressure point to remember even without the convenient use of the bands.

Another acupressure point I'd started to use, even before the cancer, is nicknamed the 'Great Eliminator'. Now, like never before, it was coming into its own. Initially I was reluctant to use the technique for fear of disturbing, over stimulating or interfering with one of the cancer treatments, but soon realised that it was my own imagination that was disturbed, stimulated and interfered with! Dorothy put my mind at rest and encouraged the gentle prodding.

To find the Great Eliminator follow up the fleshy mound between the thumb and first finger until you feel a V formation of bone. Gently exert pressure on the area with your thumb for five seconds, then release. Repeat three times.

It certainly worked for me.

There is a slight warning concerning this point in that it should not be used on women who are pregnant. It's that powerful.

I was quite pleased with my ability to cope with work, and the men were being as helpful as they could be, for men. My idea, and their's of 'tidy up' were not the same. Some of the Latin American students could not understand my change in demeanour and asked what was wrong.

"Estoy un poco enferma," I attempted with my very rusty, post-Pedro, Spanish.

"Tu faltas una vacación en España." They offered, as advice.

"No es possible, por que tengo . . . tengo."

I asked an English speaking Colombian what was the Spanish for cancer.

"AIDS," he said, with great enjoyment, as he continued thumping his pottery.

"Thank you Rubin, very helpful. Sinvergüenza," I added, which is the only Spanish word of abuse I know.

The clay was in constant need of kneading, and, like tidying up, they thought it was *my* job. Not necessarily my job, as in 'teacher' but more as in 'female'.

"No way Jose," I declared, especially to the laid back Latins.

They did their best, and they did quite well, but I could never resist giving the clay a final pummelling.

Big mistake.

Towards the end of the day I was vigorously kneading, in a one and a half hand action, when a sharp deep pain shot across my lymph gland area, and ricocheted across my breast. It seemed to stop my breath for a split second but I had to sit down to stop my panic from spreading.

What the hell was I doing jeopardising my health for a lump of clay?

I was frightened.

The following morning I remained in bed until it was time to go to visit Lily again.

As soon as I entered her room her eyes lit up.

"My dear, your Aura's a lot better, and your skin is a better colour, and your eyes are clearer."

"That's because of you and Robert."

"And you . . . don't forget you are a great healer as well."

Lily herself was in a bad way. She had been woken in the middle of the night by an intruder, and although not physically hurt, was very shaken.

Despite my protestations she insisted on 'doing' for me for five minutes, until she was forced to retire to her room.

During her session with me she announced suddenly: "You will get better."

"I know," I said in a peremptory manner.

It had never occurred to me that I wouldn't get better.

Was this a blanket refusal to accept that things could go wrong or just an inner refusal to allow anything to go wrong?

What did I know?

After Lily retired to her room one of the helper/students continued with the healing. There was nothing wrong with her style or approach, but it was rather like making a hair appointment only to find that your own favourite stylist was on holiday.

I couldn't relax.

She didn't know how I liked it.

At the end of the session she bent and kissed my forehead.

??? or !!! or why not. I couldn't make up my mind why this had been done.

After fifteen minutes rest I went downstairs to the communal area for a cup of tea.

She-of-the-kiss ignored me.

I don't like her I muttered to myself. I've had enough false kisses in my life and I felt she had intruded my kiss-space.

Healing sessions tire you, or perhaps they just calm down the system? At any rate, the car drive back across North London seemed an age.

I slept.

Waffles was not in the best of spirits either and instead of her normal crepuscular activities she seemed to sleep for 24 hours instead of her normal 22 hours.

At six in the morning Waffles demanded food.

Good, I thought she can't be that bad, as she wolfed (catted) it down. It returned at high speed in a neat, near perfect, state.

Waffles!!!!!

After half an hour of compulsory pampering to calm her down, while she demonstrated her appreciation by breathing regurgitated Whiskas fumes into my face, she demanded more food. But this time it remained intact.

If only humans had the same power of recovery.

I sat in bed and looked over the pile of books bought for me, or recommended to me, by interested friends and colleagues. One, entitled 'The trials and persecution of Gaston Naessens' was about the revolutionary new treatment—or medical quackery that was being debated in Canada. Gaston Naessens's elixir of life named 714-X, claimed to have restored to perfect health 750 out of the 1,000 cancer victims who had sought his treatment. This had naturally sent waves of panic through the medical profession, especially as his qualifications, obtained in France, were not recognised in Canada. Thus, he was a charlatan.

But is he?

The book was far too medical for me to understand totally, or even, come to that, partially understand.

But I wish him well.

I also had Louise Hay's 'You can heal your life' and the follow up book of Bernie Siegal called 'Peace, Love and Healing'.

I also found two books on Homeopathy in an attempt to understand, not just Homeopathy, but Robert.

It was here that I learnt about Christian Samuel Hahnemann, who is considered the founder of Homeopathy.

He was, by today's standards, a very brave, or foolish man, as he set about experimenting with various substances.

He started with a bark called cinchona, which is the source of quinine used mainly in the treatment of malaria. He discovered that by taking this mixture he produced the symptoms of the disease for which the substance was produced to cure. When he stopped taking it his symptoms gradually disappeared.

He carried out many similar trials on himself and friends and 'proved' 90 different drugs. These provings became the basis for his 'Materia Medica Pura', which was first published in 1811 and became a classic textbook for serious students of Homeopathy.

His treatment of soldiers in a typhoid epidemic, where only one soldier out of 180 cases died, made him famous.

He was aware of the effects of minimal doses, and by experimenting discovered that the more he diluted the drug the more powerful it became.

The process of dilution is not only strange but also defies belief that it can have any effect on an illness.

A 'remedy' was mixed with water or alcohol to the ratio of one part to ninety-nine; and this is where it starts to sound ridiculous. He banged it on a hard surface thirty times! The solution was called 1c. This mix was then further mixed to the same ratio of one part to ninety-nine, and banged again thirty times!! This was then called 2c.

This process was carried out thirty times in all to produce a potency (potency ?) of 30c.

Today, using machines, this can be diluted up to 100,000 times!!!

A cynical friend of mine with an over-active scientific brain refuses to acknowledge that any effect can be produced with these dosages. He scientifically worked out that it would probably need a pill the size of the world to get one molecule of the original tincture.

I found that a bit hard to swallow!

However, he had to admit by empirical research that it did work, as he witnessed his niece being cured of asthma with Homeopathic treatment when all other allopathic remedies had been tried, and failed.

He was 'furious'.

I also came across Miasms and Psoras, which partially explained my gonorrheoa connection.

A miasm is the inherited effect of a disease that has been suppressed; in other words it is the vital root to all disease.

The most ancient miasms are called Psoras: namely Syphilis, Tuberculosis and Gonorrheoa. The residue of these ancient diseases are the consequences of these Miasms.

This would then explain hereditary illnesses and in my case, if I am descended from the 'Gonorrheoa family', then added credence would come with the knowledge that my mother had been crippled with arthritis. That too is supposed to have its roots in gonorrheoa.

The list of characteristics of psoric people, I liked, indicating that I was part of a group who were intelligent, sensitive, hard working, inventive but also nervous, suffering from headaches, restlessness and craving unhealthy foods.

(*Wrong!-ish.*)

If that wasn't bad enough the Sycotic miasm (Gonorrheoa type) are a nasty bunch who are greedy, vindictive, irritable, violent and crave beer.

Very interesting, but it all adds up to the known fact that you can't choose your family but now it seems you can't choose your Miasms or Psoras.

One other thing I've learnt is that I can now spell 'gonorrheoa'.

My Spruce Flower and Gem remedy had arrived and I had been advised how to take it. After all my reading I now knew that it probably didn't contain any Spruce, but as it was distilled in brandy, I could certainly taste that. Four drops at a time, three times a day. As I had decided to stop drinking alcohol, although this was more through no desire than common sense, it was a rather harsh medicine to take.

The effect of the Spruce was immediate, at least I hoped it was the effect of the Spruce? I felt as if I had suddenly been asked to carry an extra large rucksack up a mountain after an all night party.

I felt drained.

I rang Robert to seek advice and he confirmed that this is how Spruce can make you feel. Basically, it directs the body's energy to the area that needs the help, leaving the other parts to fend for themselves.

Now he tells me!

But at least I know that this extra tiredness has a positive outcome . . . if I can only keep awake.

The next day I was due for my visit to Lily. I was already drained from the onslaught of the Spruce, but still staggered across London to keep my appointment.

I was edgy and unsettled.

Lily had been ordered to rest by her doctor, so I had to

make do with one of our chats. While we were talking, two friends, who had trained with her, arrived and entered into the conversation.

"Cancer," said Jane. "Who's got cancer?"

"I have."

"Ooh! let us do some healing on you," she pleaded.

"Us?" I enquired.

Into the room came Declan, Jane's partner.

"Us," she declared.

I looked across at Lily to see what her reaction would be.

"Go with them, they're very good. Different, but good," she said.

Jane and Declan certainly were different. For a start there was Declan's spiritual being or side-kick called Jenny. She went everywhere with him.

"Come along," called Jane, as she left the room. "Come along Declan and Jenny, in fact both Jennys," she said with a chuckle.

The four of us walked to the treatment room.

Jane stood with her hand resting on my solar plexus chakra and Declan described what he saw or, to be exact, what Jenny saw.

(I think).

Apparently he, she, or both saw grey lines travelling over my chakras and a gold dome over my right breast.

"My right breast," I enquired.

"Don't worry," said Declan, "that's good."

Jane then put two rocks on me, one called the Peacock, which she placed on my abdomen and the other, which she delved into her bra for, was placed on my heart chakra.

She also started to sprinkle salt all over me.

What is going on!

Meanwhile, Declan is quietly writing something on a small

48

piece of notepaper. He rips it out and places it face down on the table.

"Is your cancer a punishment?" Jane asks Jenny (2) through Declan.

"No."

"Is your cancer a means of control?" she asks again.

"No."

"Is . . . is . . . oh, I don't know what else to ask," she says looking at Declan for help.

He remains quiet.

"Have you had any traumatic experiences in the recent past?" she asks me.

"Where do you want me to begin?" I start to rattle off event after event, as I had done with Robert.

"I see, you tend to attract, or demand, attention, don't you?" said Jane.

Here we go again, I thought, it usually ends up being 'my fault'.

Declan suddenly announces that he's not convinced that my cancer is related to the present.

I rattled off teenage traumas.

"Further back still," he demands.

"What was your childhood like? Did you have a good relationship with your mother?"

"Oh yeh, fabulous. She threw me down the bottom of the bed when I was a few days old and told her husband to take the bastard away. We had a fabulous relationship," I spat out.

"That's it," they cried.

"That's what?" I demanded.

Declan asked if I knew what an Affirmation was. "Well, sort of, but what do you mean?"

49

He told me to raise my arm out straight and say to it: "I am as strong as steel, I cannot be moved" over and over. Then I had to prevent him pushing down my arm, which I managed. He then got me to lower my arm and tell it several times in quick succession: "I have no power".

"Now raise your arm again," he said.

I attempted to raise it, but he quickly and easily pushed it down. The whole process was reversed and it was back to normal.

"That's an Affirmation," he said. "If you tell yourself something over and over again it imprints it in your energy and psyche."

"I see," I muttered, slightly impressed or overwhelmed by the two of them.

Declan then turned over his piece of paper.

On it was written: 'I, Jenny, forgive my mother completely, now.' I was told to write it out 70 times a day, until it clears.

"Clears?" I query.

"You'll know," they replied, somewhat mysteriously.

I also had to write out: 'I, Jenny, forgive myself completely, now' . . . but not for a few days.

They then talked a lot, threw salt around the room and over me, and generally took off into their own world.

WHAT WAS GOING ON!!

I was left for a few minutes, to rest.

Eventually I joined them all for tea. As I entered the room I had intended to say: "what was all that about?", in a calm and amused tone, but I think I had been a little overpowered and it came out in a far more aggressive manner.

They all looked up in surprise.

50

"I need to be in control," I demanded, "and I haven't the faintest idea what that was all about."

"Oh, you like to be in control, do you?" said Declan quietly.

"Your subconscious will know what was happening," said Lily, observing my confusion.

Oh, good, I'm glad part of me will know.

I took my leave of them, brushing salt from my clothes as I went. I then painted a picture of the encounter: my arms are in a gesture which meant: 'I don't understand what is going on,' and I didn't. But, it was an interesting experience and I arranged to see them again.

Really?

Could it be my openness to all this weird behaviour that gets me into so much trouble?

Probably.

Later, at home, Ellis hugs and kisses me.
I'm so surprised I don't know whether to cry or hit him.
I do neither.
What a strange day.

The next morning I start on my homework of writing out my Affirmation:
I, Jenny, forgive my mother completely, now.
I, Jenny, forgive my mother completely, now.
I, Jenny, forgive my mother completely, now.
etc etc.

I got bored, so wrote in the margin. 'I wonder how many times each word will appear at the start of each line?' and 'she's still giving me hassles, even though she's been dead twenty years.'

I also wrote the last line in perfect *italic script*; and by the side wrote: she'd complain if I didn't make an effort.

In the evening I had a meal with an old friend, Erl. He-of-the-cynical-scientific-mind. He paid me a compliment.

Cancer of the colon ran in his family and he had just had one of his regular check-ups.

"Your attitude and approach to cancer has really given me a boost," he declared. "If I do get it myself, I won't be so panicky."

He described watching his exploratory probings live on close-circuit TV in the hospital, and expressed his desire to obtain a video of it next time.

"What for?" I politely enquired.

"Well, it will make a change as an After Dinner presentation . . . instead of our holiday in Majorca, what about a trip up my arse?"

He started to chuckle.

Yes, Erl, a great change.

The next day my sister announced that she had been sent for a Mammogram because of a lump that had just appeared.

!!!!??

Are people jealous, or what?

She too declared that she would have been frightened if she hadn't seen how I had dealt with it.

Glad to be of some use.

(*Well, Bernie did say we were nice people.*)

My own breast was becoming a bit of a problem at night. It was tightening up and getting hard, so that when I moved, the weight pulled the mass about, and it was very uncomfortable. But I should expect that shouldn't I?

52

The next day I popped in to see Dorothy. It was meant to be my last Visualisation coaching session, but as I had got it off to a Tea, we just sat and talked.

She was very impressed by my approach.

"Gold star?" I enquired.

"Gold star and A+."

She was pleased that I had been a positive role model to my sister and Erl and said that more individuals with a good approach like mine were needed to spread the word that cancer isn't automatically an impossible thing to overcome, or accept.

Bobby Moore had just died of cancer, and, although I have no wish to belittle his family's suffering, he was yet another Star or Personality, who had hit the headlines because of cancer. It was all a bit too vague and out of touch with the ordinary person in the street. Almost, in fact, making it seem that only famous personalities died of cancer.

I'm ordinary. There wouldn't be a spread in the papers if I died. Would that make my suffering and my family and friend's suffering any less?

Or, am I being unreasonable?

I visit another friend who I haven't seen for over a year. He listens in awe and horror as I relay to him my life in 1992.

It seems that every time I see him another handful of life's shit has been thrown at me.

But he too is impressed by my attitude and approach, and states that he is almost 'pleased' that I've got cancer because it's made me even more amazing and wonderful.

(*Glad to be of service!*)

He brings out a box of American Indian 'Medicine cards' and shows me how to use them.

He gives me the set and on it writes a dedication:

"There are many ways and means to help one on this journey.

Love, Charles."

Thanks Charles.

I read: "To understand the concept of medicine in the Native American way, one must redefine 'medicine'. The medicine referred to is anything that improves one's connections to the Great Mystery and to all life. This would include the healing of body, mind and of spirit. This medicine is also anything which brings personal power, strength and understanding.

(*I could do with some of that!*)

I had to find the token animal for each of the seven directions surrounding my physical body; in them I would find lessons to help me through my journey.

Spreading the cards out in the prescribed manner and allowing the choice to be intuitive the following animals became my guides.

The Fox gives me the ability to be 'unseen' and weave through any situation or location. I would be "wise to observe the acts of others rather than their words."

(*But the words 'I love you' have never meant anything to me!*)

The Grouse is a symbol of personal power. I am the centre of a whirlpool. "I should analyse the way I move through the world. What reaction do you create with the energy you send to the universe?"

(*Usually, everyone thinks I'm so independent ... they leave me!*)

I am a rare Snake person. These people "experience and live through multiple snake bites."

(*But, I think this time I've been swallowed by a python!*)

I need the "Armadillo's protective coating to deflect

negative energies." I must find strength in my vulnerability and create.

My (contra) Beaver shows that I am being "asked to open new doors to opportunity. Meditate and Visualise the goal you wish to accomplish, and be willing to work with others to achieve that end."

(*Thank heavens I have cancer, or I wouldn't be writing this book.*)

My Raven warns me that "if I have wished harm to another—beware—you have asked harm to teach you."

(*Tempting!*)

The appearance of my Buffalo means "that prayers were heard." It willingly provided for others, so did not run away from the hunters (nor Lion?).

(*!!*)

I was too tired to venture fully into the world of animal guides, as it was not as simple (or flippant) as I've implied. I did however write down the appropriate animals . . . and time will tell.

The swings and flatness of my cancer never followed any discernible rhythm. One day I could be relatively well . . .

(*It's those relatives again*)

. . . and the next, feel disorientated, lethargic and drained of energy.

Nevertheless, *I* insisted on doing my daily Visualisation.

I hadn't reckoned on Waffles.

If I'd had the energy to think clearly *I* should have realised that first thing in the morning, when she was having her daily constitution of quivering by the cat flap, was not the best time for me to relax.

She 'knows' when I need to be alone, except that at times like this she insists on helping (with a capital H).

I would lie on the floor having turned on my relaxing

meditation tapes of peaceful music, and start the slow countdown to relax every part of my body.

It is then that I'm aware that she has re-entered the room. I know she's there although hasn't made a sound.

(*What is she doing?*)

I'd then be aware that she was sitting near a foot, which is open to attack.

Lick, Lick, Lick, Lick.

(*Go away!*)

She would then tread softly to the next naked vulnerable piece of flesh and sit for a few minutes until I'd relaxed again.

Lick, Lick, Lick, Lick, Lick.

(*GO AWAY!*)

This tender torture would continue until I had been circumnavigated. Her disbelief that I could ignore her was alien to her limited mental capacity, which worked on a quick response of stimulus and reward.

I wasn't always sure who was rewarding or rewarded.

But, suffice to say that it was unheard of for her to be within a few yards of me and not be acknowledged, called for, stroked or threatened.

My inactivity baffled her.

With one last attempt she would stand astride me and caterwaul until I opened my eyes.

I'd look up to see an irate, wide eyed cat, screaming down at me. Once I was alert, and giggling ... she would walk away ... and sleep.

Tyrants make slaves.

I know. I know.

I could then, and only then, return to my Visualisation.

I had over the past weeks been expanding my experiences

with strange yet relaxing sensations courtesy of the Visualisation. My head became detached from my body, and I was simultaneously floating in mid-air yet glued to the floor.

For a child of the '60s, who at that time never participated in anything stronger than half a bitter, it was amazing.

(It was also why I remembered the '60s.)

I was hooked.

And, there was no side effects.

I had a rough few days following my visit to Charles, although the visit itself had no direct connection.

I just seemed to get very tired even with the simplest of activities.

Visual impairment, headaches, sinus problems, all helped to debilitate my energy.

I had difficulty in sleeping, partly because of the discomfort, but also because I couldn't relax enough to sleep. Many a night I would be working on one of my paintings until the early hours of the morning.

The weather had turned cold and the snow seemed to make my breast throb.

The disruption of sleep and rest did not help my work at the prison. The journey to work involving over 600 gear changes (I got bored counting after that) did not help matters, as my left arm, under-arm, lymph system and breast were really painful by the time I arrived.

I slept as much as I could during the lunch break but, with the constant banging of doors and jangling of keys, it was not easy.

At the other end of the day I had to face the long drive home again. The closure of exit 2 on the M1 meant that I had to divert via Brent Cross, sitting in long traffic jams and wishing I wasn't there. By this time I had difficulty in changing into reverse gear as, with my car, it requires a downward push. I prayed for an easy parking space outside the house; if none existed I'd have to park some distance away.

My next visit to Lily was due, and I expected Jane and Declan also to be there.

Lily announced that my Guardian Angel was looking after me.

(I tried to imagine my Armadillo or Buffalo with wings!)

But if this was so, why was I feeling so rough?

Jane and Declan did not appear.

I had seen Jane write the appointment in her diary, so where were they?

After a while Lily phoned Jane, who rushed round as soon as possible, apologising as she entered. She had not transferred my appointment to her main work diary. Still, she was here now and healing began.

Jane felt that my energies had become less blocked and that my Aura was clearing, especially round my solar plexus.

She discovered the tender area on my back, which on many occasions had caused me to leap in the air if touched accidentally by someone in a crowd. It was in direct line with my solar plexus, and could have been the body's manifestation of an energy block, perhaps?

I expressed my surprise at the style of treatment that I'd received from her and Declan last week.

"It was meant to unblock you, which it is doing," she offered.

She asked me to continue writing out the Affirmation about my mother for another week.

I was surprised she hadn't wanted to 'mark' my homework, or to check that I'd even done it.

"I knew you'd do it," was all she said.

Am I that easy to mould?

Probably.

Lily asked me directly: "Do you really want to get better?"

"Yes."

"Really?"

I thought for a while.

The cancer had given me something concrete to fight for (against?) and I had taken control of *me* again.

However, post-cancer?

What does that hold for me? A return to all my financial, personal, redundancy, relationship problems in a country with a bleak economic future and an appallingly complacent and arrogant government.

Did I want to stick with the cancer?

NO!!!

But, I had to admit that Health equalled getting to grips with the old problems, with other liberally sprinkled on top.

It was not going to be easy.

I had brought with me my early paintings as well as a new painting, which I chose to call a 'cancer document of the first six weeks'. Both Jane and Lily were impressed and delighted at my use of colour.

Jane picked up one that I had done nearly twenty years ago; it showed a swirl over my left breast!

She took that and two others to show to Declan.

"They will be safe with me," she insisted.

And for some reason I believed her.

"Will you design our book cover?" she pleaded.

"Delighted."

"You are a sensitive person, who has not learned to protect yourself against the unpleasant forces in the world," she crowed.

"Tell me about it . . . !"

I liked her.

Well I would, wouldn't I? It was a rare treat to be with someone who thought I was talented and sensitive.

Appreciation had been a bit thin on the ground lately.

It made a change.

Or was I jumping in with both feet again?

(*Watch this space.*)

Pre-cancer I had arranged to teach an introduction course on Massage and Aromatherapy at one of the local Community Centres with which I had been involved, before redundancy and local government cuts decimated the whole programme.

Could I cope?

As usual the women were a lovely group and they took on board the fact that they would probably not get the exact course they had signed for.

The second week of the course coincided with my third Chemotherapy session, so I had arranged for two willing, but terrified, volunteers, to substitute for me.

My first evening with the group went well, although I don't remember too much about it.

"See you in two week's time," I called out confidently.

I was overtired and couldn't sleep until 1 a.m., but was pleased that I had at least taken the class, and that they all wanted to come back.

I woke at 5 a.m. I had been dreaming about the prison, which wasn't really there.

In the dream I drove around Hertfordshire trying to find it, realising that I was going to be late.

(Not an Arien characteristic.)

It kept moving.

When I finally caught up with it, it had changed its function and was now a Rest Home for Ex-Prison Teachers with no where to go.

WOW!

All my dreams, since the diagnosis of cancer, have been like that.

In reality, I drove straight to the prison, which was still there, worked my half day, drove back, and slept seventeen hours. I returned the following day for a full day's teaching.

My cancer diary simply stated: 'No energy'.

Su had originally taught me Aromatherapy. In the first few weeks of cancer when I was telephoning everyone I could think of who might have knowledge and concern, I thought of her. She told me of Gaston Naessen's book and offered advice on Massage and the use of oils with cancer patients.

She also recommended a Crystal therapist called Harry Oldfield.

Crystals?

I liked the sound of that.

I made contact, but was disappointed to discover that his clinic would be far too long a drive, especially after a treatment session.

"One of our Practitioners is in Muswell Hill. Is that any better?"

"Perfect."

I rang for an appointment.

Trish, the Practitioner, accompanied by an assortment of dogs and cats welcomed me, noisily, at the front door.

I walked into an ordinary, suburban front room and felt slightly let down.

Crystals:

Crystals conjure up dark exotic images to me. The least she could have done was wear a flowing robe and talk in riddles.

I sat in a lounger.

Min, the dog, offered me an empty Whiskas tin, then sat and stared at me.

This is more like it.

Trish decided to use Electro-Crystal Therapy.

Now you're talking!

Eer! What's that?

Basically it is a treatment for energy imbalances using crystals stimulated by pulsed, high frequency electromagnetic waves, generated by a battery operated unit. The gems and/or crystals are in sealed tubes and loops containing a saline solution to enhance the effect. Depending on the needs of the client the crystals are pulsated at different frequencies.

A plastic loop containing fragments of crystals is handed to me.

"Place this over your breast, please."

"Okay."

Another loop was handed to me.

"Place this over your right hip, please."

"Okay."

See how trainable I am?

I get confused when a tube containing crystals is handed to me.
"Put this over your left him, please."
"Okay."
A Walkman is put on my head.
The electro machine is then switched on.
No hum, heat or beat.
It doesn't seem to be doing anything.

Trish observed that I was remarkably cool about the procedure considering I hadn't known what was going to happen.
Why shouldn't I be?
Six weeks into cancer with my horizons stretched in all directions, plugging myself into a portable battery operated spaghetti junction of loops and crystals seemed very normal!

Min is still looking at me.

We chat for about an hour about cancer and attitudes and treatments and diet, while two dogs sleep at our feet.
All her animals had received treatments and responded well. The cats, especially, would walk in the room and select a suitable lap depending on the client's course of treatment.

Trish's plan was to boost my bone marrow and calm the tumour.
(*Please calm it, it's too active. Why does it still hurt?*)

I expressed my disappointment that she hadn't covered me with rocks and crystals and, before I could react, she flipped an arm on the lounger and I was horizontal. I was given a crystal to hold in each hand and three more were placed directly onto my body. A beautiful Amethyst was then swung backwards and forwards across my body, and a Crystal pendant is dangled over me.

She felt the energy, she said.

I have to confess, I didn't feel a thing.

Amethyst is beautiful, though.

I asked what would be good for me to buy for home use: Amethyst Geod and Rose Quartz.

I buy them.

I treated myself to an evening, (or part evening) at my Odds and Sods of North London Greek restaurant.

It was the weekend before my next Chemotherapy. If I wasn't feeling up to a bit of entertainment now, I never would.

Mac was already entrenched at the bar.

"Hallo Love. How are you?"

"Fine."

"What sort of treatment are you having now?" he enquired.

"Well, I'm going to Colour Therapy, I'm doing Visualisation every day, I've started Crystal-Healing and I'm painting pictures and keeping a diary and . . . "

"You're still having Chemotherapy though, aren't you?" he interrupted quickly.

"Yes, of course, but all the other activities are keeping my interest and my spirit alive; in fact they are keeping *me* alive."

He beamed down at me.

"Thank God someone like you has cancer . . . and not some poor sod who couldn't cope."

I laughed, but several heads swung round in the restaurant after the first part of his statement! If they were expecting me to thump him, or burst into tears, they were wrong.

A little later in the evening, when more banter had occurred, and more beer had been poured down his throat, he declared:

"You've got bollocks."

"No, Mac, I've got ovaries."

"It's not the same," he insisted.

"Well it is to me," I snapped back.

For the rest of the evening, whenever he heard anyone saying something stupid, a muttered 'ovaries' could just be heard.

'Ovaries.'

"I like it," he repeated gleefully, to himself.

Hangover?

I'd had a minuscule amount of wine, surely not enough to give me a hangover?

Experience proved that I could easily wake feeling as if I'd drunk too much without any alcohol touching my mouth for weeks.

So, I ignored the sensation.

I had arranged to visit an old friend and ex-colleague, who not only has cancer but shares another 'snap' with me.

In 1981 we both had a Hysterectomy on the same morning, although not at the same hospital.

The small-ish education department was delighted to have both of us off work for three months, at the same time.

(I don't think!)

We had a lot to share then, and we were about to share a lot, more now.

Snap.

65

We were both wearing black trousers and bright red jumpers.

Frances had been to the Bristol Cancer Unit and had lists of helpful foods to suppress or fight cancer: carrots, pears, avocado, greens, kiwi fruit, etc, etc.

Yummy.

Exchanging thought processes with someone with cancer was very therapeutic for me. In the past few days I'd only just realised that I ran the risk of becoming isolated in my own world.

Everyone had been looking at me to define what 'cancer' meant to them, but I hadn't really talked about it with someone who had firsthand knowledge ... and could therefore knock a ball around for a bit.

We even acknowledged our predilection for rubbish.

"I hate to say this, but I watch all the Soaps on Television and get very upset if I have to miss one."

I waited for the gasp of horror.

"Me too."

Giggles.

When I related this conversation with another mutual friend she couldn't see the point.

"But, I watch all the Soaps, and I don't have cancer" she said, slightly baffled.

Snap.

"I'm going to an amazing Homeopath," I casually introduced.

"Oh, it's alright, I go to one as well. It's a bit far, Bethnal Green actually, but it's well worth it."

"Bethnal Green?"

"Yes."

"Robert?"

"Yes."

"What do you make of him?"

"He's interesting."

"Interesting?"

"Yes . . . interesting," she deliberated.

We looked at each other, and giggled.

I slept a lot over that weekend, despite the fact that it should have been one of the better phases.

(*Why was I so tired?*)

There had been a constant unpleasant sensation in the breast area, which I had been trying to ignore.

Ignore? This may be too fixed a concept, but what did I know about the effect or efficacy of Chemotherapy?

Surely there's a lot going on in there?

More strange dreams:

Every toilet, drawer, cupboard, pot and pan was overflowing with human excrement, which I was trying to hide or flush away. The more I tried the more it grew.

I wasn't very popular.

One more day at the prison and then a few days' leave to have my third Chemotherapy.

(*Very noble, aren't I?*)

The date?

9.3.93.

I pondered on the symmetry, and was reminded of another major medical day in my life, which was also a significant date. Significant, that is, to a student friend of mine who beseeched me not to have my major Operation on that day. Not only was 18.3.81 palindromic but, if all the numbers were added up, was divisible by '3'.

So?

"That's terrible," she insisted. "Things will happen."

I laughed, and ignored her panic.

She helped herself to my boyfriend.

I never forgave her.

Putting those ancient thoughts aside I took the bus to the tube station.

Every bus in the region seemed to converge at the same time, and having no change I found myself in a long, slow-moving queue of passengers all renewing yearly passes.

A commotion had started to gather momentum near the ticket machines.

Perhaps commotion is a little strong for most descriptions, but not with this female. If it can be carried out with great gusto and flare, as well as having everyone looking at your perfect black, red and white ensemble, then so much the better. 'Red Lips' had arrived, and in tow, her 'Slave', who hovered and fawned persistently.

Shit, I thought. Just the people I don't want to bump into.

I hid behind my Guardian.

Seventeen minutes later I purchased my ticket.

(And they wonder why people try to board trains without paying.)

Deep breath.

Enter out-patients at the Middlesex Hospital.

Pre-Chemotherapy blood extracted from me.

Results phoned through to the ward.

Walk across the road to the main hospital.

Deep breath.

Along corridor to . . . I end up in the Oncology out-patients department by mistake.

Clare manoeuvres me back along the corridor and up a staircase to Latymer Ward.

Deep breath.

I don't know anyone!

And they don't know me!

Clare leaves.

I sat in the small waiting room.

An elderly couple sat opposite.

Obviously one of them was going to have Chemotherapy, but which one?

They both looked grim.

I tried to make conversation.

They stare at me.

(*Why am I talking so much?*)

Deep breath.

My name was called by a doctor, and I entered a small curtained off examination area.

"How has it been?" she enquired.

"A bit hot, some pain and discomfort, and there seems to be a sort of ache down the side of my body.

But, there's obviously a battle going on in there?

(*Why am I talking so much?*)

It's to be expected.

It's normal isn't it?"

Deep breath.

She examines my tender, painful, inflamed and enlarged breast.

"I think I'd like to have Glen's opinion on this," she states, and leaves me to get dressed behind the curtain.

If I had any thoughts going through my head, they were well and truly knitted up into complicated patterns.

I'm good at that.
But, why was I shaking?

She returned, but not with Glen.
  (*Where's Glen. I need Glen.*)

"I've talked it over with Glen and we aren't happy with your progress."

I stare at her.

"We don't see much point in continuing the Chemotherapy. It doesn't seem to be helping."

I stare at her.

"What happens now, then?" I managed to ask, as everything started to take on an air of unreality.
  "Well, there are two options."
  "What are they?"

Deep breath.

  "You could either have a course of Radiotherapy, but I don't think that would be any use because your tumour is now too large . . ."
  (*What is this woman saying?*)
  ". . . or we might consider surgery."
  "Surgery? What do you mean by *surgery*?"
  I could feel the panic and disbelief well up and consume me.
  "Mastectomy."
  "NO!!!!!!"

Shallow breath.
  Rapid, shallow breath.

70

She called across to the reception desk to cancel the Chemotherapy from the pharmacy.

"Can we discuss this a while?"
   (*Everything's come to a complete stop.*)

"Miss Cole . . . "

"I need to ask you things."
   (*and rapidly going backwards.*)

"Listen to me . . . "

". . . why can't I have some more Chemotherapy today, and we can discuss this next week?"
   (*This is not happening!*)

"It's not advisable to have any Chemotherapy today. If you're booked in to have a Mastectomy next Monday or Tuesday, and you are full of chemicals, they wouldn't be able to operate."

"Next Monday or Tuesday . . ."
   (*I've lost it. I've lost control.*)

"I've written you a letter . . . (*Can we start this conversation again?*) to see Professor Taylor . . . (*this is out of control*) . . . on Thursday. I've explained your reluctance . . . (*reluctance?*) . . . to an operation, but I've also explained the seriousness of . . . (*this isn't happening.*) . . . the situation, and the necessity to act quickly," she was trying to explain.

"I know you aren't happy with the outcome," she added.
   Happy?
   "I'm not saying that I'd rather die than have a Mastectomy, but it's close . . ."

71

(Did I really say that?)

". . . We've had some lovely times together and I'm not giving up that easily," I added.

An anonymous brown letter was placed in my hand and I left the ward.

I ripped it open.

It asked Professor Taylor to examine my breast and the details, and to help make a decision. It noted my reluctance to an Operation.

I walked out of the hospital.

I arrived home.

How one became the other I'll never know.

The walk, tube, station change, bus, walk, is a blank.

I wasn't feeling anything.

Not a thing.

I pressed the automatic button to reach Ellis.

"Hallo," said his voice.

". . ."

"Hallo?"

". . ."

"Is there anyone there?"

"Ellis . . ."

"Jenny, what's wrong?"

A rush of jumbled, frightened, out of control words burbled from my confusion.

"I'm on my way."

By the time Ellis reached home I was hugging, or hanging on to, a pillow; rocking backwards and forwards, and screaming.

He held me, and the pillow, tightly until I sank into an exhausted heap.

Ellis then 'took over'.
　He phoned Dorothy.
　He phoned Glen.
　He phoned Harry Oldfield.
　He phoned Su.
　He phoned another consultant.
　He phoned Quebec. (Gaston Naessens).
　He phoned Bournemouth (Gaston Naessen's contact in England.)
　He phoned . . .

I slept in a state of exhaustion.

Dorothy phoned back, but I found I couldn't speak.

Ellis fielded them all.

Breakthrough: Dorothy had made contact with Glen and had arranged for us to see him the next day. We may have to wait for a while, but we would be seen.
　I manage to speak to Dorothy, who assures me that my reaction was quite understandable. It had reopened all my traumas of '92.

I was no longer in control . . . again.
　And I was frightened.
　Very frightened.

I turned the light off at 9 p.m.

I turned the light back on at 3 a.m.

For the first time since November '92, Waffles was not asleep on the nearby pillow.

I looked terrible and felt even worse.

I was not in control of my brain.

It refused to stay on one topic for longer than the split second it took for me to realise I didn't want to think about it.

In the morning Ellis and I sat in the kitchen, silent and drained, then ordered a taxi to the hospital.

The out-patients was crowded. I realized I looked as stunned as everyone else.

Rebecca was surprised to see me.

"What are you doing here? You had your Chemotherapy yesterday, didn't you?"

The raw and exposed nerves that I had been trying to control were released by this concern. It triggered another cascading flow of uncontrollable fear and I burst into tears.

I don't remember her words, but she held my hand and spoke softly with a skill for calming which she should patent.

The panic subsided.

But the wait continued.

Finally, Glen was available and I found myself reliving the conversation word for word, as he stared ahead with a grim expression.

My grievance was not the diagnosis, as such, but the surprise 'attack'. Up to that point I had believed that I was in control of what happened to my body.

Handled correctly, I could accept a Mastectomy, if it were necessary, but only if I was part of the decision-making process.

Glen could not apologise enough for the trauma I had

been put through, but asked to examine my breast before he committed himself to any further comment.

"That's a relief," he said. "I was expecting much worse."

My tension began to diminish.

"What does that mean?"

"Well, I'm the first to admit that it's not responding as quickly as I would have expected or desired, but it is responding.

"When I was 'phoned and told that your breast wasn't 'responding at all to treatment and had perhaps got worse', I gave my advice based on what I heard. The problem is that the doctor who examined you had not seen it when you had first come in . . . so did not have a base line to work from."

This was exactly what the Oncology department from UCH had been fighting about when the merger was first discussed. They know that continuity is paramount in cancer treatment but under the new structure this was now impossible.

They know.

I know.

But apparently others, with the power, don't want to know.

At the UCH this would never have happened, as everyone was available in the one small, cramped, Dickensian, but human department. If Glen had been required to add his knowledge to a particular case he could have stepped across a corridor and seen for himself, without abandoning his own continuity of work.

At the Middlesex the Oncology out-patients, Chemotherapy ward, Radiotherapy planning and Radiotherapy treatment rooms were all separated by corridors and staircases, relying on the telephone to fill the gap of human contact.

It doesn't work. I know.

The need for one doctor to follow through a patient's treatment can be demonstrated by my Gynaecological experiences.

Every six weeks I would attend out-patients with the same problem. That problem being that I was not functioning properly; I was bleeding and in deep pain every day. Everyday, that is, for two years! I saw a different doctor each time I attended and as my file grew thicker and thicker, so did my waist. I was offered various treatments, the most bizarre being that of constipation granules.

Constipation granules?

What each doctor didn't see was the steady, then rapid, disintegration of a reasonably presentable young-ish female with a good figure and flexible mind, to an overweight, sluggish, unattractive drudge who was totally neurotic.

(*What do you mean, nothing's changed?*)

They only had a snap-shot instead of a home-movie.

This to me has always been the one and only failure of the NHS, fabulous staff working in a structure not designed for people who are ill for longer than one hospital appointment.

But the solution is not to force people into private medicine, as most do not have the money to be forced.

"You're the first, but you won't be the last, to suffer under this new merger," Glen confessed.

"I intend to write to Virginia Bottomley and let her know all about the so called Patients Charter," I insisted.

"Good."

Speaking to all the staff I got the feeling that no one liked the new arrangements because of the fragmentation and if they didn't like it, why should the patients?

Glen knew about the appointment with Professor Taylor at the UCH.

(UCH? I thought it had merged with the Middlesex? They may have merged, but as one person said, 'you can't get a quart into a pint pot', so some of the departments were still on the UCH site.)

(*Of course they were!*)

He asked if I would like him to come with me to see Professor Taylor to ensure the continuity.

Oh, yes please.

My pressure cooker tension had reduced to a simmer and now the adrenalin was also in retreat.

I slept.

Dorothy rang me later in the day and was relieved by the outcome. I praised Glen to the sky, especially his asking my permission to attend the session with Professor Taylor.

My thoughts and feelings mattered.

Dorothy assured me that Prof Taylor (as he was affectionately called) was also a 'Goody' and not knife happy.

That's a relief.

One thing had been bothering me though. What if I hadn't had someone like Ellis to fight on behalf of my brain—which had atrophied on hearing 'Mastectomy'. What if I'd agreed while still in a state of shock?

"I wouldn't have allowed you to have a Mastectomy without first being counselled," she informed me.

"That's a relief."

"You're doing fine," she added.

"Well, I think I've earned my ECaP brownie points."

"You have indeed."

The following morning, although calmer, I had difficulty in concentrating on anything that required a commitment of grey matter.

Su had sent me some tapes about a product which had amazing results in, yes you've guessed it, America.

It has to be a cultural divide I said to myself, as person after person eulogised in their over-the-top-ain't-life-wonderful fashion. It reminded me of a meeting I had been lured to by an acquaintance promoting Herbalife. One by one all the agents stood on chairs and raved how Herbalife had changed, nay revolutionised, their life and health. My acquaintance stood and declared that he'd discovered so much energy since he started to take Herbalife that he found he didn't need to sleep until 2 a.m., and he always rose at 6 a.m. to start work. Soon, he continued, he would need even less sleep.

So much so, I told him afterwards, that he was probably getting up before he went to bed. He almost, not quite, but almost said yes.

(Amazing what a few 'herbs' can do!)

By the end of the meeting people were queuing up to cart off crates of this miracle compound. But they all had an unreal look in their eyes, as if they had been present at a religious cult meeting.

Perhaps it's healthy to be cynical?

(I *was*.)

However, the tape I was listening to about Barleygreen made a lot of nutritional sense. Modern day farming methods and the stress of life in cities was destroying our nutrients, which we need in order to remain healthy. Barleygreen, it seemed, kept healthy people healthy and helped restore to health those who were ill.

Su had given me the name of an English woman who not only took Barleygreen herself, but could also organise some stocks for me.

My curiosity got the better of me, and I phoned.

Kathleen's praise of the product was similar to the

Americans' but it was very British. I believed her when she said that years of minor but debilitating illnesses were now a thing of the past since she began using Barleygreen. There were no religious cult ravings here, I thought.

She had to import it from the States, which was a complicated business owing to import and excise duties. At £25.00 (plus) a jar was it worth investing in a sample?

It wasn't the main thing on my mind at the moment, so I shelved it temporarily in the back of my storage box for future reference.

Another journey by taxi to UCH.

Glen, in a white coat, and Professor Taylor entered the clinic side by side like two trouble shooters. Dorothy was already busy making the area as comforting as possible, watering flowers and displaying her 'Breast Counsellor in attendance' board.

I felt safe.

I could trust two out of the three, at least, to treat me with the kid gloves (disposable, for health reasons) I needed.

Suddenly, I was whisked away to await in a tiny room for the two men who would be deciding my next few months.

Professor Taylor wanted to see the recalcitrant boob straight away, so Ellis and I found ourselves whisked into another room, and left alone, for me to undress. It occurred to me that Ellis hadn't seen me even partially unclothed for well over a year.

I was embarrassed . . . for him.

The room, the size of a large cupboard, suddenly also had to accommodate Glen, Professor Taylor and a nurse. There was no space to swing a cat, which was good, because Professor Taylor made a good attempt to swing a boob instead. I'm sure he knew what he was doing but it looked, and felt, as if he were clinging on to my breast and attempting to walk round the room with it.

It didn't particularly hurt, which surprised me, but it was an unpleasant sensation. My liver, stomach, ovaries (?) and various glands were prodded for good measure, and I was asked to dress.

There then followed a question and answer session.

"When and why did you have an Hysterectomy?"

"1981, and, etc, etc."

"Why were you put on HRT?"

"Because . . . etc etc."

"Do you have any Menopausal symptoms?"

"Such as?"

"Hot sweats at night."

"Yes, but I've been having those since I was a teenager." (true!)

"Mood swings?"

"I'm horrible all the time." (looking at Ellis)

Neither of them were convinced that I was going through an early Menopause, but that was something to be investigated at a later date.

"Stop taking the HRT." Professor Taylor insisted.

"I already have."

"Good."

The decision.

(My heart was pounding.)

Six weeks of Radiotherapy. Then, other things if that wasn't successful.

"Such as?" I quickly interjected.

"Hormonal intervention, and if that doesn't seem to work there are other things we can try."

"Such as?"

"Radiotherapy and Chemotherapy combined or . . ."

"What?"

"Things," he said, trying not to grin at my urgency.

Glen then saw us on our own to answer a list of questions Ellis and I had prepared in moments of clarity.

Glen expressed his surprise that I hadn't noticed the improvement in my breast, but put it down to my being in a state of shock when he had first seen me.

"I wasn't in shock," I insisted.

"But, you weren't reacting like someone who'd just been told they had cancer."

"I wasn't in shock, honestly. I hadn't really been fully aware of the state of my breast because as it became more and more tender I just wanted to leave it alone. Not in a 'what you can't see can't hurt you' state of mind, but I wanted an expert 'to take it away and repair it' state of mind."

"I see."

"So you weren't in shock?"

"Not at all."

(Not *with the cancer, I thought to myself.*)

Home to exhaustion. My adrenalin was well and truly drained and I slept for hours.

Another painting was born from this experience.

It was a quick delivery.

I am depicted in the healing colour of pale green, but my colour is draining fast. I'm being held back from continuing my progress by a doctor. In my hand is a purple flower of healing, but it is wilting in the rush of steam from a pressure cooker, which is on overdrive. The hospital is a strange shaped corridor with a 'no entry' sign attached to a padlocked door. Above the corridor are my crystals, chakra colours, gold star, A+ and ECaP; as they descend into the

81

corridor they lose all their colour and turn into dull greys. I stare up at a knife and the key to the padlock.

Underneath is written 'UCH + Middlesex Hospital = UCLH Trust'. (University College London Hospital Trust.)

I had crossed out 'Trust' and scrawled 'CHAOS'.

It took only four hours to paint . . . boy did I feel better.

The evening was filled with outgoing phone calls to allay the fears of friends whipped up in the frenzy of panic, and incoming calls from those who had been crawling up the grapevine.

Anita, as usual, telephoned out of the blue, but her calls usually coincided with some latest development.

(*How does she know?*)

I told all, including my hunt for a strange powder called Barleygreen.

"I've got some of that," she announced calmly.

"How, why?"

"I picked up a jar when I was in Canada, but I prefer to eat seaweed."

(*Of course you do.*)

"So?"

"You can have my jar."

The hunt was over even before it had started.

We also discovered that we were both seeing Robert the next day, so a swap could take place.

This was getting easier and easier.

Robert was horrified at my experience.

"Well done National Health Service. In the present demand for efficiency they've managed to cram several years of trauma into a few days."

"Quite."

I told him I was having difficulty in fitting in all the tablet

82

taking. Many had to be taken with food and water at set intervals during the day, but the Homeopathic pellets could not be taken within half an hour of food or drink. I was having to devise a military precision chart to work out how I could take all these different items and find time to relax, feed the cat, and sleep.

"Don't get neurotic," he said.

(*Get?*)

"It only requires a space of ten minutes either side of food or drink."

"But in this book I've been reading it says half an hour and don't brush your teeth with peppermint toothpaste and . . ."

". . . let me have a look at the book."

He snorted.

"I taught the author in 1980," he remarked casually.

He didn't seem impressed.

"So, it's your fault?" I opined (provocatively).

"The trouble with some people is that if they're taught in 1980, they remain in 1980. It's now 1993. Only ten minutes."

"Got it?"

(*Got it?*)

"How's your month been?" he asked.

"I yelled at Ellis."

"And?"

"And, nothing."

"How was he when all this trauma was exploding around you?"

"Brilliant. I couldn't have got through it without him."

"How did he respond?"

"He hugged me for a long time."

"You women will do anything for sex," he quipped.

I gave him one of my 'looks'.

83

Then he started again.

"What are you going to do with the rest of your life?" he asked again.

"Well . . . don't laugh, but I want to write a book." (He didn't laugh!)

"Go on."

"I just feel the need to write something that isn't along the lines of 'aren't I brave', or 'how I beat cancer'."

"Go on."

"More a book on the insights, experiences and self-determination which accompanies cancer, along with the role of Complementary therapies in the treatment of the whole person (and not just the cancer) . . . all mixed with a liberal dose of humour."

"Great. Cancer patients have to change their lives or they will get 'stuck' with the cancer. The important thing is to aim for something higher than yourself. What are you doing about it?"

"I'm already keeping a journal, writing down my dreams and producing strange paintings."

"Great. Go for it."

"I will. I have."

He added that most cancer patients arrive at a 'sticking point' where they almost decide to give up the struggle. But there were even Homeopathic remedies for that.

More questions and answers.

"Does the breast feel tight?"

"No."

"Is it painful?"

"No."

"Does it hurt when you breath in?"

"Yes."

"Yes?"

"Well you see my bra elastic is getting too tight."

This time he gave me one of *his* 'looks'.

"Right," he said. "Throw away your remaining tablets . . . "

"I don't like waste."

"Throw away your remaining tablets, and take these."

Specific instruction again. Tablet number one: now, 5 p.m., 8 p.m. Tablet number two: one to be taken three times a day. Tablet number three: one to be taken on days of Radiotherapy.

"What do they do?" I enquired.

"These Radiotherapy tabs? Oh, these are wonderful. They make your healthy cells invisible to the gamma rays."

(*The Fox element's working then?*)

"Of course they do."

I also remembered a statement made by one of the speakers on the Barleygreen tape. "It's amazing how broadminded you become when your life's at stake."

I'll go along with that.

I made the wrong decision to catch a 253 bus, destination Finsbury Park. It ended up there, but not before touring London under the direction of a driver who obviously had no belief in a timetable. He slowed down on approaching traffic lights, so he was able to stop when they changed to red. He stopped when anyone put his or her hand out. He waited until new passengers had settled themselves in their seats etc etc.

The whole journey took an hour and a quarter.

Is there a Homeopathic remedy for London Transport fatigue?

I'd only just arrived home when I realised that I was expected at my crystal session. I was cold, so put on the first available jumper that hadn't been totally covered in cat's hair.

I needn't have worried because as soon as I entered

Trish's front room a strange looking black cat jumped up on my lap, curled up, and went to sleep.

(I've always wondered how a totally black cat can leave white cats hairs on a black jumper?)

Trish 'told me off' for wearing black next to my skin.

"Very negative," she insisted.

"I'll try to do better," I mumbled.

The week had taken its toll and I remained in bed for twenty hours.

That evening a friend, who is also Waffles's 'grandmother', joined me for a meal. Rosemary was delighted at the help Waffles was giving me and declared that she was a much nicer, well balanced cat than her mother, Pancake.

(Waffles—well balanced?)

"Which boob is it?" she asked.

"The left."

"Right," she mused.

"No, left."

Giggles.

"I've got tickets for a requiem," she said with some urgency.

"I'm not quite ready for that."

Giggles.

The conversation continued at that level all evening. What hope was there for Pancake and Waffles?

As I had been given a medical certificate for two months' sick leave, I wrote to the education department telling them of the six to eight weeks of Radiotherapy and that I was feeling particularly frazzled by last week's cock-up. (Cock-up? Shouldn't that be Boob?)

I would try to visit the department every now and then, but they mustn't be surprised to see a naked Boob walking in, complete with a set of keys around its middle.

That will be me.

I was preparing them for the effects of the Vanishing tablets.

They'd never really understood me . . . I doubt now if they ever would.

I wanted to prepare myself for the next round of new experiences.

Radiotherapy.

Thinks? I don't know anything about that.

I reached for my copy of 'Our Bodies, Ourselves' and flipped casually to the chapter on Radiotherapy.

Quote: 'As long ago as 1946 it was recognised that Radiotherapy did not help and possibly even exacerbated the disease', and 'Many Radiotherapy departments in England have long queues and a lot of outdated equipment'.

Gulp!!!!!!

I turned to the front of the book, and there it was: Printed and Published *1976*.

I threw the book away, and made a mental note to always look at the publication date before reading any material.

I wrote to BACUP (British Association of Cancer United Patients) for their current pamphlet on Radiotherapy, as well as one on Chemotherapy and Breast Cancer.

My breast started hurting again. I hoped it was the Homeopathy.

The next day was to be the start of my Radiotherapy. However, I hadn't realised that so much preparation was needed.

In Planning, Glen arrived and started to draw purple lines on my chest and neck area. It was very uncomfortable for me, as I had to lie with my left arm stretched backwards to enable the lymph glands to be exposed. The lines were straightened up by a nurse with a ruler and set square and then marked with Gentian Violet, a semi-permanent liquid, which stains everything it comes in contact with. Then, in best Blue Peter tradition, a cardboard cut-out of the cross-section of my breast was produced and a spirit level perched on top to ensure the correct position. Many measurements were taken and these I was told would be fed into a computer to programme the level and depth of the radiation waves. By using a computer there was very little risk of my lungs or other vital underlying organs being frazzled as well. I was warned that I would not be able to wear a bra for some time, as the whole area would be sore. I had already stopped wearing a bra, as the swelling was making it so uncomfortable. I was my normal self on one side, but the other was like Dolly Parton with a booster silicon injection. I had searched for Boob tubes in my local shops, but fashion dictates that only young trendy bustless creatures need these items. I did eventually have some given to me and although more comfortable on the skin did not give the support my tumour required. It was now quite heavy and any movement caused great discomfort. Even my arm ached. I was unaware that I permanently held the arm across the body to support it, but as this created a platform for the breast to perch on, perhaps subconsciously I knew what I was doing?

I was told not to use soap, only baby talcum powder, and no deodorant, as these all contain metals.

No deodorant! Don't worry, they said, the sweat glands dry up and any underarm hair will fall out, so after a while I won't pong.

(*Great, can you do the other one while you're at it!*)

By the end of the Planning my arm had to be prised away from the bar I had been holding on to. All the blood had drained away from my hand and the whole area was tight with pain from being stretched into such an unnatural position.

It really was bad in a bad way. Up until then I hadn't realised.

Despite the discomfort I drove to keep my appontment with Lily, Jane and Declan.

Once again, Jane and Declan didn't turn up.

"It's just not good enough," I argued. "They are supposed to be involved in healing and caring for people and they consistently let me down . . . and they have my paintings . . . and Declan said he'd send me a special tape of meditation for cancer, which never arrived . . ."

I was hurt and angry.

Lily sympathised.

She was not well enough to give me any Healing, but I was handed over to one of her helpers.

It was not the same.

I was becoming agitated having to wait for the start of the Radiotherapy treatment. Apart from the necessity of waiting for the computer programme the Radiotherapy unit was in the process of being refurbished and would not be ready until the following week at the earliest. Meanwhile, wasn't this giving the cancer a chance to procreate? It was unpleasant, to say the least, to think of cells multiplying at their leisure.

(*Get out of me!*)

I had a meeting with Dorothy, and she calmed some of my agitation. As my knowledge grew, the more I realised I didn't know certain fundamental concepts.

"What's the difference between a tumour and a cancer?"

"A tumour *is* a cancer. 'Tumour' is more commonly used

because people find the word 'cancer' so hard to say," was the simple reply.

(*cancer, cancer, cancer, cancer, cancer, cancer, cancer, cancer, cancer, cancer.*)

"What does Oncology mean?"

"The study and treatment of cancers."

"Oh, (silly me)."

In a medical dictionary I had (the sort of book you read whilst peering through gaps in your fingers) it states simply 'the study of tumours'.

"Dorothy, what's a 'tumour'?"

Su phoned in great excitement. She had just seen an article about a German treatment that was achieving very good results on Inflammatory Breast cancer; she promised to send me a copy.

The next day brought lots of post crashing through my letter box. The usual scenario in life is that the postman gets bitten or chased by the family dog. In my household, I get savaged by the cat. Waffles has nerves about her station and if she is asleep on me, any noise in the house is enough for her to leap up on to a high platform . . . using me as a springboard!

Four letters or communications for me.

Envelope one: a poem from my boss about touching 'eternity' and 'outstretched hands' reaching for the aforementioned eternity.

Okay, I can cope with that. Nice poem.

Envelope two: BACUP pamphlets. I opened the one on Breast cancer. Talk of benign and malignant tumours (that word again) and the possibility of cells spreading to other parts of the body.

Under 'Stages of Breast cancer' I read that:

'Stage one: The tumour measures under two centimetres.'

'Stage two: The tumour measures between two to five centimetres.'

'Stage three: The tumour is larger than five centimetres.'

'Stage four: The tumour is of any size.'

(*What about a size 36D, going on 38D?*)

Now I could see why they said that it would be better if I didn't read anything on Breast cancer.

One section of the pamphlet interested me. 'Contraception and Hormone Replacement Therapy'. It states: 'As the cancer may be affected by hormones, women who have breast cancer are usually advised not to take the contraceptive pill. The same advice is usually given about HRT.'

Very interesting.

While waiting for one of the Planning sessions I had read in a magazine that 'HRT increases the risk of Breast cancer. This may be because Breast tumours are oestrogen-dependent and therefore grow more rapidly due to the treatment. Consequently HRT may unmask a tumour earlier. This could explain why women on HRT who are diagnosed as having Breast cancer have a better prognosis.'

My brain couldn't work out if this was a good piece of information or not. On the one hand, could my being on HRT have been one of the triggers? Or, could it also have caused the cancer to be detected sooner because of the speed of the growth?

The only delay had been the forty three days wait for the UCH appointment. If I had only been more alert to the pain of my breast instead of the pain of my life, perhaps I would have reacted like 'Red Lips' and demanded an earlier appointment.

'If only' . . . a prevaricator's cop out.

By the end of the pamphlet I had to acknowledge that I did have a potentially fatal disease and that, even if it is cleared up, I may have years of problems and that it is often impossible to predict if the cancer has gone completely.

Acceptance is one thing. Information in black and white is another.

I prefer my acceptance . . . and fighting determination.

Several people had warned me of the negativity of the average cancer ward in a hospital, as opposed to the heart surgery ward.

Is it this negativity about the uncertainty of cancer that makes people give up, or the disease itself?

Envelope three: a book and card from my niece, Niah.

That's nice.

The book was 'The Cancer Journals' by Audre Lorde, published in 1980.

It chronicled her confrontation with cancer, her Mastectomy and her view of the heterosexual and male-dominated medical profession.

I was assured it would be an easy read 'and yes, Audre Lorde died last November (1992) but she didn't leave quietly' added Niah.

(*Jolly good.*)

I successfully ignored the horror stories of Chemotherapy and Radiotherapy, which had persuaded Audre to have an immediate Mastectomy. I admired her flow of writing and descriptive powers of the hurt she felt 'abandoning' her breast, but her total dislike of the heterosexual world left me feeling worried about the amount of energy she had used up in this process.

She praised the woman who had come from 'Reach for Recovery' (an American based group) to help her through the difficult time after surgery, but 'thought what a shame such a gutsy woman wasn't a dyke'.

I remembered my time in ILEA (Inner London Education

Authority) and Camden Adult Education Institute and thought what a furore I would have caused if at a management meeting I had passed comment that a particular teacher was brilliant, but that wasn't it a shame she *was* a dyke!

I was also amused by the reasons she gave for refusing a prosthesis: it was all a male conspiracy as they, and society, found the concept of one-breasted women too hard to take.

'The fact that the fashion needs of one-breasted women are not currently being met doesn't mean that the concerted pressure of our demands cannot change that.'

My mind zoomed off to the British Telecom advert featuring Beatie and a harassed shopkeeper.

'Yes, Madam, we have it in the pink and the green and the blue and the yellow, in all of the styles and in all of the sizes.

'What was that Madam? No, we do not have those particular styles with the left breast missing, only the right.'

The mind boggles.

I thought of the dictates of fashion. I have always been excited when an article has declared that 'Breasts are back' and then have an emaciated size 30A model stuff some cotton wool under her breast to elevate it to a 30B, and then be called curvy.

That fashion is usually short-lived

The fact that 60% of women in England now take size 36B (or C) makes a mockery of the models used to promote clothes. And, they wonder why the rag trade is in difficulties.

Other passages in the book leapt out at me. 'The battle will continue to rage between Surgeons, Radiographers and Chemotherapists about whether it is better to mutilate us, radiate us, or poison us.'

Yes?

'There has been a marked increase in Breast cancer in women since 1961: 21% of cancer deaths among women are due to Breast cancer. Over the years, the incidence, mortality and survival rates from cancer of the breast has remained relatively unchanged.'

Yes?

Did I need this?

Envelope four: the article about the new wonder cure by a German doctor, sent by Su.

'Inflammatory cancer the most lethal form of Breast cancer,' it stated.

I was glad there was nothing else to open; I could feel myself closing in.

I was very unsettled. Couldn't sleep. The lymph area had a constant dull ache, making my imagination run riot.

That night I dreamed of my own funeral.

The next morning I had a shower, and practised not getting the breast and shoulder area wet or soapy.

I felt a little better.

I visualised for half an hour.

I felt much better.

I went out and bought some beautiful loose-fitting clothes.

I felt wonderful.

I had managed to internalise all the gloom and doom and store it away in the 'relevant but not appropriate to me' file.

Life goes on.

There was no point in thinking of the bleakest scenario or I would find myself the Star player.

Back to the Middlesex and the start of the Radiotherapy. At last. Glen had to make a few more markings on me and I learn I'm the first breast patient to be measured on the new machine.

I'm then taken to the basement.

Potters know about basements. It must be the same for Radiographers.

Although the room was newly furbished, and therefore wonderful, I wouldn't have known. It was a typical hospital basement; no daylight, heating pipes everywhere and nowhere to sit without being in someone's way.

My name is called. "Mrs Cole."

(*Here we go again.*)

A huge machine called a Mobiltron awaits me. I have to lie on a fairly cold surface, my arm prised backwards and gripping on to a handle. A cold spirit level is placed on my sternum. If my left nipple could manage it, it would be erect with the cold. The right one comes out in sympathy.

A temporary beam of light is directed down on to the perfect square that will be with me for eight weeks.

They praise my markings.

Everyone leaves the room.

Peep peep . . . peep . . . peeppeep . . . peep peep . . . peep . . . peep peep.

I look at the clock and time it.

About two minutes (-ish) depending if one counts the peeps or the noise of the machine whirring into action.

A radio keeps me company.

The first song I heard was 'Wide eyed and Legless' by Andy Fairweather-Low, but, as the Middlesex was where I had had all my gynaecological operations, I heard it as 'Wide legged and eyeless'.

Honest.

The Radiographers returned and moved the machine around me to Zap me from a different position.

Another two minutes.

95

What happens, I thought, if someone panics?

They return again.

This time, as the rays will be very near my throat, an extra device is added to the machine and a piece of lead is positioned between me and the rays to prevent any damage.

A further two minutes.

My arm is prised away from the grip.

I'm cold and in some discomfort, but not from the Radiation.

You don't feel a thing. Not a thing.

However, this is not what the Sun wishes people to believe.

When I was waiting I picked up the Sun to remind myself how terrible it was (well, that's my excuse), and there was an article about one of the stars from Dad's Army who was having 'Months of painful Radiotherapy'.

Absolute rubbish.

And Radiotherapy isn't painful either.

I was to return to the basement every day for thirty-two more sessions. This, in fact, was spread over eight weeks in total as Easter and bank holidays intervened.

I was receiving two 'grays' a day.

I was in a fair amount of discomfort for the first few weeks because of the position I had to hold for ten to fifteen minutes at a time but, as the rays began to work, so did my body.

On the second or third day of the monotonous journey down to Goodge Street by tube, I was silently involved in a conversation between three passengers.

When one of them left, the remaining two started a different conversation.

"Why is George so glum these days?"

"His father's just died from cancer."

"He couldn't have been that old?"

96

"Oh he was. At least mid-forties."

(*What?*)

"I don't know why they bother with any treatment. I think they should just be told that they've got cancer and they are going to die."

"Yes. It's such a waste of time and money."

I almost asked them if they would like me to drop dead in front of them, or should I wait until I got home?

The one and only time I felt nauseous was on the third day of the treatment. But I still dragged myself across London to see Lily.

"You can't have come to see Lily, she's gone to America."

"What!"

"It's been arranged for months. She hasn't made any appointments because of the travel arrangements."

"Well she did with me!"

I felt drained, angry, let down, cast aside . . . and uncared for, again.

It was too much. I let rip with all the hurt of '92 welling up inside me.

"Why does everyone let me down? I've got cancer; I feel terrible; I've travelled forty minutes to get here; Lily knew I was coming, she wrote it in her book; Jane and Declan are no better, they just dumped me for no reason and with no apologies; now I've got to drive back and . . . "

They sat me in a room to calm down.

"You must learn to ask for help," said one woman.

"I did, " I muttered, "and all that's happened is that I feel abandoned."

I was coaxed into having some healing from a young couple, and arranged to see them the following week.

But my confidence in the outfit was dented forever.

Months later I did receive a phone call from the

Chairman of the Healing centre apologising for my treatment, or lack of it!

I met Dorothy the next day and had a slight eruption when I recalled the anger and hurt I had felt in being deemed 'unimportant' even to those in the healing profession.

"They are not Healers" said Dorothy. "If they were, they would acknowledge your needs."

"I know that, but why do I get so frustrated and angry? They are the ones with the problem, so why can't I just walk away and accept that I don't want anything to do with them?"

"It's brought back too many memories and, at the moment, you haven't the energy to step aside and view things objectively."

(*True*)

But I do know that if for any reason I've had no alternative but to cancel an appointment I have always contacted the person as soon as possible to apologise and explain.

No apology ever came from Lily, Jane or Declan.

I tried to step aside.

It's not easy.

The days started to fall into a regular pattern.

Leave house at 7.45 a.m. and drive to a Northern Line station. Fit on to a train, which seemed to run in a vacuum of the normal rush hour capacity. Ten minutes either side and there would be no hope of a seat, nor a square foot for

98

my feet. I shuddered at being caught in a crush, as I felt very protective of my injured breast. To try to create a barrier between it and another individual could be misconstrued as selfishness; and unfortunately (?) I did not look ill enough to request a seat. It was therefore simpler to avoid all these problems and arrive forty minutes early for my appointment.

I could then have a cup of tea in one of the local cafes and read my Guardian. A much more civilised start to the day than being squashed boob(y).

After a while I learnt that if I hovered in the basement I could usually be seen fifteen or twenty minutes earlier.

Home by 10 a.m. . . . and blissfully back to bed.

I then had the rest of the day in which to write or paint.

My latest painting was of the Radiotherapy basement. I am lying on the table with my arm back but I am only a mere outline, as the 'Vanishing tablets' had done their work. The breast area, however, is taking the full force of the rays and is bright red and black. The Mobiltron machine, which towers above me, is sending out its deadly rays but, hang on a minute, what's that?

Flying through the air, wearing a cloak and magician's hat is Robert holding the container of Vanishing tablets. His other hand carries a magic wand, which is touching the Mobiltron machine and making the rays pink instead of deadly red.

Several friends who looked at this strange painting asked, in all seriousness, if the Mobiltron machine was in fact just plugged into the wall with a 15 amp fuse!!!

"You've got to be joking! It's probably connected directly to the National Grid," I replied jokingly. But at least I knew they had observed the small 'details' I had incorporated into the painting.

Apart from the painting and the daily Journal I was keeping, the days were taken up with sleep and my Complementary therapies. These were now becoming a lifeline to sanity. Giving me not only an interest, but helping to break the potential isolation I could have felt by not being at work . . . and not having a home life.

I needed stimulation, and my encounters with the therapists attached to the therapies certainly gave me that.

Regular trips to food shops also grounded me in everyday activities.

I had asked the hospital if there was any food I should or should not eat.

"No, eat normally," was the considered opinion.

But I asked around my various Gurus and a whole wealth of information was forthcoming.

Robert advised me not to eat or drink anything that would overtax the liver, as it had already had more than its fair share of work to do.

So?

"Avoid tea, coffee and alcohol," he said.

I could not do without tea first thing in the morning; it got my mouth working. During the day I really did try to stick to herbal teas, water or soya drinks. It was no problem avoiding coffee as I rarely liked it unless it contained cointreau and cream! As my consumption of alcohol was virtually nil, this solved that excuse for hedonism.

"Avoid meat unless it's free-range chicken."

I'm not a big meat eater anyway, so cutting out meat altogether was another no big deal.

"Eat fish but not trout or salmon reared in fish farms. They swim around in a soup of anti-biotics." That's enough to put me off trout and salmon for life!

"Eat fresh fruit and vegetables and pulses, but avoid sweets and processed food."

My eating habits have always been reasonably good

unless I've been bad with a capital B. I can quite easily demolish a box of chocolates or a double chocolate chip, dutch fudge, rocky mountain, praline nut sundae.

I always felt guilty but not that guilty! . . . Bliss.

With all this advice I did not dare buy any more chocolate, but I did occasionally dip into a chocolate frozen yoghurt . . . smallish bliss.

Beetroot juice I learnt was a great detoxifier, and the liver could do with any help it could get.

Rice, I learnt, was also a good detoxifier as the bulk of the grain passed through the body taking with it unwanted products.

(*That's a nice way of putting it.*)

I had never really enjoyed rice, but this could have been the result of my mother serving boil-in-the-bag Vesta Curry and Rice in the '60s. That and mounds of badly cooked rice, were enough to make me avoid it, as opposed to disliking it.

Now, there was a need, but to make it more acceptable to my stomach and eyes I cooked separate dishes of rice, buckwheat and lentils then layered them in small timbales, with spinach in between each layer.

By preparing ten of these little dishes and stacking them in the fridge I had a ready stock of delicious meals.

I was also becoming a pill popper: Vitamin C, Selenium, Folic Acid, Beta-Carotene, Codliver oil capsules and four large tablets of Barleygreen a day.

I had carefully worked up to four tablets as I had been warned that initially they could cause stomach upsets.

However, one day when I'd staggered in with some shopping I made the mistake of answering the phone. It was the American lady who had spoken with Ellis. She had hopes of interesting him in the importation of Barleygreen.

Boy, could she talk!

She was planning to attend a Barleygreen convention in Orlando, so I thought it would be of interest to mention the

101

possible cultural differences between American and English levels of tolerance to frenzied marketing techniques.

I thought it would help.

She went on talking as if I had never spoken.

Had I said something?

It felt as if I were talking to a recorded message.

As I started to feel my energy drain I politely mentioned that I was ill, that I had just returned from shopping, and that I really was in need of a rest . . . the voice continued.

"How many Barleygreen are you taking every day?"

"Four."

"Oh, you need to take at least twenty-eight a day to get the full benefit."

(*Twenty-eight! Has she got shares in Barleygreen?*)

With that I informed her that my vegetables, and I, were now rapidly wilting and I really had to go.

I clunked the phone down and leaving the vegetables to their fate, I retired to bed and dreamed of mountains of Barleygreen tablets.

The 'tablets' had confused me when Anita gave me her bottle from Canada, because all the promotional talk had been of powder.

Through the post had arrived a small sample of Barleygreen powder and I dutifully mixed it with fruit juice, as directed. If I say it was like drinking the dredged bottom of a pond, then I would be understating the taste sensation.

(*Keep taking the tablets.*)

Throughout my exploration of the causes and nature of cancer I was open to any insight or understanding of the condition. I had a good supportive friend, Angela, who herself had been laid low by Myalgic Encephalomyelitis.

Over the two years of her illness I had regularly phoned to check on her latest 'state of body' and now, in return, the phone calls were all flooding the other way,

She had delved into many spiritual aspects of illness and was delighted to pass on various tapes and books.

Matthew Manning's 'Guide to Self Healing' was another jolt to the complex acceptance of illness as an indication that something is wrong with the whole person.

'Illness can be a socially acceptable form of suicide.'

(*Was I that desperate?*)

Galen, in the second century, noted that only depressed individuals got cancer; Sir James Paget thought deferred hope and disappointment could bring about the growth of cancer; Elida Evans found in his study of a hundred patients that many had lost an important relationship before the onset of cancer.

I read on.

In 1969 Holmes and Rahe studied the effects that changes in life brought about in 5,000 patients.

They concluded that if there were a significant number of changes in a relatively short space of time, then that individual was more likely to become ill.

They devised a 'Social Readjustment Scale' in which they listed possible stressful events in a person's life with a value factor against each.

They claimed that if in the preceding year a score of over 300 was reached, then the chance of a serious health problem was 80%.

I have never taken to these 'quizzes', partly because I usually only see them in Women's magazines. Here the vitally important insight is to find out if you are sexually dynamic on a first date, or how would you react if you discovered that your man was having a relationship with your best friend's mother's second husband.

I only do them for fun (*everyone says that*) and am usually rewarded with the knowledge that I am pretty pathetic and must try harder.

Pen and paper in hand I started down this latest list of life's traumas.

I'm bound to get a low score, I thought, jokingly.

422!!!!!

And this was without any score points for Ellis. However, they assumed you had to be married to be stressed about a relationsip.

Not true.

But under relationship traumas there were only:

'Death of Spouse' scoring 100;

'Divorce' scoring 73;

'Marital Separation' scoring 63.

I felt Ellis had separated, divorced and died on me all in one go! How do you work out the score for 'a knight in shining armour has not only fallen off his horse, but his armour's rusted . . . and he knew it was going to happen, and forgot to mention it'?

I thought of 1992 and shuddered.

On 1st January I was officially redundant after twenty two years of teaching. My position at the Camden Institute gave me not only complete control of my working day, but the power to organise and promote many different courses, exhibitions, demonstrations and open days. True, there were difficulties with certain members of staff, and one in particular, but I loved my job as it gave me the space to be creative and productive.

It also provided me with the financial security that I had worked so hard to achieve. As a single female with neither husband, live-in partner, nor parents, I had relied only on myself since I was sixteen.

The financial security I had worked for had all disappeared.

What also angered me was that my job entailed working with what Camden described as Priority groups. I had helped to boost the number of students in this specific category from 500 to over 4000++, the name I gave an exhibition I organised just as they were tearing apart the whole concept of adult education . . . and Priorities.

No apologies.

No sadness.

No condemnation of government education policy.

From now on those in need would have to pay high fees for even the most basic class . . . if they could find one.

I started to build up a small, very small, business in Massage and Aromatherapy, but in times of recession it's not easy, even if everyone could do with a dose of Lavender.

By the start of the year, maybe sooner, I had realised that something had happened to Ellis. We had been living together for only a few months and, although I had been prepared to live through and accept a period of adjustment, I thought I would be the one to find it difficult.

Having lived on my own for twenty-three years, I had to have some horrible habits.

But within two weeks he could no longer sit in the same room as me, we stopped socialising, and I was removed to another bedroom, where I mourned and cried and raged.

Where once my sadness would elicit his instant devotion to the process of returning me to peace, now he turned away from me, from my every gesture of concern for him, for us.

I did not give in easily.

I spent most of 1992 trying to penetrate the hidden world of Ellis's emotional past.

He didn't want it found.

It was too painful.

I had lost control.

By the time I realised this it was November, and the cancer had already taken a grip.

I made up my mind to leave as soon as I could get my own house back. The culmination of saving and planning from the age of fifteen, my house represented all my achievements and had been my bolt hole when life took a turn for the worse.

I didn't have a bolt hole now. It was frightening.

I had rented out my house via an Estate Agency, who installed a refugee family, care of the local council.

In May '92 the payments ceased, as the Estate Agency was being investigated for fraud and embezzlement.

But that's not my fault.

Tough.

I received no further rent until January '93 and that was only after Ellis had spent a great deal of time and energy acting on my behalf.

At one time he was even accused by the council of working for the Estate Agents!

I had lost control.

Worse was to come. I went to the house to talk to the tenants, whom I had met earlier in the year. As part of the 'fraud' the council refused to believe that the tenants existed.

They didn't!

A neighbour informed me that the original family had moved out months ago and that since then a succession of people of every age, sex and race had moved freely in and out of the house: maybe as many as fifteen living there at any one time.

I'd lost control.

The council wasn't bothered.

In March '92 I returned to a Women's Clinic for another discussion on Hormone Replacement Therapy. By this time I was ready to imbibe anything that would make the 'hurt' go away. They had sent me to St Mary's Hospital for a bone scan, and there it was, the start of Osteoporosis.

Brittle bone disease that affects women after the Menopause because of the lack of oestrogen in their blood.

Because of my early Hysterectomy at the age of thirty-two they said I had probably started an early Menopause, hence the effect on my bones.

This reopened my memories of a thug I had lived with when I was nineteen. A charming fellow, who felt it was his duty to keep me in place by kicking and slapping me at regular intervals.

I used to hear him in the bathroom muttering to himself 'I'll kill her, I'll kill her'. It was only when I felt that death was preferable to this treatment that I rebelled.

After a particularly savage beating, through which I heard a male student colleague pleading 'Don't do that Sid', I was free.

That is why I had lived alone, quite happily.

He had now come back to haunt me, as those beatings had taken their toll on my health and helped towards my need for an Operation.

A bright glow on the horizon was that I was offered and accepted a 0.5 Lecturer post at a men's prison.

Two and a half days work a week would still allow time for me to build up my small business.

Great.

Not so great.

The incumbent art teacher, convinced she would be offered the job (and should have, as she was brilliant), was devastated.

The Education Officer promptly offered her ten teaching sessions a week, halved my administrative duties, and carried on as though everything was normal.

It certainly wasn't normal.

The animosity against me from the 'fans' of the art teacher was extremely upsetting and at times vicious. I attempted to ameliorate the situation, but it felt as if my efforts were falling on deaf ears.

Nobody seemed interested.

Effectively, everyone still went to the original art teacher with queries as she knew what she was doing, had been doing it for years, and doing it very well.

I didn't have any control.

Then there was the harassment.

Small things like a knife being held at me in a threatening way; my passage down the stairs blocked by a student; being jumped on in the kiln room for a kiss.

My fault??

Yes, my fault in that I kept saying 'No' to this particular student if his requests were unreasonable.

But, as no one else in the department had had any trouble with him, there appeared to be no case to answer.

It was 'only me' after all.

I frequently discussed the problem at staff meetings, but as I was the only teacher from the arts subjects there was no one else to back me. In fact, other members of staff *had* been having trouble with this particular student, but hadn't wanted to report it in case it might look as if they had lost control.

I'd certainly lost control.

And, I felt very unsupported and irrelevant.

In September of that year another student joined the class. It was obvious to me that he not only had problems but that he was also very disturbed. He would have uncontrollable rages over nothing, slump over his work, refuse to communicate, and threaten to smash up his and everyone else's work.

All of this I reported.

Apart from one letter from the Medical Officer stating that it was known that this particular man had behaviour problems nothing was done.

Why should anyone bother; it was only me.

November was a bleak month.

My body had already started to let me down in peculiar ways. I had to queue in the local housing department to convince them that I existed and that I was the official

Landlord (Distressed House Owner actually!) of the property where they had placed the refugee tenants.

After one hour in the queue, I felt my back seize up and I could neither walk, stand nor sit without considerable pain.

Once out of the building the pain eased off.

A few days later I woke early in the morning and my first thought was that I was paralysed. I could not move my head, neck, eyes nor shoulders and the pain across my forehead was unbearable.

I lay there trying to stay calm, and slowly tried to move my hands to my face . . . without moving my shoulders.

The whole of my head felt as if it had been beaten with a blunt instrument and even my own fingers were not welcome to investigate.

I waited until I heard Ellis pass my door . . . and called out.

He must have realised something was very wrong. Even I was surprised by the panic in my voice.

"Bring me paracetamol, Rescue Remedy, Peppermint essential oil, a cold flannel, a cup of tea," I pleaded.

Slowly, after about an hour, I could feel the intensity begin to wane, but it took a further six hours before I attempted to open my eyes, or get out of bed.

Ellis rang the prison to let them know I was not coming in.
(*Significant?*)

The next day all symptoms had vanished . . . but then, I don't teach at the prison on Fridays.
(*Very significant.*)

How much more could I take?

The next week I returned to the prison, but I could feel the unreality of my own body.

I felt as if I didn't exist.

The class went quite smoothly until that same troubled student started screaming abuse at me.

I spoke quietly to him.

He apologised.

Then he flared up again, and threw something across the room. I talked to him and he calmed down.

He apologised.

He threatened to smash up the kiln room ... "and nobody would do anything about it," he said.
  (*How right he is.*)
  I calmed him down.

He apologised.

At the end of the class I asked him to clear his work space which after some further altercation, he did.

I thanked him.

I collected all the security tools, which had to be secured in a downstairs office, and the men drifted away.

I was putting away pottery in the kiln room, when I heard my name called.

As I turned, a pottery cheese wire was wrapped around my neck, and I found myself face to face with the disturbed student.

By instinct, self preservation or just pure luck (?), I managed to place my fingers between the wire and the front of my neck, as I had twisted round to see who had called my name.

We stared at each other.

Silence.

His expression changed, his grip relaxed and I was able to release the wire from my throat.

I started, with mechanical movements, to wipe down the tables.

"Oh, I suppose you're going to report me now?" he said.

"It's obvious you don't want to be in my class and I'll do everything I can to ensure that you're not."

"What's all the fuss about. If I'd wanted to kill you I could have done."

"I'm sure."

"Look, I'm sorry," he pleaded. "It was only a joke, but it went too far. I like you really."

I walked out of the room, went downstairs, and into the staff room.

I froze.

He appeared at the door and asked another member of staff if he could talk to me.

It was then that she noticed that I was shaking and losing control.

She closed the door on him.

I went to pieces.

Meanwhile, Security went into action. He had returned to his house block and confessed that he'd garrotted the pottery teacher.

That got them moving!
  (*Shall we pick up the head first, or lock him up?*)

I remember being surrounded by Governors and Officers

and Medics; and screaming abuse at the pathetic inadequate way the prison was being run.

I don't think it did much good, but I felt better for saying it. I then had to wait for the outside police, who interviewed me for hours.

When they looked at his prison file, all they could say was how was it possible for someone as violent as that to be in a Category C prison, and on education.

It was a mystery to them.

Not to me.

Money.

It's cheaper to send someone to a Category C prison than a Category B prison.
    And sod security.
    And sod Pottery teachers.
    When I returned to work a few days later I assumed that this incident would have confirmed and highlighted all my verbal complaints.

Nothing was mentioned.

To me, it seemed as if everyone was ignoring what had happened.
    I didn't exist.

I was not worth getting bothered about.

The students were wonderful and apologetic. One man, whom I didn't know well, made a special point of coming to me to plead on behalf of his race.
    It hadn't even occurred to me to be 'racist' or 'sexist'. This person was mentally unbalanced. I didn't want him even to be prosecuted, only helped.

He was transferred to another prison for his own protection.

And?

On arrival he promptly applied for education.

And?

Luckily the non-Home Office grapevine had been put to good use and other teachers were spared the problem.

My problem still remained.

Nobody seemed bothered about the attack, so I made up my mind to mention something at the next staff meeting.

The next meeting was cancelled.

A comment of 'I could really mug you for that apple' casually thrown at me by a colleague, would not normally cause offence, but under the circumstances, the insensitivity of the comment didn't alleviate my sense of isolation.

Why was I so unworthy of protection?

I was not only cracking up again but producing a good head of steam in which to do it.

I prepared a statement that could be read out at the next meeting, and ensured that the item of 'Disruptive Students' was added to the agenda.

The big day arrived, and I was already shaking.

Some surprise was voiced at the topic but, paper in hand, I started my 'cornered animal' justification of my hurt.

I apologised for my shaky voice, but hoped they would soon understand the reason for my emotion.

I read.

"Several months ago I discussed at the staff meeting whether there had been, or should be, a 'code of conduct' for prisoners attending the department. I also suggested the need to have prior knowledge of any mental instability or violent behaviour.

Both suggestions were rejected as unnecessary.

Over the past six months I have been subjected to, or have been made aware of, the following . . . (I then read out a list of twenty two incidents relating to myself and other art staff.)

As other members of staff attending the meeting had not experienced major difficulties with either of the students involved, nothing was done.

However, one student who had verbally abused a member of staff at a concert, was suspended immediately for three months and told to apologise before he would be allowed back to education. Another student was removed completely for being a 'general nuisance.'

Although I had not had any major problems with these two students I supported in theory their removal from education.

I feel I have reasonable grounds for feeling unsupported in the matter of my personal safety."

I then waved a Home Office Health and Safety document at the silent gathering and proposed that a workable warning/suspension procedure should be immediately implemented.

I escaped the expected fallout . . . and cried the twenty-eight miles home.

The next day I had to return.

Had my message taken root?

Yes.

An incident book was set up to monitor any strange or unacceptable behaviour. I had achieved something but at what cost to my general state of health?

At the next week's meeting I had to leave early.

"I have an appointment at the clinic, nothing important, I'll see you tomorrow."

"Good luck," they all cried.

Too late.

So, 422+++ points, and a year that ended with my spending Christmas and New Year on my own, as Ellis had suddenly announced that he would be staying at an hotel.

I was not totally alone.

Waffles was her normal sleepy self.

I joined her on the hall landing for a New Year photograph.

"Happy New Year, Waffs. 1993 has got to be better," I murmured in her ear.

I raised my glass.

The automatic camera flashed.

I received a wet lick for my joviality, and she returned to her dreams.

And I to mine.

Holmes and Rahe's point system does not automatically mean that the individual *would* become ill, only that to avoid any chance of an illness, one had to adapt to these changes and learn to relax.

Simple.

Relaxation can come in many forms. Mental imagery, breathing, exercise and laughter.

Laughter?

Laughter deepens breathing, improves circulation, speeds tissue healing, expands blood vessels, and stabilises many body functions. Our thoughts can trigger the release of chemicals such as endorphins, and laughter will help.

Trouble was, I found nothing funny about '92.

That was the problem.

Now, in '93 I keep friends and associates entertained by my tales of treatments, both friendly, creative and down right 'orrible.

Perverse?

Probably

Effective?

100%.

Waffles continued to give me hours of precious support or encounters with the cat world, where few humans dare to go.

She had reluctantly accepted my Visualisation as part of the daily routine, but still sat around eyeing me suspiciously.

If she could try out, hamper, or improve something, she would. So, although on one occasion I was aware of her presence, it was not until I roused myself from the Visualisation that I realised she had 'joined in'. There she was lying alongside me on her back with her front paws flopped forward, and her head stretched into a blissful angelic pose.

What was she Visualising about?

Her need to exit through the cat flap, and return at greater speed if necessary, was a constant battle between us.

In my haste to open the flap I stepped awkwardly as I approached it, lost my balance, twisted to save my breast from being hurt, and placed one foot in her cat tray. Then I skidded along the floor wearing my new foot wear, and the other leg buckled and dumped me in a box containing old newspapers.

117

As I sat, surrounded by chaos, Waffles sat silently and peacefully surveying the situation.

After a respectable time lapse she gave a very modest cry to remind me of my task.

I let her out.

My back hurt.

Her penchant for sleeping exactly where she wanted was another obstacle course ... for me. Many a night I would stretch my legs or turn over in the night, to be met by a warning lick, an irate look, and complete disregard for my comfort.

I was having difficulty in finding a comfortable position anyway, as the weight of the breast, and the pain, required me to construct an 'armchair' of pillows. I was supported on all sides, and should I sleep, there was little danger of crushing anything that would object. I frequently woke during the night for what I called 'pit stops', but on this occasion I was confused.

A loud snoring was coming from above my head.

Levitating cat?

(*Nothing would surprise me.*)

She had precariously placed herself on the top arch of the pillow construction, and was oblivious to the danger (to me) if I had moved my head suddenly.

I prodded and stroked until the snoring stopped, and eventually a grumpy cat admitted defeat and clambered down to a safer perch.

By this time I was wide awake, and glaring at a dozing cat.

Some nights I watched her ability to sleep, with envy.

118

Most mornings I woke at around 5 a.m., but if I'd had a restless night it was possible for me to have remained awake until three or four; then after only a few hours sleep the emergency alarm reminded me of the hospital appointment.

On one of these mornings I had to leave the house without washing. I, in fact, showered, as this was the only way I could feel reasonably clean without getting soap on my Radiated area.

I then had a long wait as the Mobiltron machine wasn't working properly.

Now, this has to be more serious than a coffee machine not working, I thought to myself.

"It's alright now," they informed me.

"Sure?"

"Yes."

"Positive?"

"Yes."

Now was my time to ask about the existence of a panic button.

"What happens if someone sneezes, or moves when they are having radiotherapy?"

"We have an automatic cut-off button. Even if someone opens the door to the room it will stop the machine."

"Good."

"You seem nervous today?" they enquired.

"No, it's just that the veneer of sleep that I normally come with is lacking today, and thoughts surface."

I was led into the room for my (safe) treatment.

The next day was to be a London Transport strike, so I was required to visit out-patients for my weekly check, a day earlier.

Another doctor awaited me.

"Mrs Cole."

(*Here we go again.*)

I had been fighting a losing battle with the Radiographers to establish that my name was 'Jenny'.

The turnover of staff made my desire to be called by my first name appear as an obsession.

I gave up.

I had made up my mind that if any other doctor called into question the progress of my breast, I would re-dress, demand Glen, and refuse all offers of surrender.

My breast had turned a fairly bright shade of red and I had been doing my best to ignore the possibility that it was inflamed again.

Her response, thankfully, was good. The redness was the result of the Radiotherapy and she warned me that the top I was wearing would be too rough on the skin towards the later part of the treatment.

My lymph glands were settling down though.

It was a shame my back wasn't.

Since the encounter with the cat tray I had been plagued by a lower back pain, which would normally send me to an Osteopath.

But, there wasn't really any way Roger, my Osteopath, could have got hold of me to do his 'crunching'.

I had to suffer.

I mentioned my back to Trish, the Crystal therapist. When she stopped laughing at the description of the fall, she concentrated her loops and wands on my lower back.

It improved.

I wonder if she can work miracles on Waffles?

I had arranged to return to the two young Colour therapists, despite reservations.

The journey was appalling because of heavy rain, but I arrived on time.

I had to wait forty minutes.

They were a very gentle couple and I felt safe with them, but they didn't talk to me.

That made me talkative.

They didn't respond.

I needed feedback.

As I left the house I made up my mind not to return.

I would find something else to interest me, but I would bide my time.

Something would find me.

A more immediate problem was the rail and bus strike. Previous transport strikes had caused complete chaos in the capital and I knew I would not have the energy to battle through the traffic myself and find somewhere to park.

Thinking that the whole of London would be grid-locked by cars, a taxi was ordered for 7.45 a.m.

It arrived early, at 7.30 a.m.

And, as there didn't appear to be another car on the road, we arrived at the Middlesex Hospital at 7.45 a.m!

One and a quarter hours early.

I wasn't the only one to be caught out by this, as more and more out-patients congregated in a nearby cafe.

The owners were pleased and even contemplated putting up a sign saying 'wait here for your appointment'.

I was in and out of the basement in fifteen minutes, which meant another wait for the taxi I had ordered to take me home.

I felt as if I had been working all day, and was so tired that I fell asleep on the floor while attempting Visualisation.

An interesting article arrived, from one of my students, on research into the use of shark cartilage in the treatment of cancer.

121

'Cancer cells represent a new localised area of growth in blood vessels, as they are metabolically very active, and reduce local oxygen levels.' So, new blood supplies are formed and the cancer grows in its self-induced environment. Cartilage is the only living tissue with no blood supply, so could this, if extracted, be used to starve cancer cells? Dr Lane, a marine biologist and Nutritionalist, knew that sharks, which have a skeleton composed entirely of cartilage, were virtually free of cancer, so persuaded doctors to try extract of shark cartilage in capsule form to individuals with advanced cancer.

The tumours shrank and disappeared.

Although in the experimental stage this treatment appears not to help every cancer, it does have the advantage of fewer side effects than Chemotherapy.

Sounds brilliant.

I mentioned it to various people at the hospital, and apart from already knowing about it, they didn't seem ecstatic.

'Very expensive,' they said.

How expensive?

They didn't know.

More than the total cost of a cancer 'cure' in a conventional hospital, and the accumulated loss of the patients ability to work? I wonder.

I'm not grabbing at straws (only sharks) but why are these research projects given such low profiles?

This, plus Gaston Naesson's research and that of the German doctor's miracle injections, are possibly only three of the many independent teams trying to find a cure.

How many more are there?

Do they all get together? Or are they like the big multi-national drug companies, out to make their own glory and a financial killing?

So many people and so many claims.

Who do you believe?

A television programme reported on a therapist who claimed she could cure cancer with her special formula CH6. That, plus a machine which 'fires forces of semi-precious stones into the body', left her wide open to prosecution.

The most disturbing aspect of the case for me was that she had advertised in 'Here's Health', a magazine that I respect.

I have responded to many of their articles and adverts but would I be tempted to believe in a claim such as this?

To undertake any cancer treatment one has to have a large amount of faith in its benefits, especially as the treatment is usually worse than the disease.

A Radiotherapist told me a true story of an American who arrived for treatment for advanced Breast cancer. She had delayed approaching conventional methods as she had first consulted a Red Indian chief, who had advised her to wear a colander on her head and to pray to a particular god every day.

She didn't get better.

If I find that (misguided) trust a little frightening, what do I feel about my own belief in the methods I have tried; and how do others view me?

Being a National Health baby (1948) it would take an enormous leap of faith or madness to completely distance myself from a system embedded in my whole culture.

(*I'm also too much of a coward.*)

I'm a healthy cynic.

Despite the enormous damage done to my body by the conventional cancer treatments, I have to believe they will work.

But, they may not.

Despite the enormous benefits I feel from my Complementary therapies they may actually be doing nothing at all to fight the cancer.

But, they may be helping.

My optimistic pessimist approach allows me to weave in and out of the various options and to pick and choose what seems right for me. I could not abandon Orthodox medicine (unless they said they could do no more) but I still reserve the right to take pot shots at it. It's all part of the healing process. Object to a drug, score 50; object to a doctor, score 75; object to the health minister, Bingo!

The Mobiltron machine was not working again, but the long wait and journey home left me with a depleted and tired state of mind. I mixed some Rosemary, Pettigrain, Marjoram and Geranium essential oils together in a vaporiser and breathed in the aroma which would clear my head, soothe my emotions, help me to confront issues and lift my spirits.

If only it were that simple!

The room smelt lovely.

And I felt better.

Prove it wasn't the essential oils.

Visitors.

Rachel, a pottery student of mine, turned Acupuncturist student of someone else, appeared straight from a dental appointment clutching some freesias.

"What a gorgeous cat," she remarked to Waffles, who, for visitors, had switched to a tranquil demeanour and was posing beautifully at the foot of the bed.

"She can come again," we both thought.

Rachel told me of a colleague and friend who had recently established herself as a Healer.

I had met Paola very briefly when I was substituting for a tutor at a community centre. She approached the class to ask if she could practise taking 'pulses', but as she started to explain what that meant we raised our arms en masse like the old hands we were. Many of us had experienced Rachel feeling for our wood, metal, fire, water and earth pulses and seeing her write down ticks, crosses and dashes, which looked like nonsense to us but made perfect sense to her.

Paola herself had had cancer, so would know what I was experiencing.

"She's very good," added Rachel.

I took her number.

(*I knew something would find me.*)

The next day I had two hospital appointments; the normal Radiotherapy at 9 a.m. at the Middlesex, and one for the UCH Breast clinic at 4 p.m. I thought I was going to be seen by Glen as a routine check, but as I waited in the small room there was a gentle knock at the door.

"Come in"

(*Who knocks on doors in a hospital?*)

A lovely young doctor (LYD) came in, with a better taste in ties than Glen; but as we had never met, the series of questions that I'd answered months before, began.

"Now, I believe you are having pains in your breast," he started.

"Er, yes, but . . . "

"We haven't seen you for weeks, so has there been any improvement?"

(*Haven't I been through this before?*)

"Yes of course. Since the start of the Radiotherapy there has been a change in the condition."

"Radiotherapy?"

"Yes."

"Who put you on Radiotherapy?"

"Professor Taylor and Glen."

"Who's Glen?"

"Who's Glen!"

"Yes, I've never heard of him."

"Glen is" . . . I started my normal eulogy, talked of his concern, his lovely care and his terrible taste in ties . . . what could I say to convince this doctor that I wasn't imagining him.

LYD slowly closed my file, walked to the door, and announced he would ask the registrar if he knew anything about me.

He didn't.

There was no point in examining me, he said, as things had obviously progressed further than where the clinic thought it had got to.

"Is this another merger cock-up?" I suggested.

"I expect so, and it can only get worse," he conceded.

"Dorothy knows me," I offered.

(*Trying to play snap*)

Dorothy was duly ushered in.

"Hallo, Jenny, how are things?" she enquired.

"Fine."

We started to chatter in our normal way until we noticed that the LYD was sitting in a haze of bored maleness.

"Is this girly talk, or can anyone join in?"

We fussed over him for a while, and both said he was lovely, which lulled him into a more tranquil state . . . for a while.

"Look," he said to Dorothy, "what we have decided (*we?*) is that Jenny will return next Thursday when Professor Taylor is back and you can put him in the picture as to what has been going on."

"I'm on holiday next Thursday," said Dorothy.

"It's my birthday next Thursday," I announced.

"Oh, is it," said Dorothy. "Many happy returns . . . the big 40?"

"No, the big 45."

LYD slumped even further into his body.

"I haven't slept for days," he announced, so we cossetted him again.

"That's settled then," I declared. "Dorothy with go on holiday, I will not come to the clinic and you will have one less breast to worry about."

"Agreed," he sighed, thankfully.

I was met in the reception area by my sister Wendy and her daughter, Niah. Too much activity in the Cole/Gaynair households in July had produced a constellation of Arien-type characters, and three of us were about to have an accumulative birthday meal.

If I could stay awake.

I had also arranged to go to a lecture on Algae which Anita had recommended but, after a meal, a chat in a smoky, loud pub and a walk to the venue, I'd had it.

A numbness had come over me and all I could do was hail a taxi and pray for home.

I was asleep by 8.30 p.m.

Easter: Ellis had arranged for us to spend a couple of days at Dedham, in the same house/hotel as the previous year. I was not sure how to take this offer of a break . . . and the question uppermost in my mind was, would he book one room or two?

I didn't know how I would cope with either outcome.

We were in the same large, twin-bedded room as before, overlooking the village pond, complete with ducks, a meadow with bouncy rabbits and the Norman tower of the church.

It was pouring with rain.

We were joined that evening by friends, a young couple who lived near the hotel. I hadn't seen them for a year, mainly because Ellis and I hadn't socialised for a year.

(. . . *or anything.*)

The meal was excellent.

Although I was abstemious (for me) I did indulge in a glass of wine and a piece of gateau.

Should be okay I thought, as I felt my batteries rapidly running down. I said goodnight and left the grown-ups to finish their meal with coffee and brandy.

The next morning was not only bright but sunny and warm. The footpath to Flatford Mill started near the hotel, so we decided to set out before the weather and tourists dampened the day.

The walk was flat and untaxing, albeit boggy and cow-y. We sat by the Mill and watched everyone photographing the ubiquitous scene, and as the clouds and crowds rolled in we headed back towards Dedham.

The walk in total was only three miles and I felt fine when we returned to the hotel; but I slept for three hours in what felt like a deep coma.

The rain came down, then stopped.

We drove into the countryside and hunted for a quiet pub to have an early evening meal.

Thinking it would be the only sensible thing to do, I ordered fish.

Moby Dick and chips arrived.

I don't think I've ever seen such a large portion and I felt stumped before I'd begun.

I hate waste . . . probably something to do with the parental order to 'eat it all, or you won't be allowed to leave the table' (a far cry from today's monosodium glutamate-instant-processed food-demanding-or-they-will-refuse-to-eat-youngsters.)

(*See why I never had children?*)

However, I really do hate waste, but this fish was bigger than both of us, and Ellis had his own to worry about.

I relinquished my title of Trencherwoman, and groaned all the way back to the hotel.

I woke at 3 a.m. and couldn't get back to sleep. Instead, I had one of my phases where my mind runs rampant with all the ills of the world and the realisation that everybody wants to abuse, trick, reject and control me for their own purposes. I was too old to be of value anymore and all I had to look forward to was an unstable, lonely, penny-pinching existence.

I then panic at the negative reaction I'm causing in my chemicals, giving the cancer something to feed on? And feel even worse.

Feed? Parasite? I was reminded of a medical dictionary (1988) which stated that 'in effect, a cancer is a parasite formed from the parent's own tissues, it draws on the general supply of nutrients and contributes nothing in return. Its demands should not be enough to cause serious deprivation elsewhere, yet this is the ultimate effect unless the cancer can be treated'.

Parasites! I've had enough of them in my life, and I wasn't prepared to allow the little buggers into my body; or at least to stay there.

I switched my thoughts to another article I'd read about a woman of eighty who had just published her first novel . . . then thought of Anita, who did not fit into anyone's stereotype of a pensioner . . . and of all the other positive women I know who, come to think of it, far outweigh the number of positive men I know.

ZZZZZZZZZZZZZZZZZZ

The storm clouds had left my brain and returned to the skies over Essex. We were not London-bound though, as we had one more social/business occasion to attend to at lunchtime.

Our host, an overgrown schoolboy of fifty, reminded me of my nocturnal notions, and once again a feeling of relief came over me.

Relief did not come, however, with the food. Piles and piles of it, and this time everyone agreed it was far too much.

So was the conversation: puerile and facile.

(*I do realise that I get very intolerant, when I'm feeling rough.*)

I switched off.

I was also worried about the break in treatment. The breast didn't feel any worse but I had only had one Radiation session in the past five days.

I suppose they know what they are doing?

I was tired, drained, over-fed, aching and low.

I went to bed for the rest of the day.

Normal routine was resumed the next day.

The Mobiltron machine was working well after its four-day rest, whereas I had taken a turn for the worse.

I felt very tired and nauseous and strangely absent from what I was doing.

Still, I had a meal to look forward to with friends, in the evening.

More food?

They had suggested 8.30 p.m. as a time to meet and couldn't make it any earlier because of their various commitments.

"Please make it no later," I pleaded.

I should have known better. Indeed they were friends but ones with an inbuilt precision Greek-timing. They had never been on time in all the years I'd known them.

They arrived at the door at 9.10 p.m.

I was tired, agitated and annoyed.

One of my 'virtues', of course, is that I am always on time, if not early. I think it is an insult to the person you have agreed to meet, to keep them waiting; almost as if they are unimportant.

A theme running through my life.

Try as I may to accept other people's inability to be on time, I still find it exasperating when I'm made to hang around.

I was not amused.

Late to the restaurant, and so, late to bed.

(*It was a lovely meal and good company.*)

The next morning I looked and felt terrible.

Will, an old colleague and friend, who rang frequently to chart my progress, was due for lunch.

More food?

He didn't expect much, which is precisely what he got.

Within the space of an hour I could feel myself not paying attention and forgetting what I'd already said, so announced that I would have to take him to the station.

He understood, as even he had noticed the dramatic change in my appearance.

I slept for three hours.

But, it didn't stop there. A long standing arrangement to have dinner with some of Ellis's friends was for that night.

More food!

The meal was delicious and carefully planned around my new eating habits; the wine and champagne should have remained firmly in my old habits (for the time being) but it was my birthday the next day . . .

I was freezing, and sat with a blanket around my shoulders sipping champagne and feeling double my age.

I wanted to be in bed . . . NOW.

April 15th

Happy Birthday to me, Happy Birthday to me.

I hauled myself off to the hospital and in record time was out of the department by 9.10 a.m.

I couldn't go home though because I had to be seen by a doctor as part of my weekly supervision.

I didn't get to see Glen until 10.50 a.m.

"You look tired," he said. "Overdoing it?"

"Just a little."

He was, however, pleased with the breast, and, to make my day, extended the Radiotherapy treatment because of the disruption of the bank holidays.

Yippee.

I plucked up enough courage to ask him how rare was my form of cancer.

"We only see four or five women a year," he informed me.

"Wow!"

I did not have enough courage to ask the survival rate.

(*Coward . . . True.*)

I had already decided to 'cancel' my birthday for this year, and have an unofficial one later in the year, or have it thrown in with another of my 'wonderful' Christmases.

On informing my sister of my decision, she misheard it as 'cancered' my birthday.

I prefer her version.

Cancelled or cancered, I still expected one or two cards to be waiting on the mat.

Nothing.

(*Sod them all, she cried . . . aching with hurt*)

I zoomed up the hill to Trish for a Crystal session. At least Min gave me a soggy teddy bear . . . which he wanted back immediately.

Trish told me about Shi-take mushrooms, which contain Germanium, something that helps people with cancer.

132

I tried to investigate, firstly where to buy this exotic fungus, and secondly, to find out more about Germanium.

Wood Green's Safeway answers the first.

A book by Jan De Vries called 'Cancer and Leukaemia' informed me about the second.

It states: 'Lourdes water contains 30 parts per million of germanium in a solution of 10% concentration . . . and also that it helps improve the transportation of oxygen around the body.'

Another book I read on Nutrition simply stated that 'in organic form it is said to enhance the immune system'.

I need no excuse to eat mushrooms of any description, nor garlic (another source), so these I included in my rapidly changing diet.

Home from Trish and assorted animals.

I exaggerate if I say that the front door jammed as I tried to open it, but I did have to push against a heap of mail that had arrived second, or late first, post.

People had remembered . . . didn't they know it was cancelled?

I glowed, but it had all been too much.

I went to bed, and on my cancelled birthday I was asleep by 2.30 p.m.

Deep sleep on and off for sixteen hours, with powerful dreams of 'leave me alone' quality.

In the dream my sister had arrived to cheer me up, and would not accept that I was exhausted.

I kept falling asleep.

She kept prodding and poking me awake, told me jokes, fed me drinks until I screamed and went into another room to escape. I locked the door then curled up with Waffles on the spare bed. She objected to her space being invaded and left the room (but it was locked).

Later, Ellis arrived through the same locked door wearing flash, bright turquoise, clothes. He had been advised to alter

133

his image. He looked like a spiv. Nobody would leave me to rest, and I was desperate for sleep. One by one people turned up asking for advice or help or a favour. I just screamed at them to go away.

Eventually they did, but I woke in the morning feeling as if I'd been to an all-night party.

Mental note: do not accept, arrange or agree to so many events.

Agreed.

The Friday brought another strike on the trains, so I drove down to the hospital thinking it was the method least likely to tire me.

Wrong.

I returned to the car at 9.15 a.m. (the meter ran out at 9.30 a.m.)

The ignition made a strange noise. Now, I've heard ignitions when the tumble thingies have broken and when the battery is flat, but this was different.

I searched for a phone and called the AA.

"Sorry, there will be a delay. All our cars are busy."

I was nearly in tears with fatigue and the worry of how long it would take to get home.

I needed help and sympathy.

"Please get someone to me soon," I pleaded, explaining my medical condition.

"I will make you a priority."

"Thanks."

I retraced my steps to the car to find a posse of traffic wardens and Clampers accumulating at the end of the road.

Would they believe me that my car was waiting for the AA?

If not, I think I would be capable of doing a Red Lips special, ie, causing one hell of a scene to get my own way.

Except that I had a valid reason. She always wanted her own way no matter how it inconvenienced anyone else.

The Clampers walked past me, as I whispered my genuine excuse of a breakdown.

(I wasn't far behind, by this time.)

The AA arrived.

"This car isn't going anywhere," he announced, very nicely.

Why?

The timing belt, or something-or-other, had gone and it may have caused extensive damage to the engine.

(*Extensive? = money*)

I had to sit until a pick-up truck arrived, and my car was then unceremoniously hauled aboard.

I was so relieved that my car wasn't being towed through London traffic.

Instead, I sat in the cabin and listened to the driver telling me all about his medical problems.

We headed for Kentish Town and Mr George, who isn't a 'Mr George' but answers to that, or Peter.

Peter had looked after my cars, and me, for years. He had in fact warned me about the timing belt, as it was a built-in booby prize from the manufacturers and needed changing every so many thousands of miles. 'January' he had advised.

But in January I had more worrying things to think of than a timing belt.

So, I forgot.

My spirits flagged even further when I realised that he wasn't open.

By this time I was ready to sit down in the street and cry.

His lovely parents, who live a few doors away from his lock-up and, keep their ears open for cars, called to me.

When I explained my problem they dragged me in off the street, sat me down, gave me a cup of tea and phoned for a taxi.

Meanwhile I'd written Peter a note but he had appeared

before the taxi. After listening to my pathetic description of
'tumbly thingy noises' all he could say was that he'd let me
know.

Cheers.

The taxi, driven by a lady, deposited me home, but I was so
drained I couldn't sleep.
   But I could weep, and did.

I stayed in bed all weekend.

(*Weak-end?*)

Two boob-tubes arrived from my sister, complete with
poem:
"My dearest skin and blister, my one and only sister,
   I hope your skin don't blister when they zap you with
those rays.
I wandered round the West End, seeking something for my
best friend,
   As a pressie which I could send but which didn't look like
stays!
The only thing I spotted, which were not polka dotted
   Were these booby slings I gotted, and I hope you like
them.
(Have a go at the last line—I ran out of puff.)"

My attempt at a reply:

"My word I think you're clever.
   I'd come to the end of my tether,
   in trying to find another support,
   which around my way just can't be bought.
   Most styles are only '34'
   while I'm a '36', plus more.

136

My one and only boob-tube wear,
to keep ahoist my tender pair,
is B.O'd now beyond repair
despite my daily wash and care.
As I can't use no anti-pong,
what chance was there for 'Radion'."

I took the opportunity of bed rest to delve into the problem I had encountered over the use of essential oils and cancer patients.

My training had categorically stated that essential oils must not be used on individuals with active cancer.

Yet, browsing through a well known and respected book on Aromatherapy 'The Fragrant Pharmacy' by Valerie Worwood I was surprised, yet delighted, to read:

'In my practice I have seen many (Radiation) burns that could have been avoided if essential oils had been used beforehand.'

There then followed a blend of oils that had to be applied once a day to clean dry skin, starting 2–3 weeks before treatment.

It was not to be used on the days of the treatment, but should be continued up to one month after the completion of the Radiation treatment.

Similarly with Chemotherapy, the blend could be used, except on the days when the Chemotherapy is administered.

This treatment will not conflict with the treatment given to you by your doctor.

She also advised a change of diet, a reduction in stress, an increase in Vitamin C, and avoidance of commercial deodorants.

Deodorants?

I didn't know, because nobody told me, that deodorants

contain aluminium salts. Aluminium can be absorbed into the body and is a poison. By blocking the pores you are effectively preventing the toxins from being eliminated from the body, as well as potentially allowing the body to absorb the toxicity of the aluminium.

That information made me go all sweaty!

I quizzed the Radiologists on the use of essential oils. The older two had no advice to give, but then their training would not have included anything on alternative therapies. John, however, thought that as they didn't contain metal then they would be alright.

But would they? This was not something you could take a chance on as the negative effects would be dramatic.

I made a mental note to write to Val Worwood.

A National Association of Health Authorities and Trusts (Nahat) publication arrived the next day. I had read an article in the Guardian headlined: 'Alternative medicine costing NHS £1,000,000 a year, needs research.'

Many GP fund-holders offered therapies such as Spinal manipulation, Homeopathy, Aromatherapy, Osteopathy, Acupuncture and Counselling, but there was no agreed policy and calls had been made to look into their effectiveness and cost in relation to their benefit.

I wonder if similar calls should be made into the use and wastage of NHS drugs? And the incidences of iatrogenic complications resulting in further operations? For example, I believe that a large percentage of bladder Operations are due to problems arising from Hysterectomies.

It would be an interesting research project to take on identical groups of patients and offer only a choice of either repeat prescriptions, hospital appointments, the chance to join a waiting list, or to try a Complementary therapy.

And compare the cost.

I opened the Nahat research paper with interest. It was written in the normal boring format of officialdom, so it took a little while to realise that it wasn't talking about *Compl*ementary therapies! I turned to the front cover. I had been sent '*Compl*aints in the National Health Service' in error, or as an amusing and pertinent Freudian slip?

I 'complained' when I sent it back.

(*Well at least I'd got through to the right department.*)

I had another bad night's sleep.

I woke every hour and a half in a raging heat, as if an electric blanket had been switched on.

I was thirsty, so had a drink of water . . . which seemed to short-circuit my stomach and ooze directly from my pores.

I then became cold because of the evaporating effect of moisture on a hot surface.

I'd then snuggle down to get warm and the whole cycle would start again.

Is this the Radiotherapy, the Homeopathy or a mixture of both?

Or stress?

Basically, I felt dumped again. After Ellis's Easter attention he had reverted to one of his great disappearing acts, as if in a frightened response to recent attention he had given me.

He had tried to insist that I was the most important thing in his life, and commented on my look of disbelief.

"You have to believe me," he insisted.

"I'll try."

But it was impossible.

I had been alone in the house for seven days.

He arrived home at 10 a.m. on the day he had planned a seven-day holiday, with his mother.

"Have you arranged for someone to stay with you while I'm away?" he enquired, genuinely.

"What! Why?"

"Well you shouldn't be in the house on your own."

"I've managed quite well for the past week, so I assume I'll be able to cope," I replied, with more than a hint of sarcasm in my voice.

He said nothing, crept out of the room, and left the house as soon as possible.

I sat at the table and froze into a mental block of self pity. It had to be 'my fault'. Obviously I was unlovable.

But was I also unlikeable?

My hurt went beyond feeling unloved, or disliked. I was a non person. I was irrelevant to anyone's thought processes.

I didn't exist.

If I'd had money and energy I would have left there and then. Instead, I lay on the bed and quietly cried to myself, my brain unable to untangle the words and deeds of the man I had chosen to be with, but who clearly did not want me.

Why had he fought so hard and long to win me? Perhaps the obtaining is more important than the possessing? I certainly felt on a par with the sauna and extractor units he had installed in the house at great expense, time and effort.

He didn't use or appreciate them, either.

"1514"

"Hi Jenny, it's Angela. I was wondering if you were intending to come over tonight?"

"No, sorry I haven't the energy and I'd be lousy company."

"Oh, that's alright then. It's just that the youngsters next door are having a party, so I was ringing to warn you not to come . . . but . . . to ask if I could come to see you, to avoid some of the noise."

"Doooo come," I pleaded. "Why not stay the night," I added.

"Great. I will."

I also invited another ex-colleague to join us for an early meal. We sat round the kitchen table for hours demolishing pasta, salad, bread, low alcoholic wine . . . and men.

Do men have the ability to join with friends and freely swap accounts of personal experiences, to the extent that the sadness is reduced to a level of acceptance, or hilarity?

They should try it.

The best humour is based on relieving the worst hurt of any situation and twisting it to show the absurdity.

For dessert we had a 'peace' of Absurdity Sponge and Cream.

My spirit had been raised by the evening's company and banter, but my flesh was weak. I was ready for bed by 10 p.m. and went, leaving my understanding guests to understand.

I woke early, as usual, washed up, bought a paper and generally pottered about ready for my house guest to descend.

Not a sound could be heard.

It was not until about 11 a.m. that I heard noises coming from Ellis's room.

'The Archers' and loud nose blowing!!

For a moment my brain couldn't absorb the information. Had Ellis returned, and if so, where was Angela?

Angela, the 'Archer' fan and nose blower, minus Ellis, (phew!) descended into the main part of the house.

I offered her breakfast, which she ate, while I lunched.

Her day may have just started but I had been awake for over six hours and was in need of a sleep.

She left, to utilise her optimum level of energy in the day.

I slept, because I'd already used mine.

(*Angela, our medical afflictions are incompatible.*)

Back to the drawing board, or to be precise, back to Planning.

I was coming to the end of the first block of Radiotherapy and I now had to be re-marked to reduce the area of Zapping.

I could appreciate the improvement in the cancered area, as my arm could remain in the thrust-back position with relative ease.

But, it was still very ticklish as Glen marked out more indelible purple lines.

My general knowledge was improved by discovering that a unit of Radiotherapy is called a 'gray'. I was to have 54 grays in total, at the rate of two a day. I bet I never get asked that in a quiz; but it did come in useful towards the end of my treatment, when there was a slight confusion over the exact day of my last session.

"I'm having 54 grays," I authoritatively informed the hospital staff. "28 days x 2 = three more doses because I missed some sessions through machine failure and strikes."

I smiled sweetly.

"Where's the sandbag?" one of them asked.

"Sandbag? Am I to be thrown into the Thames for being a know-all bossy-boots?"

They smiled.

"No, it's all part of our high-tech equipment . . . it stops the head-rest from moving."

(*Phew!*)

The rooms where the Planning and Zapping take place are always cold. Well, cold if you are the only person in a state of undress.

I returned home and got into bed fully clothed to warm up.

I warmed up and became aware again of the strange body smell which had pervaded my nostrils and bed clothes since the start of the treatment.

Nobody 'complained' nor even acknowledged any strangeness of odour, so I had to believe that it was my own micro-environment kept close to my chest.

(*And armpits.*)

I remembered the advice about deodorants, so with my personal pollution in tow I took myself off to the local Health shop.

Success: a roll-on deodorant proudly claiming that it contained no aluminium. What it did contain was a selection of essential oils. Tea tree, Ylang-Ylang, Vertiver, Guaic Wood and Rose.

It was only slightly more expensive than the normal variety, but it is hard to establish the value, roll for roll, as I was only using it on 50% of my armpits!

I woke the next day to find that an amazing Rorschach Ink blot Test had been carried out on my 'chest'.

The effect of mirror imaging lines en-squaring a breast, with extra lines and marks depicting important areas, was to give my torso the comic look of a pair of goofy eyes with spectacles. I was tempted to draw on a smiling mouth and present myself to the Radiologists.

Unfortunately, (or fortunately) my nerve cracked and as vigorously as I could I managed to rub away the unwanted surplus markings on the healthy skin.

Still, great possibilities had been missed. I could have established a 'BBB' competition (Beautiful Breast Blot) with prizes for the best imaginative interpretation. Although, as one friend pointed out, most males faced with such a task would resort to the most basic archetypal response.

The left side of my body had started to look very 'sunburnt' and had the ability to flare-up to a deep crimson for no apparent reason. The most affected areas were under the armpit and the 'crease' under the breast (if one has anything over 34 inches). These areas have virtually no contact with sunlight at any time, let alone bombardment from Radiation, so they are the ones to suffer the most. But gone are the days of the horrendous Radiation burns described in text books. (I hope?) Updated machinery and the use of computers ensures a much safer treatment.

Paola returned my call. She congratulated me on my attitude, and my ability to say the word 'cancer'.

I still found it strange that many cancer patients did not refer to their condition by name; perhaps there should be a national 'coming out' day for cancer, similar to the Gay or HIV/AIDS celebrations? I have since found out that it was extremely common for whole families to be sworn to secrecy if a member of that family had cancer. This silent killer had been tolerated almost as embarrassing relations who, if ignored for long enough would improve their behaviour. This approach does not work with human rogues and it certainly doesn't work with rogue cells bent on colonisation.

She was also interested in all my other approaches and asked me directly what I felt she could offer me to help my recovery.

It was true that I was worried about the toxins affecting my organs and the possibility of lasting damage to my system. However, I felt I was in a strange dichotomy. Yes, I was dealing with the cancer and being very positive and creative, but I was very much aware that I was being churned up with anger, which disturbed my sleep and in turn caused me to worry about the prognosis.

In Acupuncture terms Paola told me, the liver is the seat of anger or that anger has the ability to disempower the liver.

Considering that my liver was under constant pressure anyway trying to filter out all the poisons, it was not surprising it was having a rough time. It could do without my contribution but, conversely, would I be feeling as negative as this if my liver was a happy organ?

My liver and I looked forward to meeting Paola later in the week; perhaps she could do something for our mutual benefit?

Meanwhile it (my liver) seemed to be playing up like a malfunctioning child who knows it is going to be taken to a psychologist. I woke every two hours during the night, and was drained of energy in the morning.

The Guardian contained an article on 'Cell Suicide', which looked into the reasons why some patients do not respond to cancer treatment.

There is a gene called p53, which programmes cells to commit suicide. However, if this gene is damaged two things can happen: a cancer develops and the tumour doesn't respond to treatment. (My CMF experience?). Research shows that p53 was a trigger for cell death but only in certain cases, implying that other factors were also involved.

This was far too difficult for me to understand fully but I was grateful that there were others who found it fascinating.

I took my weary body to Bethnal Green to see Robert, knowing that 'seconds out' would be the order of the day.

I was not to be disappointed.

I was handed packs of little round white pills.

Someone had already warned me that he would not answer this particular question, but I was not only used to his unyielding style, I had a sneaking admiration for his ability to answer nothing unless he wanted to.

He should have been in counter-interrogation.

(*He is in counter-interrogation!*)

But, here goes . . .

"Do these pills have names?"

"Yes."

"Can you tell me the names?"

"No."

"Any reason?"

"Yes."

"Can you tell me these reasons?"

"Yes."

"Well!!??"

"The problem is that if I inform individuals of the names of pills they are receiving they may casually inform other individuals who may just buy these remedies over the counter and believe they are being treated."

(*That was a long sentence for him.*)

"Are people that stupid?"

"?"

"Okay, they're that stupid."

"?"

"Can you give me an indication of the types of names?"

"A few flowers . . . some Latin names (he rattled off long complicated sounds) . . . some herbs . . . blah, blah, blah . . . Hemlock . . . blah, blah, blah."

"Hemlock!"

(*I knew he was a wizard*)

"Satisfied?" he enquired.

"Very enlightening and helpful," I lied.

I took my anonymous pills out into the anonymous road and headed north to familiar territory; just because you know something by name does it make life any easier?

The correct research paper on Complementary therapies in the NHS had arrived from Nahat. It was very short, very boring, full of bar graphs and acronyms like DHA, GPFH and FHSA, which I didn't understand. I was surprised and delighted to see that a wide-ish selection of Complementary therapies were used by some DHAs etc, but that the biggest obstacle was lack of information on effectiveness rather than cost or disapproval.

At the Middlesex the next day there was a delay with my treatment because they couldn't find the template of the cross-section of my breast; vital to ensure correct positioning.

(*Had they left it on a washing line?*)

It soon appeared and after my usual Zapping I 'traipsed' to another part of the hospital to see Glen.

At the end of my Radiotherapy I'm to return to a course of Chemotherapy but with a two week break.

(*Bliss.*)

The idea was to return me to the CMF regime and to carry on where I'd left off: ie, I was to have four more doses.

After a pleasant session with Trish and animals (and crystals) I propped myself against a mound of pillows and hunted for other information on Aromatherapy and cancer among all my books. I had been delighted that Valerie Worwood had been so positive about their use but as it conflicted with my training I wanted to have as many opinions as possible.

Here was a direct contradiction!

Patricia Davis's 'A–Z of Aromatherapy' clearly stated that it was inadvisable to use essential oils on individuals with cancer for perhaps up to two years after treatment.

(*There goes my earning capacity!!*)

I decided to write to both these established Aromatherapists not as an antagonist to their knowledge, but as an interested Aromatherapist/Cancerholic.

In the meantime I didn't personally have the courage to try any essential oils on my Radiation area, as the consequences of making an error were too awful to contemplate.

I sent the letters; it remained to be seen if I would have any replies.

On one of my trips to a wholefood shop I had attempted to buy some beetroot juice, as recommended by Paola, to help detox my liver. Freshlands didn't stock it because in their opinion there wasn't a brand that was pure enough for their stringent standards.

Okay, I'll make my own.

I purchased uncooked beetroot from the local supermarket, and discovered why it was usually sold already cooked.

I started to boil it . . . 30 mins later it was still rock hard. After an hour it was still rock hard. (?)

I flipped through a cook book: 'It can take 3–4 hours!!!, but more usually 40 mins.'

'Usual' doesn't come into my life and it had already passed the 40-minute stage, so I boiled on . . . and on . . . and on.

It was still hard-ish after three hours but the stress level of having to hang around the kitchen topping up the deep red liquid was probably in direct opposition to the benefit I was supposed to receive from the wretched stuff.

I took it out, and vowed never to bother again. However, I did discover a delicious way of eating raw beetroot, which is also good as a detoxing food. Grate raw beetroot, carrot and apple together as a salad. Different, colourful, edible, delicious and healthy.

I searched locally for non-hassle beetroot juice and found some which did not appear to be too polluted with salt.

It's an acquired taste.

Another problem arose though because no matter how delicate I was in drinking it, I ended up with deep red lips.

I thought of 'Red-lips' and searched furiously for a solution. In fact the solution, a straw, solved two problems. Not only did one avoid a circle of indelible red around the lips, but by directing the straw to the back of the throat, one didn't taste the stuff.

(*Liver, I hope you appreciate my lack of selfishness?*)

Later, I realised that by mixing the beetroot juice with vegetable juice both red lips and an unacceptable taste could be avoided.

A long weekend.

Sunday and the early Spring Bank holiday.

I had woken at 4.15 a.m. with a terrible headache in both temples and across the eyes.

I lay there and absorbed the sensation of pain and tried to make it a positive experience. I felt too rough even to reach for the paracetamol or Lavender oil.

I must have fallen asleep with my masochistic mind game but woke again at 7.15 a.m. still with a pain in both temples.

Paola later informed me that the liver meridians end at the temples, accumulating more evidence to the fact that my liver just wasn't having a great time. At least it gave me a better understanding of the cause of my discomfort; and why nothing relieved it.

I felt nauseous and 'punched' all morning but after a long sleep in the afternoon I started to rally round, although I couldn't face food.

I felt miserable and trapped.

Ellis had tried to be nice to me over the weekend and it was this constant need for me to adapt to his emotional state I found most tiring.

I could cope if he was negative towards me all the time, but these swings just seemed to me to be cruel.

(*And, I know he's not a deliberately cruel man don't I?*)

The strange sleep habits continued and I frequently woke tired and disturbed.

Waffles didn't help.

I frequently woke to find her perched on me in her 'chicken' position and no amount of twisting or turning could remove her. After one particularly tormented night when I'd dreamt of being pursued by ferocious creatures I surfaced from sleep to find myself looking down the throat of an animal; with fangs.

Recognising a broken front tooth to be one belonging to Waffles who had decided to yawn at the very time I opened my eyes, I groaned and returned to the relative safety of my safari slumbers.

I was more pleasantly woken by Ellis bringing me a cup of tea (!) but I had overslept and had no time to have breakfast before tottering out to the tube.

A headache was developing.

As I entered the hospital the Fire Alarm screamed into action and along with other early visitors I found myself corralled in the foyer.

I had the choice of being either warm and seated, but deafened by the alarm, or cold and unseated and in charge of my ear drums.

I sat, and cultivated my headache.

Peace was restored and we were allowed to filter into the various hospital recesses that would deal with our personal recesses.

As I was having my treatment another alarm started but we stood firm. Correction, they stood firm, while I lay firm.

Don't worry they said, there is an Emergency exit which leads directly into the courtyard.

I looked at my naked torso.

150

They just prevented a Fireman from rushing in to check the room.

Shame.

(*Oh come on, my Horoscope said I'd meet a dashing young man in May*)

My headache was well and truly established by now.

Such excitement.

I went straight to my session with Trish, who placed a visor type contraption over my eyes, which flashed small continuous lights if I moved.

I immediately started to play 'Star Wars'

"Children love wearing the visor for the same reason," she added.

That kept me still!

The headache diminished.

Another of my paintings was inspired by the visor, and the tamed menagerie.

It depicts me sitting in the lounger with coils and loops and wires all over my body, plus the visor. I'm plugged into the Electro-Crystal Generator, which is gently going 'tick tick'.

I looked as if I was in the Electric Chair! So, I painted in a smile just to show that whatever was happening was okay by me.

Trish is shown as a rather superior Regal character holding out to me in the palm of her hand a Rose Quartz.

Min is staring at me and next to him on the floor is the empty tin of Whiskas. I have Bernard, alias 'flat head', on my lap and Edward and Pye (the other cats) and Sapphire, the dog, roaming around the room at their leisure.

After knowing them better I realised that I should have had them on the chairs and sofas, and Trish and me on the floor.

The room had to be simplified, as the items and objects of

interest which cluttered every spare space, and non spare space, would have detracted from the overall impression.

(*Who am I trying to kid?*)

I hesitated in showing it to Trish, because all her walls were festooned with magnificent 'proper' paintings.

What would she think of my daub?

"Fun."

She took two photocopies.

Ellis, in one of his tea-bringing ceremonies, had suggested a Wordprocessor as a birthday present. I had been very ungracious at his previous attempts to suggest gifts which may be desirable, but this was more to do with my attitude to him rather than to the suggestions.

But, a Wordprocessor would be useful, therapeutic and something different to master.

"Okay."

I couldn't rest after the crystal session, so rang around various local Wordprocessor outlets and asked stupid questions to see how helpful they would be to someone who didn't know anything about new fangled typewriters.

I was offered a demonstration.

Great.

What was more impressive was that the explanation was in 'English' as opposed to Computerspeak, in 'Japanese'.

I can't remember anything he told me but what stuck in my immediate memory was that this Wordprocessor had been designed with humans in mind. The 'User's Guide' was equally impressive.

"I'll take it."

"Would you like a new one from the warehouse, which I can get for you by tomorrow, or this one, which I'll have to sell to you as a demonstration model?"

"This one."

(*Strike while the Wordprocessor's hot.*)

A problem arose after I had signed the cheque. I realised

152

that I had no formal means of identification with me. Why should I? I had temporarily left behind the world of commerce and normal procedures, and my bag and wallet were devoid of day to day accumulated officialdom.

I proffered one of my Massage/Aromatherapy business cards.

(*Never one to miss an opportunity.*)

"Will this do?"

He hesitated, but swiftly clipped it to the invoice with a movement not dissimilar to having been found with a girly magazine, or that he was riding roughshod over company procedures.

He carried my Canon Starwriter to the car and wished me luck with the book.

I couldn't wait to unpack, and putting my best finger forward began tapping.

Rather in the same way that some humans have instilled panic in me, this machine also tried to undermine my confidence. I was alright when I could see why something had gone wrong, but when without warning a line would disappear, or jump, or any number of other inexplicable actions occurred, I stared at it with my usual baffled expression of: 'Why did you do that to me?'

I battled on and was just about to hit a key marked 'Help' when the phone rang.

"1514"

"Hallo"

"Hallo"

"Hallo", accompanied by a bemused giggle.

"I've already said 'Hallo' twice, it's now your turn to say something else," I suggested forcefully (for me).

"Who's that?"

"Oh no, you tell me who you are, and then I'll tell you who I am."

"Doesn't matter," he said, in an unsinister relaxed voice, and hung up.

Was this the nice man at the Computer centre ringing to see if I am who I said I was?

Well I am.

Tap, tap, tap, tap . . . 'Help'.

(*Being me, at present, was not easy.*)

Seeing keys before my eyes I thought lesson one had gone on long enough. 'Not bad'. I tapped in five different founts, and went to bed.

I woke at 4.15 a.m. and that was that.

I saw Glen at the hospital as part of my end of Radiotherapy de-briefing and another appointment was made for the following week to arrange the Chemotherapy. He had seen me showing Rebecca my paintings and asked for a private view. He thought they were great and wondered if I'd mind lending them to the department to be exhibited.

Unfortunately I did, 'mind' that is; they were far too precious (to me) to be let out of my sight.

What I did promise were colour photocopies, which I delivered via a nurse the next time I appeared.

One of the nurses mentioned a programme she'd seen on television which was looking at the controversial use of money for research into into HIV and AIDS when so many women were dying of Breast cancer. What was my view?

(*Ask me another*)

What did I think?

Cancer is no longer an automatic killer, whereas AIDS is the next 'cancer' to consume the fears of millions. If research into AIDS can help to understand the immune system, then perhaps indirectly it will benefit cancer research?

But, I didn't feel any bitterness towards the 'Showbiz

154

Glamour' aspect of AIDS awareness . . . working in a prison I had seen too many lives wrecked, or ended, by the virus.

I was pleased, in some ways, that I had cancer.

(*What am I saying!*)

Saturday 8th May 1993: I wrote in my daily diary: 'Started my cancer book on W/P. Pleased with the results.'

One of the results of my enthusiasm I hadn't bargained for was a very stiff neck and shoulder. It had been over three months since I'd concentrated on anything, apart from my illness, and now that I was having an 'out of body' experience it was exhausting.

I retired to bed with a hot water bottle perched on my shoulder, while Waffles looked on with intense jealousy.

It had begun to feel very sore under the breast, and a restless night because of the discomfort made me investigate.

The weight of the tumour had caused the burnt skin to stretch and crack, exposing a line of raw flesh. There was nothing I could do until my next hospital visit except try to limit the damage by immobilising the breast without allowing any garment to rub the wound.

It was not a peaceful night.

The Radiographers sent me to a nurse who produced a small bottle and a cotton bud and proceeded to coat the area with Gentian Violet paint. I was expecting it to be painful and sore when touched, but instead I discovered a new ticklish area.

I couldn't stop chuckling.

I was handed the bottle with instructions to dab twice a day until it had healed.

This treatment, at least, is going to be one long laugh, I thought.

The use of this deep purple paint, which brought back childhood memories of grazed knees and elbows covered with the stuff, surprised me. Surely there must be a modern equivalent that doesn't stain everything?

Apparently not.

It's still one of the most effective antiseptics that can be used, so hospitals use it. It also explains why it's used for painting on the lines for Radiation treatment. They know it won't go away in a hurry.

Perhaps because of its tenacity, it had fallen out of favour?

It's a well known fact that once a subject becomes of interest then articles on that subject jump out from magazines and newspapers at alarming regularity. I knew I had read articles on cancer before the onset of my own disease, but whether I took any notice of them is hard to remember.

Now, I absorb every new idea on possible causes, treatments and 'cures' with a fairly objective mind. However, one article that came out of the blue knocked my objectivity sideways. It argued that childless couples, who wanted fertility treatment, should have priority over cancer patients when it came to distribution of funds.

I see.

It was a hot June. Very hot.

Normally I would have taken every opportunity to wallow in the sheer sweatiness of an oppressive London spring.

But, now, I hated it.

The Chemotherapy and Radiotherapy had tampered with my internal thermostat, and I felt I was dissolving.

My inability to cope with the heat solved the strict instructions, given to me by the hospital, of not allowing the sun's rays to reach the area of skin having the radiation. I simply avoided the sun and heat preferring a cool shady room.

It was the hottest part of the day when I drove to see Paola. In our first session we had only talked, although that does no justice to the conversation. This time she took my pulses.

Some were fast.

She took my blood pressure, the highest reading was low, indicating poisoning.

(*Slight understatement!*)

She fiddled with my feet and toes.

(*AAArrrggghhh!!!*)

Both sides of the big toe, the liver Meridians, were tender. I felt she was stabbing me with a pin.

Slowly she worked along other Meridians using such light pressure that at times I couldn't tell if she was still in the room.

She took my pulses again and was delighted to find that they had normalised.

"You are so easy to tune," she declares.

Trouble is, the rest of the week I'd have a succession of boisterous individuals trying their best to boogie on my keyboard; they were heavy handed, which did nothing for my fine tuning.

Paola had been interested in my need to paint, so I lugged my portfolio, full of past and present doodles, to the session.

I really don't care if people are at a loss at what to say about my work, but obviously I would appreciate any positive reaction.

My most recently finished painting was getting 'rave reviews', perhaps because it looked like a painting; ie, something that could be put on a wall, and look nice.

I had not only painted a proper, albeit stylised figure but had produced a cat that not only looked like a cat but was instantly recognisable as Waffles. I had visualised my Visualisation and the effect was strangely powerful. Paola was interested in my use of colour and interpreted my painting for me. The pink and purple flowers symbolised 'love' and 'communication'. The figure, which represented me had long flowing brown hair (I can but dream), which referred to 'courage'.

I had already started another realistic painting. The lower half of my naked torso, of which only the right arm and right breast could be seen, was resting on a bed of dark green leaves; my hand had started to metamorphose into one of the leaves. Waffles is using me as an island again but is sitting up and alert, ready for action.

I had begun to paint this at 3 a.m., which is the main reason I left out the head.

(*Who am I trying to kid. I can't paint heads at 3 p.m. either.*)

The leaves, also of my imagination, were even less botanical than the last and had a great similarity to my ghostly figures.

Technical and Chemotherapy-induced excuses aside, I was pleased with the result; it had a slightly surrealistic quality about it.

"In colour analysis, green is progress," said Paola. A further interpretation was offered regarding the nakedness of the figure. By having the lower body exposed I was presenting my creativity to the world. It would be through my creativity that the cancer would be fought; the water was bringing gentle waves of healing.

Waffles was depicted as alert, and ready to help me through the next part of the treatment.

The lack of a head? Well, Paola thought this showed that I was fully aware of the rational aspects of the process and had consciously accepted the situation, so there was no need to include the head.

(*I know better. I'm just a lousy artist—or am I?*)

She then started on the Healing by balancing and directing the energies to help my body fight the cancer. As she worked she said she had 'seen' a magazine and suggested that while

I waited for any positive reaction to my book I should submit something shorter, to test the water.

Strangely enough, although I semi-dismissed her suggestion, I did send off some of my poems in response to an article in the Guardian.

And waited.

Surprise, delight and a boost at a very low ebb in my 'journey' I found myself signing an 'authors consent' form for one of my poems to be included in an anthology of women's poetry depicting life in the latter part of the twentieth century.

As I remarked to interested friends when they asked me the title of the work; 'Rape', it is not the sort of poem one would recommend to one's maiden Great-Aunt. Then she realised that, as a maiden Great-Aunt, I had written it!

(*Life is stranger than fiction?*)

Paola also suggested that I changed my image and suggested . . . a hat.

Nah. I've never worn a hat, mainly because my hair looks such a mess when the hat is removed. Not for me the shampoo advert thick lustrous locks which cascade into a bouncy, perfectly styled fashion accessory. Static electricity, gravity and pressure have total control over my delicate tendrils, which incidentally had withdrawn further into themselves with the onslaught of cancer.

Nah, I repeated to myself.

Her other suggestion to place a cabbage leaf over my breast to reduce the effect of Radiation, was received with greater enthusiasm, not least because it provided inspiration for another painting.

But then again?

I had, on good advice, bought a piece of orange Calcite for energy. As I clutched it I was convinced that my hand felt tingly. Surely not? I transferred the crystal to the other hand. There it was again. It was as if a small current was being directed through my skin. Was I imagining it?

The next day I saw Trish and she didn't think it strange for me to have experienced the sensation.

Oh well then, I thought, I will just have to add that to the accumulation of new and strange events that were becoming so commonplace to me. So much so that I was now blasé about them.

My friends, however, continued to fear for my sanity.

I rushed home from my visit to Trish, as I was expecting a visitor.

At the age of thirty-five I had taken out a ten-year Insurance policy thinking that a small pile of readies in my mid-forties would be quite a good idea. I had images of a tour of South America investigating the ancient cultures and crafts, or a room extension, or a new car, or . . . anything but the current necessity to re-invest, as a future, sans job, dictated.

I had, as requested, telephoned the office of this large organisation to arrange for the agent to relieve me of the Policy Document (and sign for it) as it was too precious to risk the mail.

Mail/Male? Similarity of sonics failed to alert me to the extra similarities that both, at times, produce. They either fail to deliver, or one is inundated with junk.

George (his name has been changed to protect the company) should have caused clanging warning bells when he announced over the phone that 'something greater than both of us had brought us together'.

I couldn't see the connection really, as all I had informed him was that I had no intention of taking out another policy . . . just Give-Me-The-Money.

We sat at the kitchen table with me clinging onto the radiator. I was going through one of my 'can't get warm phases'.

George started the ball rolling, as I handed him a herbal tea.

"Your treatment is obviously working . . .

(*Thank you*)

. . . but it will get worse."

(*Eh?*)

"Your hair will fall out."

"No it won't," I replied sharply.

"You must become a vegetarian," he continued.

"Why??"

"We are not designed to eat meat," he said with great authority.

"Wrong," I said with equal authority, inconveniently forgetting the enzymes, etc, with which we are equipped for dealing with meat.

"You must give up alcohol."

"Why?"

"It's bad."

"Then why did Jesus turn water into wine?" I retorted smugly, knowing by now that I had some religious nut on my hands.

No answer.

(*One to me, I thought, making a mental mark with my finger.*)

But there was no stopping him!

"You are lucky . . . you know you've got cancer. We, out there, don't."

"So?"

161

"We are all going to die . . . sooner or later. Your cancer is an indication that your time is coming sooner."

(*Yours isn't far off either, matey.*)

"You must say prayers. Sit in the garden and chant to Krishna."

I was beginning to slide down the radiator in my desperate need to sleep but I was fascinated by this complete stranger's need and determination to force his beliefs on me. Perhaps my constant battle to keep my eyes open lulled him into a false sense of believing *I* was half-way there . . . wherever that was?

He continued.

"Cleanliness is next to Godliness. You must keep the house free from germs and dirt," he declared, looking round the kitchen and especially at the food Waffles had dragged across the floor.

He then proceeded to tell me how to put a few drops of Eucalyptus into a bucket of water and how to use a mop.

(*Bloody cheek!*)

"I'm going to get a friend to phone you. He's a solicitor. He will get your estate in order . . . and help you make a will.

"I beg your pardon?"

"It's for the best."

"But, I'm leaving it all to Waffles," I announced, as the soon-to-be wealthy cat sauntered into the kitchen and demanded fresh food.

He finally left, after apologising for leaving the tea.

(*He probably suspected, quite correctly, that the mug hadn't been sterilised.*)

"Bye."

"Bye."

I was exhausted, cold, mentally stirred, but not shaken.

162

"Why," horrified friends demanded, "did you allow him to browbeat you like that?"

"Why didn't you throw him out of the house?"

"Why didn't you report him to his company for over-stepping his professional brief?"

Why?

I was determined to give him free rein to see how far he'd go.

The fact that he galloped off into the sunset was another interesting aspect for my book.

After he'd gone, I slunk upstairs and, before my memory faded, wrote down our one-sided conversation.

Good stuff. Good stuff. I thought.

But, perhaps it would have been less fraught if he'd only tried to sell me a new policy?

I fell into a deep, undisturbed, sleep with the Rose Quartz on my breast and my right hand clutching the Calcite.

I woke, very refreshed an hour later, still in the same position. Any unannounced visitor would think they had walked in on an Ancient Sacrificial Ritual of a Vestal Virgin.

Vestal Virgin I ain't.

More a . . .

Voluptuous vamp?

Vivacious Vamp?

(*Hardly, in my present mental and physical state.*)

Medically-challenged Middle-Aged Woman, is perhaps a more appropriate, albeit American, description.

(*Close enough*)

I thought I would be feeling better now that I no longer had to trek to the hospital every day, but my drain-ed-ness was greater than in the eight weeks of the Radiotherapy.

Perhaps I was a Radiotherapy Junkie? and was missing my daily fix?

I was not so much going through 'Cold-turkey' but 'luke-warm Budgy'.

(Cold-turkey for the uninitiated is the term used by drug addicts for the process they go through when suddenly cut off from all drugs. The body goes into withdrawal symptoms and one of the physiological side-effects is that the skin becomes goose-pimply, like a plucked turkey.)

My sleep patterns were very disrupted, and, with that came disruptive thought patterns. I don't think it matters which came first; I think they just happily co-existed and fed off each other for mutual benefit.

My brain was over-active and I drifted between sleep deprivation experiments and frightening dreams of vulnerability and fear.

In one dream I had just plannted a bomb in Stroud Green Road and was sheltering in a derelict shop. Next to me was a man who had also planted a bomb, but he had had to rush out and dust his as it hadn't gone off. As an armoured car rushed by we both pretended to be ordinary shoppers. I buy two packets of nuts and some porridge oats, but am horrified to be charged £14.00.

I complain about the price, but the shopkeeper explains that he is forced by the government to increase his prices by 10% per day. Nobody seems to think this is strange. Nobody does anything about it.

The bombs explode and apart from a few individuals looking from windows, they were largely ignored.

There was no public transport in London anymore, so I set off towards my house in Wood Green on foot. I hadn't been there for years but I had heard about The Problems, so made sure I had a piece of heavy wood in my hand for protection. I had to be careful that no one saw me, as vigilante groups patrolled each road to ward off Outsiders.

When I reached 'my' house the door was open and I could see piles of bills on the mat.

I entered.

The only furniture left was an ironing board, which stood in the middle of the main room.

I closed the curtains.

And left.

Not knowing if I had been on a film set for '1984' or that life in London was really getting too much I stumbled through the morning until it was time to see Paola.

Despite my nocturnal wanderings my Pulses were better, but she did worry about my ability, or inability, to take on the problems of the world.

My normal attempts at relaxation were based on concentrating on the Third Eye (Ajna), which is situated at the centre of the brow. Imbalances of this Chakra can cause sleeplessness and mental stress.

(*I know!*)

Paola suggested that I was perhaps too 'head based' and set about teaching me another breathing exercise: I had to hold my hands just below my navel then breath in slowly through that area to the count of six, and out to the count of six.

While she fiddled with my feet I practised this method, but constantly found my breath 'creeping up to' the third eye. After a while I could imagine my breath sinking into my abdominal area but it always wanted to rise from my head. Very frustrating. I could feel it homing in on my head, ready to stir up a tornado of sensations.

Must practice.

I had already acknowledged that I would need another

career once I was better/cured/in remission. The thought of lugging sacks of clay or massage tables around to earn a living did not seem to be the best idea for someone trying to conserve energy.

Paola suggested a Healing course.

"You are doing a good job on yourself, why not spread your skill?"

(*Why not indeed.*)

My breast became hot and red by the end of the session, yet Paola hadn't touched me at all—powerful stuff.

I related this incident in a phone call to friend. His cynicism of all my Complementary exploits produced the comment: "That's all the beetroot you've been eating and drinking coming out."

(*Ho Ho.*)

The next day I was alerted to a programme on Radio 3 about The Hornsey College of Art Sit-in: 25 years on. Kim Howell MP, a fellow student (made good?), was re-living the days of Student Revolution in North London and assessing the impact of the Event.

Memories.

I had left school believing in the intrinsic good of educational establishments. That was all shattered when, as a student and staff group, we had the temerity to voice our opinions about the poor quality of the courses. For our concern we found ourselves branded as 'Selfish Trouble-makers' and locked out of the main college grounds.

Seven weeks of debate, consultations, 'Happenings' (well, it was the 60s!) and a sense of responsibility towards our future resulted in local authorities threatening to withdraw grants, expulsions, incriminations . . . and a college which not only lost its credibility as a place of learning but also its name. It was consumed by Middlesex Polytechnic.

"Baldness and respectability a quarter of a century later . . ." said Dr Howell.

Baldness? No, despite Chemotherapy.

Respectability? Yes, I still feel it is respectable to stand up and fight for what you believe in.

But education, it seems, is still not pro-student. It's so depressing.

I found myself crying with the effort of it all.

Dorothy phoned to thank me for the Visualisation painting and wanted my permission to show it to her cancer support group.

The fact that my painting had provoked so much attention perhaps partly diminished my belief that I had left Hornsey unable to create two-dimensional work of a standard befitting four years of art training. But that was one of my objections all those years ago!

I was due at the Middlesex Hospital on the Friday and had started to ask around for a companion to accompany me to the poisoning.

Nervous?

It was a mini-crunch time for me. I was to return to Chemotherapy, but as it hadn't worked before, why should it work now?

Jo volunteered, but because of work schedules, had to meet me down town near the hospital.

I had already had a blood test, which had been surprisingly oochifying and, after a quick lunch, Jo and I walk into Latymer ward where the Chemotherapy is administered.

I had to have a pre-Chemotherapy check, so down we went again to the Oncology out-patients area, and waited.

Glen was not available, so I found myself with a new-to-me-doctor discussing my future.

She started:

"We can give you the CMF Chemotherapy again, but as you are aware it didn't do what we had hoped."

"Uh hah."

Silence.

"Alternatively, we could give you a stronger Chemotherapy; but it has stronger side effects."

"Such as?"

"You will lose your hair."

Silence . . . then my brain began to respond.

"What if I started on the CMF and, if it wasn't working, switch to the full strength variety?"

"We really wouldn't know just by looking at the breast how effective it was being."

My brain responded, rustily.

"Give me more information."

"With the stronger Chemotherapy there is less chance of you needing a Mastectomy."

"There's no choice then, I'd rather lose my hair for a year, than my breast forever."

Feeling a bit stunned, but happy that it had been discussed with me, I re-joined Jo.

I was not able to have the treatment until the afternoon, so Jo and I departed for Dillon's bookshop and London University.

I bought Brian Keenan's 'An Evil Cradling', and John McCarthy and Jill Morell's 'Some Other Rainbow'.

Strange choice some would say?

Perhaps not the happiest of literature, but solid indications of courage, strength and survival.

I needed inspiration and a belief in the ability of humans to live through adversity.

Jo had to leave, as the day had become drawn-out and time-consuming. I assured her I would be alright on my own, as I had already entered the Chemotherapy ward and met the new batch of nurses.

I felt safe.

I had to ring Ellis to let him know why I would not be home by the expected time.

I told him my hair news, adding that he would appreciate only too well the concept of baldness.

"Yes," he said wistfully. "But you know that yours will grow back again."

"I know," I declared emphatically. Then added (a little unkindly): "Na nah, na, na, nah."

He took it well.

I was suddenly reminded of George's prophesy of "You will lose your hair" and Paola suggesting that I change my image, and buy a hat.

(*Very interesting.*)

I returned to the ward to be met by Rebecca. She gives me a booklet informing me of the chemicals that I'm about to have poured into my veins and their side effects:

Vincristine: Jaw pain, Peripheral Neuropathy (Pins and needles to you), Constipation.

Adriamycin: Nausea, Hair loss, Discolouration of urine (red).

Cyclophosphamide: Strange taste in mouth, Nausea, Vomiting, Bone-marrow depression, ie, susceptible to infection.

Piece of cake really!

I was pleased that Rebecca warned me of the 'itchy bottom syndrome' as she administered the Adriamycin, because it was more like having drug crazed ants rampaging about in one's underwear.

169

My breast also tingled alarmingly.

She grinned; and slowed down the rate of the swarm.

Wow!

Wow! again. This was all very powerful stuff.

I waited only ten minutes for a taxi to arrive but was already having difficulty holding on to reality.

Ignoring the Soup and Soaps I had expected to consume I dived under the duvet and wished the world would go away.

I felt as if I had been put in a spin dryer, and was devoid of any constant recognisable sensation.

I slept (and spun) and woke (and spun) on and off for hours.

On one of my spins into wakefulness I peered at Waffles, who I thought had just made a choking noise.

But, then again, she was absolutely still.

I stroked her.

No movement.

No prupphh.

I stroked her again.

No movement.

My God she's dead!!!!!! I screamed.

I picked her up by the neck and started frantically to shake the inert body.

"Waffles, Waffles!" I sobbed.

A wide-eyed and startled Waffles flailed her legs about to assure me that she was very much alive, and angry.

She sat glaring at me and would not be consoled until she had washed and soothed the ruffled fur. Only then would she permit me to try to reassure her that I had her (my) best interest at heart.

She started towards me for a cuddle but took one sniff and retreated in a graceful U-turn, and, at a safe distance, looked at me again with suspicious eyes.

I really did pong, so staggered on elastic legs to the bathroom for a shower. Why couldn't I walk straight? Why did everything move as I approached? Why were things being deliberately awkward to me?

(*Why indeed?*)

I returned to my bedroom by the same route, keeping my hand firmly on the wall which refused to stay solid and a rail that jumped around.

I sank into a comatose sleep.

I dreamt that I was being given a Shiatsu neck massage. It started off well but soon I realised that two pressure points were being painfully provoked by unyielding fingers.

"Let go!!" I screamed, throwing myself and the Shiatsu Sadist around the room.

"Let go!! I can't breathe."

The fact was, I couldn't breathe. I woke to find that my throat had constricted, blocked my trachea, and I was making horrible noises in an attempt to get air through to my lungs.

There was only one thing for it; clear the throat by making even worse noises and consciously relax the muscles. It didn't un-jam immediately, but, while sounding like a cross between a donkey and a bagpipe, I managed to inhale enough air to keep me from blacking out.

Normal breathing returned but I was left shaking, exhausted and frightened.

A similarly shaking, exhausted and frightened cat stared at me with wide eyes from the bottom of the bed.

"Waffles, I'm alright now. Come on baby pussycat."

She hesitated at first, but then carefully worked her way up the duvet keeping her eyes firmly on my face, which she then proceeded to lick very gently; despite the smell

(*Cat lovers, I know, will appreciate the symbiotic relationship.*)

Thirteen and a half hours later, and millions of revolutions in the spin dryer, I surfaced to another day.

Where had Ellis been throughout this ordeal?

All night Poker, of course.

(*Where else?*)

I felt terrible: nausea, headache, stomach rumblings and shaking all over. I couldn't face tea or water or anything but I'd been given strict instructions to eat or drink something with the anti-emetic tablets. I had so many to take! Eight Dexamethasone and eight Metoclopamide per day.

Correction.

The nurses had looked at the prescription and suggested that I took only half the amount, and see how I coped with that, as they are very potent.

But trying to take even two tablets was a daunting experience. I glanced at all the food possibilities and shuddered. Eventually I prepared a cup of hot water with a pin head amount of Marmite in it and a dry matzos. It was the slowest 'meal' I've ever had, but at least it remained in my stomach, along with the tablets.

So far, so good (ish).

I felt the need to drink water, which slowly diluted my red urine to a delicate shade of pink. Pity it did not do the same for my complexion; I looked ghastly.

I tried to recount my experiences in my make-shift daily journal without over-dramatising the events. It wasn't until I came to type up the account that I discovered that I had said the same thing three times! That I had said the same thing three times! That I had said the same thing three time . . .!

I did not write anything of great interest. All I seemed to have done (three times) is have a shower and note that I hadn't got pins and needles or an aching jaw.

As 'bed time' approached Waffles, quite understandably, retired to an open drawer wearing a World War Two pith helmet and waving a white flag. Her nervous face peered out until she was convinced, in her own mind, that there would not be a repetition of the inexplicable violence.

Then slept.

I also wanted sleep but the 'spinning' that was keeping me awake did not stop until at least 12.30 a.m. Perhaps I had, at last, burnt out the motor?

I woke with a start.

If it hadn't been for extreme exhaustion I would have felt ready for anything.

I couldn't relax or sit or read or stroke Waffles without feeling that I needed to do something else more . . . more . . . more.

I didn't know what I wanted but what I was doing was simply not enough.

The clock stated that I had been asleep for only one hour!

I paced around the house unable to do anything. If I thought of an idea it flooded into my brain like a phosphorous flare and I marvelled at the brilliance of the event, if not the concept. I turned on the radio and became angry and irritated at the crassness of the topics people found to talk about at 3 a.m.

You'd think they'd have better things to do than listen to idiots discussing the social implications of hairy nostrils, yellow lines and shoe laces.

But then what was I doing?

There must be something better to do?

There was—I attempted to throw the radio across the room, but as it was attached to an electric wire it swung in an ungainly curve and crashed against the side of the bookcase. Must remember to buy a wire—less my phosphorous thoughts phosphored.

I was awake for the rest of the night, so I am unable to state that I woke up.

Sunday.

Camden Lock.

Hat.

I'll do something useful and buy a hat, I told Ellis. I felt full of energy, which seemed a little strange in the circumstances; but welcome, as a relief from the agitated inaction.

The Hatters were very helpful and gave their honest opinions, whilst I pulled faces at my mirrored image.

"Why push all your hair inside the hat? It would look better if you let some of it show," one said.

"It's falling out," I explained.

(*Does it?*)

"Have you been to see a doctor about it? gasped another, with great concern."

"Yes," I said, laughingly. "That's why it's falling out."

I demonstrated with a gentle tug just how easy it was for my scalp to relinquish its crop. The amount of hair between my fingers surprised me, let alone the stall holder. I had expected one or two stray strands to show willing to the showy bravado, but not the large tuft which I had to curl round and round between my hands to reduce the size before finding a bin.

It had taken only two days for the poison to start work.

Hats in hand I returned home and experimented with different scarves and different angles.

It will do.

It will have to. I have no choice.

I buzzed through the day not doing anything, yet filling it with nothing.

I must be tired!

I wasn't.

(?)

Lights out 10 p.m.

Lights on 12.30 a.m.

I picked up Brian Keenan's book and lived for a while in a Beirut cell. One tormented night he lit one of his precious candles and observed that 'the Candle flame seemed to still and calm the mind'.

Paola had also mentioned the spiritual calming of candles and how they cleansed the atmosphere. I had recently bought a metal candle holder in the shape of a frog. At the time I thought it strange, as I was not particularly fond of frogs, but I had to buy it.

Now I hunted for cast-off candles from abandoned dinner parties and romantic nights and offered my frog the choice of green or red . . . He chose red.

It was very soothing and enchantingly mystical.

That night belongs to one of life's snap-shots, where sensations and atmosphere and just 'Being', blend into the tools of memory for no other reason than it happened.

There was no further sleep, yet I did not feel tired.

I was so delighted that I had not been laid low by this extra strength poison, that it flitted only vaguely across my consciousness that perhaps all was not as well as it should be.

But for the time being, I wallowed in the warmth of the beautiful spring day, and donning my new hat and personality, drove to my session with Paola.

She was delighted with my energy levels, which indicated to her that, however hard the decision had been to go on to VAC, I had absorbed the consequences in a positive manner.

During the Healing I felt a strange vibration in my cheek, then was aware of an Indian Guru walking away from the table. He crouched down in the corner of the room and gestured towards us, saying, "I'll leave you both to it. You seem to be doing alright on your own."

I snapped into a more normal state of awareness. I found myself lying on the table with Paola standing next to me, with her hands hovering six inches away from my body.

"Did you recognise him?" she asked casually.

"No, not really."

He did, however, look like a cross between Ghandi and one of my pottery students!

"Try and think who it might be," encouraged Paola.

(Mmmm??? —did I want to know?)

I had more than enough energy after my session with Paola (and Indian) so my planned trip to the hair salon in Paddington which provides National Health Service wigs, took place.

I'd had to go to the Surgical Equipment office at the Middlesex hospital to obtain a special form that entitled me to a hairy covering. The female, who dealt with me, had the most beautiful, dark, glossy, wavy hair cascading down her back.

"Hate you," I said, smiling sweetly at her.

"I know what you mean," said one of the office workers who, like me, looked as if she would benefit from a wig.

Luckily, Miss Beautiful Hair accepted my 'vitriolic' outburst with good grace and with the practised acceptance of one who knows that they have something which is the envy of most.

(ggrrr!)

In the salon I was shown to a private cubicle at the back of the shop. I had been expecting rows of identical wigs, screaming NHS or at most, a choice of one or two styles. I had even heard that there were thousands of Hillary Clinton wigs going cheap and wondered if, with the NHS cuts, a job lot had been negotiated?

"What style would you like?" said one of the trained Wiggerettes.

"Something similar to my own . . ."

(*Dull, mousy, lank, badly cut, boring . . .*)

". . . so that the contrast isn't too dramatic," I suggested.

My hair colour, minus the grey, was matched to a number on a shade chart.

"This is the shortest layered style that we have," she advised, as she lunged towards my head with one quick movement.

An ancient Joan Collins, wearing a dark brown bird's nest, stared back at me.

Horrors!!

A fit of giggles took over.

"I don't think so," we both said in unison.

Wiggerette disappeared to conjure up another style while I amused myself by seeing which areas of my head would release hair the quickest.

"I think this bob cut will suit you," she said, diving for my head. In a flash I was transformed into the Jenny Cole of 1963.

Brilliant.

The shade was lighter than my natural colour, but this seemed to compensate for my natural grey highlights, with the added advantage of nòt making it look so much like a wig.

The long thick fringe would also come in handy if my eyebrows decided to give up as well. Would other hairy areas suffer? It's not something that anyone talks about. 'Hair' implies 'on the head', but as I was soon to discover, it means everywhere.

(*I wonder if the NHS do a Lady Godiva wig?*)

The wig was curled up in a neat box like a friendly hamster and I was told how to look after it. It sounded easier than my own.

I had expected to be tired with all this activity and excitement but I remained alert and frisky all day.

Too alert and frisky.

At the back of my brain I remembered that Rebecca had warned me not to take the anti-emetic tablets after 8 p.m., as they may cause me to feel a bit high. So, that was the reason I wasn't sleeping?

Silly me.

I took the last tablets at 6 p.m. and willed my exhausted brain to sleep.

It took several hours before I finally drifted off.

I woke one hour later!!!

I calculated that I had only had a maximum of five hours sleep in three nights. Surely that was wrong?

I worked on the Wordprocessor and failed to 'save to disc', so proceeded to type it all over again.

I did some Visualisation.

I read and got angry.

I watched television and started to scream at the characters.

I made some tea.

I tried not to think of my hair falling out and started to cry.

On and on the night progressed as I felt myself unable to cope with the excessive sensations and agitation that roamed around my head and room.

At 5 a.m. I had breakfast.

(*At least I'm not nauseous.*)

I found myself swaying and rocking to and fro when I sat down and pacing backwards and forwards when I was standing.

I picked things up and threw them down immediately.

I scribbled notes I couldn't understand.

It all seemed so normal.

At 10 a.m. I phoned Latymer ward and spoke to a nurse. I tried to express my worries but it sounded tame compared to reality. She advised me to stop taking the tablets, especially as I was no longer feeling nauseous. "They *do* make people feel restless," she said.

"I know!"

I drove to my pottery class and amazed everyone, and myself, by going into mass production on the wheel.

I wedged clay.

I kneaded clay.

I would not sit down.

I chatted.

I walked around.

"Sit down!" they ordered.

I sat.

I stood up.

I told Gill and Rachel of my 'visit' by the Guru-type-figure.

"What did he look like?" they agog-ly enquired.

"A bit like Glen."

We all turned towards Glen (of Indian extraction), who was happily potting to himself at the other side of the room, and only half listening to the conversation.

"I went 'missing' for a while yesterday . . ." said Glen nonchalantly . . . "but I don't know where you live, so it couldn't have been me."

He couldn't understand why we were all laughing.

I returned home to a message from George informing me that he would phone again and that he hoped I was well.

(*Why?*)

P.S. Had his friend (fiend?) the solicitor contacted me yet?

I make several phone calls and am soon made aware that my voice is high and speedy.

Friends express concern.

"I'm fine," I declare.

I watch the news and explode at a top Tory minister, (wifey alone earns a vast mega-buck salary in the City) who announced that he felt it reasonable that individuals should pay £30.00 per night for a stay in a NHS hospital.

Does he indeed!

This added to my sense of unreality. I no longer wished to work out fact from fiction as fact seemed more unreal.

I 'short circuited' myself at 8.30 p.m. and slept.

I woke at 10.30 p.m. with my stomach in turmoil. It was shooting acid around my body. I had never suffered from bad indigestion, so could not relate the sensation to the condition. But, acid indigestion in my toes?

Anything was possible.

That night everything was possible.

I tapped out two more pages to the tune of St Vitus dance.

I couldn't rest, or be active.

I tried to read a book but became angry with myself for having to move my head left to right all the time.

Everything became increased and magnified.

Waffles became a Tiger.

(*On my bed!*)

A Moth became a Bird.

I could see a Bucking Bronco leaping around my bedroom . . . but, hang on a minute, I was riding it as well . . . as well as observing.

(*Seems reasonable.*)

"Who's a beautiful Pussy cat," I murmured, as I stroked thin air. I wondered why Waffles was eyeing me in a strange way.

My stomach and breast felt full of sulphur.

The Radiation had dried the skin so I proceeded slowly to rub cream on to the affected area.

As I progressed across the sore breast I felt something hard and shiny move (?).

Furtively looking down I was convinced my nipple had fallen off.

I stared from the beetle-shaped object in my hand to the end of my breast and back again.

Slowly, very slowly, I convinced myself that I wasn't falling to bits (physically) and that the beetle was nothing more than the hard crust that had covered the nipple during its descent (inversion) into cancer.

I peered down lovingly on a brand new pink, untouched, un-Radiated nipple.

Aarrh.

Sweet.

But the night was still young, so I propped myself into a sitting position and declared: "You can't get me now, I'm ready for you."

And so I remained until dawn and beyond, fighting off creatures and sensations and thinking that the world had perhaps become just marginally a little more weird.

Ellis greeted me with a bright 'good morning' and the offer of a cup of tea.

By the time he'd returned I was asleep (not aware that I was awake) and he had to leave it by the bed.

I woke, and seeing a cold cup of tea, demanded another.

It arrived.

It went cold.

It was taken downstairs by me.

I greeted Ellis.

"I think I'll make some tea," I announced.

Back to bed and a one-sided conversation. I was aware that Ellis found it all amusing, but I couldn't work out why.

He left for America.

I was hanging on to what reality I had left inside me, which wasn't much.

Gradually the morning progressed and I phoned a few friends to tell them I didn't know who I was anymore.

(*That also seemed reasonable.*)

I was becoming well enough to know that I was feeling terrible.

Frances became apprehensive about my garbled ramblings of Bucking Broncos, Tigers and Moths the size of birds.

(*Can't see why?*)

Why don't you ring Robert?" she advised.

This I did, as the acknowledgement of my condition speedily flooded my panic button and left me shaky and weepy.

Robert answered in person.

I blurted out my . . . my what? I don't remember anything apart from blurting out.

Silence.

Is he there?

(*Speak to me!*)

"Sulphur and Nux-vomica Homeopathic tablets," he states.

"Thank you."

I was in no fit state to leave the house, but was also incapable of remembering who I knew locally.

(*Don't panic—keep calm.*)

I flicked through my address book looking for another North London post code: Jo.

Thankfully she was in.

By this time I was weeping and disorientated and could only just deliver my message.

I rocked myself back and forth until Jo, with sanity reinforcements, arrived.

She was confused in the shop when asked if she needed Series 6 or Series 30.

"What's the difference?" she asked.

"Well, normally people have the Series 6, but if it's for an acute condition you'll need Series 30."

"Believe me, this situation calls for Series 30," said Jo grabbing the tubs of strange-sounding pills and whisking them swiftly to the strange-sounding Heap of Torment.

I dissolved the tablets in my mouth and within a very short time I felt the raging subside.

I was soon asleep.

My dreams were of a succession of tiny tubs of Homeopathic tablets offered to me by a female. Every time I took a tablet I woke with one less symptom. This happened throughout the night until I woke in the morning, with a headache, but normal.

(*Normal for me.*)

"Why?" friends demanded, "didn't you ask for help sooner?"

Basically, because I was having a Bad Acid Trip, and, not ever having had even a Good Trip (or indifferent) didn't realise that things weren't as they should be. It was only as I started to have Cold turkey that pockets of understanding started to question the world I had lived in for five days.

I knew there was a reason for my being a drug-free art student in the Sixties; I'm just not cut out for the altering of my consciousness to that level. Life itself has always given me enough Uppers and Downers to do that.

I phoned Frances to thank her for suggesting Robert and Homeopathy.

I reached for my Homeopathic book:

Sulphur was for acute conditions. Restlessness. 'Wishing to touch something'. Over-sensitivity. Sick head. Vomiting.

Nux-vomica was for conditions such as fast pace. Over stimulation. Mental strain. Irritability.

Brilliant.

Ellis phoned from America and expressed relief that I was out of the nightmare even if he hadn't realised that I'd been in one.

"I knew you were a bit 'on edge', but it sounds as if you've been over the mountain and down the other side."

(Quite.)

So, I felt wonderful even as I lay in bed with an appalling headache.

The pain across my eyes and temples also indicated that my liver was objecting again.

But it was truly magnificent to feel so lousy.

I prodded Shiatsu points to help relieve the pain, then delivered myself to Trish for our weekly session.

I had made myself get into the habit of wearing the wig

before it was really necessary, so expected Trish to be confused by my appearance.

We both looked completely different, but my tongue had been relaxed and confused by the drugs.

"I have a reason for my hair to look like this. What's your excuse?" I blurted out, before realising that it wasn't quite what I'd wanted to impart.

Luckily we have the same type of humour, and as I fumbled over my words to explain what I actually meant she explained the reasons behind her perm.

(*Oh, right, a perm.*)

She worked on my stomach and head for the whole session gradually reducing the pain to a more acceptable level.

Heavy duty Chemotherapy is not easy to shift.

I had been warned not to use soap on the Radiation area for at least two weeks; this had been surpassed by three days. So, celebration time. . . . A Bath.

I longed to relax and soak and wallow in warmth and comfort, especially now I felt so frazzled by the Trip.

To be on the safe side I opened a new pack of 'soap' which claimed that it was a moisturising bar.

Bliss.

I carefully dried myself without rubbing the Radiation area and felt clean for the first time in months.

But within seconds my skin flared to a bright red and remained like that until a layer gave up.

I hadn't even used soap, according to the advert!

The Radiated area continued to turn bright red, and hot, whenever it felt like it, for weeks. I was assured this was fairly normal and could even occur long after the treatment.

I rang Dorothy to discuss this, and my Trip. In one of her

lovely understatements she calmly told me: "I think you've had an adverse reaction to one of the drugs."

No! Really?

It was not normal though and she advised me to inform the doctors so that the same reaction did not recur.

"Don't worry", I informed her, "there is no way I will take the Dexamethasone again."

I hate to think what might have happened had I taken the dosage prescribed by the doctor!

(*Jumped off Archway Bridge, perhaps?*)

Sleep, sleep and more sleep.

The following day a friend and I went to the 'Festival of Mind, Body, Spirit' at the Royal Horticultural Hall.

I went straight to the Kirlian photography stand. On previous visits I had not so much avoided it as ignored it. Now, armed with a body that definitely had something wrong with it, would this technique unearth my problems? I felt like a walking Market Research product.

The 'photograph' is actually an impression of the electro-magnetic field surrounding the hands. I was sent into a mini darkroom and asked to place my hands on a sheet of photographic paper resting on a metal box. Through this would pass an electric current and take a 'photograph'. When I was informed that I would feel a tiny crackling sensation I pulled my hands away and asked for an exact definition of 'crackling'. It wasn't that I thought they electrocuted paying festival visitors, but I didn't really think I could cope with any sudden or unpleasant sensation (again . . . so soon). He gave me an indication of the process by placing his own fingers on the metal plate. Sparks crackled, but he stood alive and well, and there was no smell of singed hair. Commonsense told me that they would soon run out of interested patrons if the whole experience was at all unpleasant, but for once in my life I was being cautious.

(*And about time too!*)

I placed my hands on the paper and . . . it was rather like gentle electric pins and needles, lasting only a few seconds.

The photograph is developed there and then and you are passed on to an 'Interpreter'.

I could see the look of horror on his face, as my nearly blank photograph developed. This look of disbelief and discomfort was transferred to the Interpreter who spent a long time wiping away the excess developing liquid.

Silence.

"It's alright," I assure him. "I already know what's wrong, so whatever you want to say is okay by me," I said, reassuringly.

His shoulders visibly dropped.

"You're very ill," he said finally.

(*Tell me about it!*)

"What indicates that?" I said, staring at a few black fuzzy markings, while all around me other Kirlian photographs looked as if a child had gone berserk with an ink pot.

"No palm print from either hand: that indicates a major illness."

"And?"

"Virtually no left hand, which indicates that your energy has withdrawn deep inside in an attempt to reserve what it can."

I inspected the space where the left hand print should have been. 'No print' was an understatement.

"The right-hand print is a little more pronounced. This shows a major change in life, i.e., a change in direction. There is an amazing outpouring of creativity and you are still 'entertaining' people with your energy."

I waited.

"That's all I'm able to see," he confessed. "There's so little for me to work on."

I could see other Kirlian participants glancing towards my specimen and perhaps wondering if I was about to demand a refund.

I found the lack of print interesting and I mad a mental note to have another one taken when I was better-er.

I strolled past the Astrology Booth and despite having some first-hand experience of the format I asked for a Reading. I gave by birth date then had to return twenty minutes later when the computer had produced the chart.

I returned on the dot to be told that I was a typical Arien; always on time.

(*Perhaps I should find myself only Arien friends?*)

Once again, I did not divulge the information of my cancer.

Sneaky? Perhaps.

"You are living in a state of great upheaval and change. Something dynamic has changed your life . . ."

She consulted a large directory.

". . . it began December or January."

(*Wow!*)

"Whatever you are going through has a good outcome," she continued.

Smiling. Enquiring?

"I've got cancer," I confessed.

"There is still a good prognosis," she insisted.

Consulting my chart (and Uranus) she talked of my fragmented early environment and that I had been kept at an emotional distance for most of my childhood.

(*True*)

The sixth house, which relates to Health (Leo) noted that my 'Heart' is damaged. (*True*).

The fourth house (Moon) is my Saving Grace: without it I would be a 'nasty piece of work'. (*Ask my friends!*). As it is, I'm over sensitive and vulnerable. (*True*).

People deplete my energy, because I don't protect myself.

(*Double true-ish*)

I was asked to return for a different reading—on my progress. Okay.

Meanwhile I drifted off to the Aura photography booth. I was asked to sit and place my hands on some 'electrodes' at either side of the chair.

Smile.

Flash.

A polaroid photo of me surrounded by red, yellow and orange clouds was handed to me along with an Interpreter.

"You are very strong."

(*Not at the moment, I'm not!*)

"Your Aura is very high; higher than the average. You are a pioneer, always active and interested in travel and new ideas. I've started on a new direction, which is creative and a challenge. Intellectual. I need to know what is going on."

I asked if the photograph could show any depletion of energy, or danger signals, as I was a little surprised that it looked so uniform and vibrant.

"No, the camera isn't that sensitive," he explained.

I have to confess I was disappointed with the session. It had taken on the atmosphere of a side-show at a circus, and from what I could see most people had yellow and red around them.

I'll have to think about this. I felt uneasy about the 'results'.

Clutching my photo I returned to the Astrology booth. This time I was handed over to another female, who dealt with more medical aspects of Astrology.

I'm asked about the cancer.

I talk of my 'enjoyment' of the cancer, a statement which I know baffles and annoys some people.

"You are very susceptible to drugs," she announced.

"In what way?"

"They have a very harsh effect on your system."

(*She's telling me!*)

"That's interesting. I've just had a five-day Acid Trip followed by Cold turkey . . . courtesy of the NHS."

"Really?"

"Yes. Come to think of it I had a similar experience on a wonder drug called Danazol, twelve years ago."

"What happened with that?"

"Well, I boarded a bus and started to walk towards the back to find a seat. The bus had to climb a steep hill to the next stop and I felt myself getting angry because everyone was looking at me. What's the matter with them?

"It wasn't until we reached the next stop that I realised that I hadn't moved at all, only walked on the same spot. No wonder everyone was looking!"

Suddenly, the Astrologer peered at me more closely.

"I know you," she insisted.

"What?"

(*Don't do that to me in a Mind, Body, Spirit Exhibition!*)

"Did you ever go to a Herbalist near Highgate?"

I racked my brains.

Slowly, I remembered that many years ago an Acupuncturist had sent me for one session to a Herbalist. I had only been with this female for under an hour. This couldn't be her could it?

It was.

"How did you recognise me after twelve years?"

"Your eyes. They say just as much as your words."

She then told me, in great detail, the events that were happening in my life at that time.

Creepy.

"I can't possibly give you an accurate health reading in ten minutes," she confessed. "Would you be prepared to see me for a full session?"

"Why not."

She handed me her card. If she hadn't recognised me I would have recognised her name. My eyes may have been the same (plus maturity lines) but she had changed from a short dark-haired female to one with long blonde luscious locks.

More difficult.

I had overdone it.

As soon as I got home I crashed into a deep sleep.

I woke with a sore throat and so consulted my BACUP pamphlet on symptoms of Chemotherapy. Nothing specific-ally on sore throats but I noticed that they suggested that I stayed away from animals.

I can think of one animal who would object to that!

The sore throat continued.

Then my stomach seemed to be very acidic and full.

Then a headache started.

I've been overdoing it, I thought. I'll go to bed and in the morning everything will have settled down.

Wrong.

I woke at 5 a.m. with sinus pain to add to my discomfort.

I felt poisoned.

My stomach was on fire.

I had sulphuric acid burning my intestines.

Trish had been concerned by my condition, so rang to see if I had improved.

Terrible.

My disorientated woeful voice prompted her to lure me up the hill for an extra session.

I go.

But not before I change from my black jumper to a red one. I didn't want to have her chastising me again.

She worked on my head, sinus, stomach, solar plexus and breast, which felt like a Hot Cole (sic).

By the end of the session I could breathe more freely, my stomach was resting and the breast had reduced to a blow.

"Don't wear red next to your breast," she warned.

"Sorry," I mumbled, not daring to confess that I'd only just changed into it.

The next day, the stomach having rested still continued to cause great discomfort.

I couldn't rest.

I couldn't even do my Visualisation, as the supine position put extra pressure on my abdomen.

I was a mess.

My sister Wendy phoned. She had only just got back from Spain.

"Are you alright?" she asked, with her 'I know you haven't been' voice.

"Why?"

"Because last Tuesday I couldn't rest I was so agitated. Several times I wanted to phone England to see how you were, and spent hours walking backwards and forwards to the phone box. Where were you on Tuesday?"

Where was I?

Knowing (or not knowing) the state I was in during the Trip and Cold turkey I wouldn't have been at all surprised to learn that I had, in fact, been in Spain.

My stomach continued to have its own rampant bush fire of sulphuric acid, which spat out angry offshoots of corrosive venom to the far corners of my toes and ears. I could no longer distinguish between my sinus, liver or digestive headaches; they had merged, congregated and gone wild. I felt dizzy, disorientated and downright poisoned, which of course I was.

By the next morning my stomach had become bloated but the headache, although bad, was just about passable. I had to creek my way to the hospital for a nadir blood test. Eight components of my blood were low but, as yet, there was no need for any action. I remembered Rebecca's enthusiasm about my blood in January when things had only just started. I didn't feel as bad then as I did now; could things get worse?

(*Just you wait, I should have said to myself.*)

The nurses were horrified by my nightmare trip and started to look up the offending substance in their Directory of Drugs.

The patient may become 'on edge or jumpy' was the worst side effect they could find. In reality that had been my best condition.

Am I that delicate?

While at the UCH having my blood tests I popped in to see Dorothy for more soothing words and encouragement.

"How're you doing?" she beamed.

After recalling my adventures I announced that I had made a decision not to return to the prison.

"At last," she declared. "It's only taken you five months to realise that your body could not possibly cope with the stresses and strains of that kind of environment."

It's true. I didn't know and nobody could tell me when (or if) I would be fit enough to work, let alone lug sacks of clay, stand all day and absorb negative waves in the process.

(*Crime waves?*)

What I would do was a mystery to me, but at present it was of very little importance. I could barely walk.

Paola, sensing my mental state, asked me my attitude to all my inactivity.

It was certainly strange for me not to be rushing around at 110 miles per hour and even stranger not to be doing *anything*.

Had this happened to me in January, perhaps I would have found it difficult to cope? But now, surrounded by my network of Therapists, whom I trusted with my body, I was prepared for them to nurture me and take the strain. Quite happily.

"Good," she said.

She was also pleased that I had decided against continuing at the prison. (Even if the choice was about to be taken away from me with the new contracts.)

"What did prison mean to you?" she probed.

"No support, no value, harassment, rudeness, frustration, threats . . . do you want me to go on?'

"NO . . . throw it away."

I had felt in 1992 that I was being buried so quickly under layer after layer, that my own strength was unable to break through. I was determined not to let that happen again, and was pleased by my refusal to allow characters like Jane and Declan to start the process all over again.

I felt with the cancer that I was shedding layers of unnecessary rubbish that I had hauled around for years.

It was somehow rewarding, but I knew I had a long way to go.

Paola found that my liver and colon were overtaxed (surprise, surprise) and suggested that I may like to see her

Chinese Herbalist. It would mean discontinuing my Robert visits, as the herbs did not mix well with Homeopathy.

I reassured her that I was perfectly happy with Robert, as he was no ordinary Homeopath. I had complete confidence in him.

Such trust.

I visited Robert the next day.

He took one look at me and dragged me into his room ahead of another client, who was late for her appointment.

"You look as if you needed to be seen quickly," he observed.

(*Ah, sweet, He cares.*)

I was clutching my stomach and could not straighten up with the pain.

"Can you suggest anything that I could eat that would perhaps calm my stomach?"

He looked at me in his silent way, then said: "This is what you do."

I was all ears.

"Buy some Slippery Elm. . . ."

"Right."

". . . and some goat's milk."

(Pause)

"Do I eat or drink them?" I prompted.

"No, prepare the Slippery Elm and consume it on its own. Leave the unpasteurised goat's milk in the sun for a day, then transfer it from the carton into a jug and leave it to ferment for two or three days. It may separate, but don't worry about it."

(*Are you listening, stomach!*)

"It's brilliant for the stomach, as it is full of vitamins and minerals that you need. It's been noted that communities that include fermented food in their diet live far longer than other groups," he concluded.

"Anything else I should do?"

"Yes, take the Nux-vomica and Sulphur during the next session, it will help to flush through the poisons."

(*A pleasant, caring Robert. What's going on?*)

"Sometimes I wonder why I'm on Chemotherapy," I quietly whimpered.

"I wonder as well. Why are you?"

"I don't have enough faith or madness not to be on it."

"Fair enough."

"Talking of madness, though, I had a visitation from an Indian Guru.. . ."

"Strange how it's never a little man wearing a cloth cap and clogs," he interjected.

"Welcome back, Robert."

I thought I had seen some Slippery Elm at the back of a shelf, but to be on the safe side I purchased some more at my excellent local Health shop. The assistant was very helpful and consulted a Natural Healing book to discover how to prepare the powder.

Once home, I measured out the milk and started to heat it gently adding the advised amount of Slipper Elm. the 'mixture' got thicker and thicker.

(*I thought I had to drink it?*)

I attempted to pour the gunge into a bowl and was surprised at the speed with which it transferred itself. Perhaps I wasn't paying attention, I thought, but I could swear it leapt.

I cornered a small spoonful and, as I raised it to my lips, watched it crawl and ooze away from the centre of the spoon, over the rim, and back into the bowl.

(!)

This stuff's alive, I thought, and tried again.

The nearest description I can muster is that it is a cross between porridge with thoughts of escape; mercury for its speed and ability to fragment; and 'the creature from outer space' for its ability to ooze, change shape and re-group.

But, once captured, it didn't taste bad at all: a sort of mix between porridge and semolina.

The thrill of the hunt had been too much though and after corralling the last spoonful I retired to bed ... with a gurgling tum.

It took ten days for my sulphuric stomach and headache to finally depart and I looked forward to eating something else. The only problem was that my appetite had diminished with the pain. As the pounds rolled off, I started to look, for the first time, as if I had a serious illness.

That I could cope with, but what I was finding unliveable with, was the daily task of removing hair from any food or drink I had prepared, sweeping the bed clothes and unblocking the sink. For such fine hair there seemed to be a vast amount of it everywhere (except on my head) which was now tender to the touch, as though bruised.

I suddenly decided to take the bull by the horn (Cole by the hair) and shave it all off.

Dare I?

Dare I not?

It will be like having a baby I told myself. Awful while you're doing it, but the end result will be positive.

Dare I?

I took control.

I knelt down on the floor over an open newspaper and picking up a pair of nail scissors hacked off several lumps.

Now there would be no going back.

Waffle's eyes opened slightly from her peaceful slumbers at the foot of the bed.

They closed.

I reached for the electric hair clippers and in the best Australian sheep farm technique whizzed several times across my tender scalp.

Chunks of hair dutifully plopped on to the newspaper.

Waffles, by this time, with eyes steadily widening in disbelief, then horror, then fear, dived under the bed for safety.

I felt for any last remaining tufts and satisfied myself that as far as unsighted-clipper-hairstyling went I had reached the summit of my ability.

Now for the participant's reaction!

Allow yourself to burst into tears, I counselled myself.

Slowly, I raised myself from the floor and stood facing the mirror.

Open your eyes coward, I hissed to myself.

My eyes opened.

First reaction?

Not bad.

Sigourney Weaver need have no worries that I will audition for Star Wars 99 but it wasn't as bad as I thought it would be.

The Clipper setting had not taken the hair to the scalp, so I had a nine o'clock shadow to play with; and play I did.

What a sensuous experience being able to stand under a shower and feel the water on your head! It felt like velvet.

Waffles emerged gingerly from under the bed and, sitting at a safe distance, stared at me.

When it finally penetrated her brain that she was not to have the same treatment she came to investigate.

Second sensuous experience!

The rasp of a cat's tongue on a newly shorn head.

I don't know who was more surprised, or delighted?

And as a small bonus the wig fitted better.

The exhilaration of the moment had passed and chatting to Paola I remarked that it was only now that I felt as though I had cancer, i.e., I felt terrible. You mustn't think that way, she insisted, what you are feeling is the effects of the treatment and not the cancer.

She was right.

Throughout the course of the treatment when friends rang to enquire about my progress (or the cancer's decline), I had to admit that the *cancer* was the least of my problems. In fact, at one stage it felt as if my breast was the only part of me that was not falling to bits or malfunctioning.

The latest malfunctioning were my fingers! Numb pins and needles. Very strange, but just about bearable.

Two phone messages.

One from 'George' hoping that I was 'progressing' . . .

(*Does that mean dying?*)

. . . and wishing to hear from me soon.

This was the third message he had left, and I'd had enough. I wrote telling him that if he bothered me again then I would inform his company of his Unethical Utterings.

I never heard from him again.

The second message was from my new general practitioner.

"Nothing to worry about, but, could I please ring the surgery?" requested the receptionist.

(*Nothing to worry about, what?*)

With my heart pounding I rang the Receptionist, who is probably now called a Medical Office Manager.

"Oh yes Mrs Cole (!) we haven't seen you since the new doctor arrived over a year ago, and were wondering if everything was alright.

As part of the new Patient's Charter we are offering a Mini Health Check."

(*Phew!*)

"Ah, well you see, I haven't been into the surgery because I'm in perfect health . . . except I've got cancer," I heard myself say.

I meant it.

I had no intention of sitting in a germ-infested waiting room for any length of time, with my battered immune system, so I made an evening appointment for the following week.

At the very least it would be an opportunity to introduce myself, but I couldn't really imagine what she could tell me about my health that I didn't already know.

The next day I was visiting Elizabeth the Astrologer, who was attempting to do just that.

What she had been particularly interested in was how a strong dynamic person could be so plagued by major illnesses.

(*So was I.*)

It didn't help that a long time ago my body had been 'poisoned' by the constant use of antibiotics and other prescribed drugs. I had also exhausted myself by being over optimistic in what I thought I could achieve, eg in the prison and with Ellis.

Years ago I had somehow lost my 'fear', and therefore my ability, to protect myself.

I had been conned by Ellis.

My 'partner' had, she felt, helped in the creation of the cancer, as it had manifested itself as a Raging, ie, an Inflammatory cancer of the breast.

(*Which he'd never liked!*)

Where the cancer had decided to attack was influenced by the feminine Venus/Moon in 1992. My Hysterectomy had reduced the options, but it had still found its way to one of my female 'bits'.

Now with Jupiter (improvement) in transit over Neptune (health) I was ready to use a sieve to shake through the shit.

She warned that the second week in August would be bad in that I may feel that the cancer was on the rampage again. But, I was not to worry. The apprehension and the problem would pass.

Jupiter over Sun in October or November would signal a period of solitude, or, creativity.

January '94 would also be an important month and a time I would need good energy. It would be a time of change or flare-up.

(*Gulp!*)

A home is important to me as I have a lot of emotional energy tied to my physical environment.

I will rid myself of my cancer by my Creativity and over the next two years I will find the meaning of my sicknesses through writing.

(*I'm already working on it.*)

I found her interpretation of my chart un-nerve-ing-ly accurate and I made a conscious decision *not* to note down in my diary the exact future periods she had talked about, but instead, to wait and see.

It had also given me much to think about and for a while my sleep was fretful, as our chat had churned up sensations, memories, fears and regrets.

To amuse myself I washed my wig. 'Dunk up and down in cold shampooy water' . . . the instructions said 'rinse, then leave to dry naturally. Never use heat of any description,' it warned.

I hung a bedraggled, drowned rat over the shower unit and for some reason expected the synthetic hair to drip dry in a few minutes.

Wrong! Because of the humidity it took over 18 hours to dry.

But, unlike my own hair, it bounced back into its perfect style in minutes.

Trish time again.

As I started to chat about my week she seemed a bit distracted, occasionally looking under the sofa, or nudging a mat.

"Trish, what are you doing?"

"Looking for a frog."

(*Naturally*)

"A frog?" I enquired politely.

"Yes, Min brought one in and it's escaped. I know it's in here somewhere.

So, with two dogs, three cats and a frog within easy reach she started to wire me up to the generator.

Suddenly I develop a cough, a dry, ticklish sort which you know is not going to go away easily.

"Good heavens, what's the matter?"

"I feel as if I have something in my throat," I croaked.

(*A frog, perhaps?*)

Strangely I've never coughed at Trish's house ever again, but she did eventually find the amphibious creature.

The second Chemotherapy session had arrived. Ellis had volunteered to sit with me, but because of all the pre-session rigmarole I advised him to arrive later.

To keep up my morale, I had made the decision always to put on my best clothes, spend minutes (not seconds) on my make-up, and adorn myself with jewellery . . . just for the Chemotherapy.

Many a time I sat looking as if I were about to attend Ascot, and many a time others must have sat looking at this weird female, wondering why she had bothered.

(*Why do individuals facing Execution make an effort?*)

Blood tests and a chat with Glen took up several hours, mainly in waiting time. I told Glen of my horrendous experiences and he duly wrote down in my notes 'Acid Trip followed by Cold turkey'—very medically described! He did however put me back on Odansetron, the original anti-emetic, which was a relief.

I had a further wait in Latymer Ward for the Chemo-therapy to arrive from the pharmacy. It was such an extended wait that by the time Ellis arrived (and he was late) he assumed I had been 'done' and started to bundle me out of the hospital.

While we waited Clare plumbed me into a saline drip.

I'm glad I sent Ellis to get my prescription and sick note because there was some difficulty in finding a vein that wanted to yield to the needle. I had become extra sensitive to any piercing of my skin, however expert, but on this occasion several nurses themselves cringed at the effort required.

Ellis would not have survived.

OOOhh!

It was at this point that I discovered that the famous 'itchy bum' liquid was also the infamous Dexamethasone; so with that hallucinogenic liquid reaching the parts that other

Chemotherapies take hours to reach, it was no wonder that I started to feel terrible almost immediately after the first session.

I could feel the difference.

I remained awake for most of the day and even managed a reasonable night's sleep.

If the worst is over, this will be a piece of cake.

I should have said 'crumbs' or something stronger . . . if only I'd known.

I had little energy and felt slightly vacant, but the next few days passed with ease. I had become more and more interested in nutrition because of my firsthand experience and the advice, or lack of advice, I'd received over the months. I decided to send off for a correspondence course in nutrition which, hopefully, could become part of my rehabilitation into the the World of Thinking. It might even provide a suitable qualification on which perhaps to base a new career. (?)

My appetite had not been brilliant over the past few days but at least I did not have the 'traumatised gut' to worry about, only the preparation of the Slippery Elm, which was keeping me alive and amused. I was also consuming quantities of All Bran, partly because it was all I could face, but I did have a mega problem of Total Blockage again. The pain and discomfort began to mount and exploded as a headache at midnight.

The physical explosion occurred the next morning.

Meanwhile I was trying to ignore the ominous feeling that the sulphuric pain was about to return, but return it did. This time I knew that it would continue for ten days and that nothing would ease the constant feeling of being eaten alive from the inside out.

Life tried to prod me into activity; the prospectus for the

correspondence course arrived, I saw Paola and Trish, I tried to write down the weird and wonderful dreams I was experiencing, and I arranged an interview with an investment adviser.

Investment is for the future and the (healthy) young man had to ask what prognosis I had for my cancer. I gave him one of my world-weary looks and informed him that if I knew I was going to be dead in a few months would I be trying to invest what little money I had? No, I'd spend, spend, spend.

(*Would I?*)

As I was determined not to be dead just yet, then I wanted my money to work for me. If by chance I were to die suddenly (and that option is open to everyone) then it was irrelevant how much money I had, or did not have.

He fumbled with his papers. I could see he was ill at ease, but this was more to do with the fact that his computer had broken down and he looked as if he was unsure of how to use a pen.

He promised to phone with some proposals.

I waited.

Meanwhile, Jane (of Jane and Declan) had left a message on my tape in response to a firm letter I'd sent her regarding the return, or rather non-return, of my paintings.

"You're absolutely right," she chortled. "It's appalling what we've done to you. Please phone me."

I didn't want to phone someone who reminded me of my powerlessness and vulnerability. Instead I phoned my niece, who was only too pleased to go round personally to retrieve them.

Jane's excuse was that she couldn't find an envelope big enough.

Interestingly, my niece posted them to me immediately.

The whole episode had taken nearly three months to reach a satisfactory conclusion . . . and it left an unpleasant after-taste.

Taste was not high on my agenda with the continuation of my inflamed gut. Porridge, Slippery Elm, Yoghurt and All Bran were all I had eaten for twelve days. At my next hospital appointment the nurses decided that I should see Glen. My haemoglobin level had dropped to 10.1 and they were concerned about my constant pain. Glen gently pressed my swollen gut and muttered "Vincristine".

It's hard to believe that such a pretty plant could cause such damage, but of all the drugs and potions poured into me, this was the one that had reduced me to such a pathetic state. Vincristine, the chemical derivative of the Periwinkle, attacked nerve endings and in my case specifically the large intestine and finger ends.

There was nothing he could do about it but the effect would wear off, as I had discovered on the previous occasion.

The solution was to halve the dosage on the next Chemotherapy session.

I couldn't wait.

(*Half the pain for half the length of time?*)

The journey, the blood test, the wait for Glen, the prodding of my swollen gut and the tightness of a hat I was wearing was all too much. It brought on a headache, which had me weeping with pain in unison with my gut.

This was not funny.

I needed to feel better as I had another appointment with Robert. He took one look at me and asked how dead I was.

"Pardon?"

"You were 'half dead' when we last met . . . how 'dead' are you now?"

I could see what he meant.

Could he suggest something to help boost my red blood count?

He could.

"Blue Green Algae."

"And where does one get that from?" I enquired, dreading the thought of wasting energy hunting down this particular Algae.

He didn't know, but from somewhere in my brain I remembered that Anita had given me a leaflet about some funny stuff she was taking instead of Barleygreen.

Wasn't that Algae?

It was.

I rang the number and was invited immediately to attend an evening lecture and to try some of the powder in a freshly juiced Juice.

Juice? What about the tablets?

I staggered down to Marylebone and into the mews accommodation, where 'Seven Ray' resided, and came face to face with Jane! I'm not sure if she recognised me, as I was wearing one of my hats, pulled low over my head, but she didn't try to talk to me and soon left.

What a relief. I really didn't have the energy for any 'verbal'.

I managed to stay only for the first part of the lecture then had to activate a full retreat. I was in no fit state to be wandering around London so, bottles of dark green tablets in hand, I retraced my steps and was asleep by 8 p.m.

Exhausted.

I was looking forward to a new television programme called 'Magic or Medicine', which aimed to look at the growing interest in Complementary therapies, their uses and their effectiveness.

The presenter (an oncologist) capsulised the interest in Complementary therapies by the fact that they were client not symptom-based.

(*Well, that's not a bad place to start!*)

This seemed to be the only aspect the programme could find that had any benefit over Orthodox treatments, ie, that it gave the individual control over their illness by working on the Life force/Qi/Hatha and helped the body heal itself.

But the overall presentation and conclusion of the programme was very condescending to non-conventional methods.

I listened and watched with mounting disbelief as the one-sided and dismissive approach swept aside treatments that had been in existence long before 'modern' medicine.

Every night following the programme I had disturbed dreams of my own death, especially when a statement was made that: "Women with Breast cancer who use both Ortho-dox and Complementary treatments are more likely to die".

This I can do without, I thought.

(That statement was in fact proved inaccurate in a court battle; the research techniques used in the study left a lot to be desired.)

But at the time of the programme I felt as if the whole rationale behind my approach to cancer had been wiped away and discredited . . . with no defence allowed.

How dare they! I raged, too traumatised by the onslaught of the programme to fully put all my thoughts into a cohesive argument in defence.

Orthodox medicine cannot abide other methods which cannot be measured, tested or bottled. Our bodies *have* to be more than a set of statistics and data—thoughts, beliefs, needs, determination and Cole's pig-headedness cannot be empirically measured, so are not relevant?

(*Let's dismiss all the Religions, as well!*)

After each programme it took me several days to regain my fighting spirit, but if according to the programme a fighting spirit was irrelevant to whether I survived or not, why bother?

Because *I* am important and how dare anyone tell me I'm not!!!!

On a more pleasant note, I still had the sensation of being eaten away by sulphuric acid. That, plus anxiety over the programme and a night of little sleep left me drained and tetchy for my session with Trish.

Perhaps it was lack of fight that allowed me to hand over my feet to Trish for some Reflexology.

I hate my feet being touched!

Suffering in a state (other than) of silence she prodded and poked until she traversed my digestive area. AArrgghh!

"The descending colon is a bit unhappy," she remarked with a grin.

Many other parts of me were also unhappy, but as I knew it would be doing me good I tolerated the onslaught and apologised to my feet afterwards.

"How do they feel now?" Trish enquired.

"Um?"

"Abused?"

"No. Actually they feel relaxed, lovingly mangled, but relaxed."

"Good, I'll do this more often."

Me and my big mouth.
(*And small feet.*)

Slowly the inflamed abdomen subsided, which allowed me to continue with one of my paintings. My African Violet had suddenly blossomed, producing over thirty magnificent deep purple flowers. It was too powerful a vision to ignore.

The problem was though, that as my concentration span was short and patchy, the plant was painted at different times of the day and in different light quality. The warm weather didn't help and as the plant responded to the heat it was like trying to paint from a speeded-up film. For some reason, quite understandable to me, I painted in my torso as the backdrop and positioned the violet over my abdomen.

Between my body and the crook of my arm Waffles was on a small raft in a turbulent sea, gazing into the water, as if it were a Crystal ball.

The whole effect was again mystical and a bit disturbing; but then again my whole life had taken on similar 'adjectives'. I felt pleased that my creative ability had not completely deserted me, but the fact remained that I had managed to be creative only in the three days before the next treatment.

Tomorrow the whole process would start again.

Paola warned me to take it easy. Get Ellis to do the shopping, washing up and cleaning. If anyone had ever witnessed Ellis attempting these tasks they would know why more energy is used in the process of watching!

She also drew me a Protection Pyramid; when encountering negative people or events I was to imagine myself surrounded by three shells of protection. Pink for physical energy, Blue for Inspiration and Gold for Soul energy. I enclose this within a pyramid, whose outer layer is Blue, for Inspiration. The base on which I stand is Green for Progress.

(Mm! not sure about this?)
"Interesting," I offered as a response.
"Try it," she insisted.
(Mmm!?)

Breakfast television had a short item on the benefits of breast feeding a child for at least three months. Not only does the child have a good start in life but it helps prevent Breast cancer.

It's the roundabout and swings syndrome again.

Research always seems to show that if women have babies, early menstruation, late menopause, breast feed or don't have babies, late menstruation, early menopause, do not breast feed, . . . then they have a greater or lesser chance of developing cancer in various places that have, or have not, been used during their lifetime.

(If you see what I mean?)

As women we're damned if we do and damned if we don't. I personally wouldn't add a baby to the equation.

At 8.30 a.m. I'm driven to UCH by a volunteer friend, or perhaps that should read, a friend who volunteered.

(But who knows?)

By 9.30 a.m., having been phlebotomised (new word?), which showed my blood to be descending into a fairly useless liquid, I entered Latymer ward at Middlesex Hospital.

At 10.15 a.m. I began waiting for the doctor to give me the All Clear to have my top-up poison.

It's reassuring to know they want you well before trying to kill you again; similar, I suppose, to a medical before an execution?

I described again, the horror of the inflamed gut and true to their word I was prescribed only half the amount of Vincristine.

211

However, some concern was expressed over my chronic constipation.

Not a good idea.

(*They're telling me!*)
I was given a prescription for Co-Danthrusate (go, dance thru . . . ta) which I was to start taking immediately for the benefit to be realised.
And I know what that means!
Wait, wait and more waiting.
Finally at 11.30 a.m. the drugs arrived from the pharmacy.
Horrors, officially I'm still written up for Dexamethasone!
Scream, rant, rage, shan't, won't, can't . . . They took me off and substituted Ondansetron.
Whew!
But what if I hadn't been paying attention?
(*I would have been in the tumble-dryer again.*)
Arrived home at 1.00 p.m.
My friend was exhausted by the process . . . I had simply switched off.
I had, in total, fourteen hours sleep apart from regular Pit-stops.
I was shaky and sinusy, though there was no comparison to the previous sessions. I did however have a tightness across my lower abdomen.

I can live with that.

What I was finding more and more difficult to live with (or not as the case may be) was Ellis's lack of presence in the house. It was hard to accept that even the most basic humane gesture was missing from an individual who had vowed to help me rid myself of cancer.

That night, alone again, I was kept awake by the sound of a party somewhere along the road.

People go out and enjoy themselves, I mused, not with jealousy or disapproval but with the realisation that my entire social life had ceased long before the cancer had moved in.

Other people enjoyed life. I could not imagine myself with enough energy ever to participate again.

The front door bell rang!

I ignored it.

It rang again!

I reached slowly for my dressing gown . . .

Thumps on the door!!!!

I crawled slowly (how else?) to the front door and whispered: "Who's there?"

"Is Mark in?"

Mark? There was no man in this house, let alone one answering to the name of Mark, but I wasn't going to let a stranger know that!

I persuaded the young reveller to depart but my heart started beating to the rhythm of the party music.

I was alone, defenceless, tired, ill and frightened . . . but somewhere deep inside me I knew that I was also angry at being left to fend for myself at such a vulnerable time.

What was Ellis playing at?

(*Simple—Poker.*)

My abdomen continued to rumble until 'D' day arrived. Chemotherapy and Odansetron (blockage producers) versus Co-Danthrusate (Dynamite) = the nearest any human being can come to experiencing the scientific conundrum of 'an irresistible object being met by an unstoppable force'.

I have the answer: AAAARRRRGGGGGHHHHH!!!!!!!!

213

Waffles came to investigate the screams, but wisely sat outside the bathroom. Gently swaying side by side, using one eye then the other to peer through the gap in the door, she kept watch on my agony.

Several stones lighter (it felt like boulders) I staggered to bed and collapsed in an exhausted heap.

Waffles investigated my lifeless form. She placed her front paws around my neck and proceeded to offer me the comfort another life form could not.

I was in a deep negative rut concerning Men.

Paola said I had to learn to protect myself by not being so open all the time. This she had to agree was probably difficult, as my personality was open, even when I thought I'd closed it.

"I've had it with men," I raged.

"You only feel that way now," she counselled.

"No! It's more than that. I don't, and never have, gone round looking for a man. I prefer my own company rather than any man who doesn't interest me, just because social protocol prefers it if I enter a restaurant with this appendage."

(*He can dine alone, simply because of his appendage!*)

"Finding a man is like looking for a job," Paola insisted. "You wouldn't buy any old newspaper to find a teaching job, would you?"

"No, I'd buy the Guardian and Times Education Supplement," I admitted.

"Of course you would; and you wouldn't just stick a pin in and apply for the job advert it landed on?"

"No."

"You'd select the job that would offer you the best and most suitable prospects of a rewarding partnership," argued Paola, really rising to the metaphor.

"Problem is ... we are in the middle of a recession," I quipped.

Boom, boom.

(Female wanted: must be under 25 years old, blonde, no brains required.)

Patricia Davis, one of the Aromatherapists to whom I had written, had replied. Her letter expanded on the advice that essential oils were too powerful to be used on cancer patients, mainly because their detoxifying properties could release stored Chemotherapy into the blood stream, causing dangerous side effects.

(More dangerous than the Chemotherapy itself?—surely not!)

She had researched the subject with doctors from the Bristol Clinic and with French Aromatherapists who had worked for the Marie Curie Foundation.

Fine.

My question is why hasn't a British professional Aromatherapy organisation carried out similar investigations?

Why indeed.

With 250,000 people in Britain a year being diagnosed as having some form of cancer, and 300 women a week dying of Breast cancer, surely this is something that should be redressed?

Too many people are not receiving, or are avoiding, essential oils, which could help them both mentally and physically.

I decided to wait and see whether I received a reply from the other Aromatherapist, weigh up the arguments, then write to my professional association.

(Here you go again, Cole, won't you ever learn? ... No!)

Another organisation I had just been introduced to was the British Association of Complementary Therapies. I rang them to find out where I could have an Aura photograph taken.

The (naff) one I'd had taken at the festival had mysteriously disappeared!

They gave me two numbers but advised me to contact Wendy Rose at Winfalcons in Surrey.

Jo and I travelled down that afternoon.

What a difference!

This Aura photograph had so much more detail and different qualities of light and colour. It confirmed my suspicion that the festival photograph was not worth the photographic paper it was printed on. That one had indicated that I was hale and hearty; this one showed many problem areas . . .

Wendy talked into a cassette, while analysing the print: "You are using up more energy than you are taking in . . . you can see it's getting wispier and wispier. You mustn't let it go on for too long or you will be in serious danger of running on your reserves . . . There is a curve of green showing that some form of 'healing' is taking place, but there is still a long way to go before you know if it has worked."

(!)

At this point I told her that I had cancer, as I didn't want her to panic at what she may be about to tell me.

"Okay. These three white blobs indicate stress, which isn't surprising considering your state of health . . .

(*It's not my health that I'm finding stressful!*)

". . . This deep blue shows me that you have the ability to come in on yourself and to meditate, but there is a danger

216

that you are holding too much inside . . . You must break out and express your anger, even if it means writing 'cancer' on a box, taking it outside and jumping up and down on it."

(*Like it.*)

"Decisions had to be made and there was no point in waiting to see what happened first. *You* have to make the decisions . . . As the Indians say: 'You won't know the way out of the swamp until you've placed one foot forward'. It may be the wrong direction but at least you will know it's the wrong direction and can start again . . .

"Wear yellow and orange for decision making," she added.

(*Yuk!*)

"The light around the throat shows that you are a good communicator . . . You have the ability to make others feel better . . . You are creative . . . The Heart chakra shows blue for withdrawal and turquoise for spirituality . . . You have a great awareness of consequences."

(*That I do know!*)

"People come to you with problems and leave when they feel good. You are then left drained. You must hold up a 'mirror', so their negativity is directed back at them," she advised.

"At the moment you must not take on board everyone else's vibes . . . You have a good sense of Right and Wrong . . . You feel for the underdog and the world as a whole, but you take on too much responsibility. There are things you cannot ever achieve, but you still try . . . and deplete your energy even further, I bet? . . . You've had several incarnations and what is happening to you now is Karmic."

"Was I that bad in a previous life?" I queried.

"Not necessarily."

(*Whew!*)

She continued, "You've been a Healer and will continue to be so . . . The cancer has given you an added dimension . . . Perhaps you will eventually work in a Hospice."

She paused.

"Have you sufficient emotional support?"

"No."

"You need more emotional support."

"Easier said than done."

"Scream for help from your Guides, use everything possible to regain your strength."

"Okay."

"Have you a Purple Plate?"

"A what?"

A large credit card-shaped piece of purple metal was brought in and handed to me.

"Can you feel a tingly sensation on your fingers?"

"No, sorry, my fingers are presently 'at rest', ie, 'not working'."

I glanced at the accompanying literature. "The atoms and electrons of the aluminium have been altered so that the plates are in resonance, or in tune, with the basic energy of the Universe. They function as transceivers . . . creating a field of energy around themselves that will penetrate any material substance by osmosis. This energy is very beneficial (the life force energy) to all life . . . plant, animal or human." It could apparently alter the taste of wine, energise drinking water, change the taste of coffee, cure sickly house plants, help people to sleep or wake, and help injuries, etc, etc.

There were also reports of plates 'disappearing'.

(*I think this calls for another Mmmmm???*)

Jo and I left.

Well, what did I think of all that?

It was all too much to take in. She read all that from a photograph?

Jo was agog at the Purple Plate and insisted on shoving it down her trousers.

What she was aiming for I do not know!

I should have sat on the Plate as we drove home.

The M4, M25 and the North Circular road are not the best places to be for peace and tranquillity.

When we reached our local shops, Jo leapt out of the car to go shopping, and by the time I got home I had rehearsed a message for her answerphone.

"Where's my Purple Plate? Don't tell me it's 'disappeared', I won't believe you."

She phoned almost immediately, giggling. It had fallen down her trouser leg with a loud clang in the supermarket, but it was now safely indoors.

I went to reclaim it.

Later that evening I had the plate balanced on my left wrist, which had not been right (!) for nearly two years. The phone rang.

It was Frances. We chatted about various things then got on to the Magic or Medicine programme. I could feel myself getting worked up again and in a strange sort of desperation used the plate as an example.

"I'm sitting here with a piece of purple metal on my wrist."

"I see," said Frances, who was used to me springing strange concepts on her.

I tried to explain the theory behind the plate's energy, but even I had to admit it sounded a bit far fetched.

"If it works—great. If it doesn't then I'm quite prepared to have a laugh," I admitted.

I flicked the plate off my wrist and for the first time in months I could bend it back into a 90 degree angle, without pain.

Boy, was I surprised!

From then on, I frequently balanced the Plate on my wrist to continue the 'treatment' and soon transferred it to the breast whenever it felt hot and bothered.

Like Jo, I too sometimes forgot it and on undressing at night a loud clunk would remind me of its presence.

Trish knew all about the Plates and although she had no idea why they worked, they did.

Life was getting more and more weird . . . or was it me?

The Diploma in Nutrition correspondence course had arrived. I opened the first lesson and started avidly to read . . . and . . . um . . . is it me or is this completely incomprehensible?

Perhaps I wasn't really ready to attempt any studying?

There appeared to be no structure to the course and it wove between assumptions that the student would have prior knowledge of technical terminology and the use of 'non-English' to explain complicated concepts. It appeared to me that the very least one needed was a Degree in Chemistry and Physics!

What was even more confusing was that an up to date book I had bought on Nutrition completely contradicted 'A Fact' in the correspondence course!

Still, thinking that the problem was with my brain and/or my inability to grasp boring chemical equations I handed it to several intelligent and verbal individuals. Luckily they too found it impossible to understand; even Trish, who had studied the subject only just managed to grasp the explanations.

Action: I rang the Consumers Association and the Citizens Advice Bureau for their opinion and then sent a carefully worded letter demanding my money back.

Result: I received a cheque in the post and a letter from the principal. I recognise that style, I thought, as I waded through appalling English and explanations. He must be a one man band. I was lucky to get a satisfactory result but how many youngsters, having failed to get into college have applied for one of these courses, and then given up, believing the problem to be with them? And how many foreign students, who believed they understood English have given up because they thought they had over stretched their ability to comprehend the language?

I shudder to think.

Ellis did one of his 'appearing' acts and offered to take me for a Tapas meal.

(*Not my Birthday, is it?*)

During the meal he started to talk about his Poker playing 'friends' and various other males.

"They don't want to be married," he announced. "Basically they do what they want to do and sod the relationship."

(*Sounds familiar!*)

He then ran through a list of men who had time-consuming Hobbies and Pastimes, to the exclusion of their wives.

"Just like you," I uttered, bravely.

"Er, yes, I suppose so," he had to concede.

"I don't think men should get married . . . but don't tell the Tory party," I spat.

The Tory party had had a blitz on broken marriages and single parents . . . mainly blaming women for the break-up of traditional family values.

Yet, as far as I could see women had adapted to the new Order or lack of Order. They had had to expand their lives and were now free(er) to be who they wanted to be.

Men on the other hand had shrunk. They had lost their

total power over women and could only reclaim it by threats and violence, or avoidance. They could no longer function in a relationship because they were expected to be an equal partner, a concept too frightening and unnatural (ie they haven't tried it before.)

If they had money, they did their own thing and the power of their money ensured that their women would not scream too loudly. If they didn't have money, they could just disappear.

(*Don't get me going!*)

It was all too depressing and here was Ellis talking as if none of it was to do with him.

He probably firmly believed that it didn't.

I went straight to bed and slept for ten hours.

The next night, however, was a different story.

It didn't help that I had difficulty in relaxing and feeling sleepy, as opposed to tired. I turned the light off and on many times . . . until a loud, piercing cat's scream startled me into action.

Waffles! and by the sound of it another cat had somehow got into the house and was attacking MY cat. I got down the stairs, as quickly as I could, expecting a furry fight in the hallway. Nothing! No sight or sound in any of the downstairs rooms?

Another howl alerted me to the back of the garden. There was Waffs being laid into by one of the local feline thugs. Passing the fruit bowl on the way out I hurled myself . . . and a grapefruit, into the dark and pouring-with-rain environment, emitting a ferocious mother cat scream.

The black cat fled.

Waffles, large and puffed up, but with no more damage than a deflated ego, threw herself into the kitchen and demanded food.

It was only then that I relaxed enough to start giggling; without turning a hair(!) I had rushed into the garden totally naked (sans wig, even) and hurled a grapefruit at a cat.

Gosh, I hope the neighbours weren't looking out of their window to see the fight!

Waffles decided to sleep for the rest of the night in the next room. I could not sleep and had to make frequent visits to stroke her.

She finally took pity on me and joined me on my bed; perhaps she was just embarrassed by my naked intervention?

Under the circumstances, who could blame her.

And, under the circumstances, who could blame me for feeling unworthy of attention, or for having a go at the root cause: Ellis.

He just could not grasp how alone and isolated I felt in the nights following Chemotherapy.

On the previous occasion he had not only been absent (playing Poker) on the night of the Poisoning, but had also managed to stay away for a further four nights in that week.

I told him his lack of concern was appalling.

He agreed.

I asked him if he could appreciate how frightened I was when alone in the house? When I had to crawl on hands and knees along the corridor, as my legs were incapable of giving any support? When I had to inch my way downstairs step by step, for fear of falling?

He could.

He agreed with every angry statement I made . . . and that was the problem. He knew what should be done, but was unable to match intent with action. I would have to remind him every day of my hurt for him to sustain any improvement. Left alone, he goes to ground and hibernates his humanity.

The next day his 'guilt' drove me to an art exhibition. The hour-long journey each way was too much for me and I don't remember any of the exhibits, but it was at least an Outing.

Ellis slept in the car.

Onwards and Upwards to Bethnal Green and to the second awkward man in my life.

I was late.

He gave me one of his looks.

I gave him one of my looks.

After our normal provocative and enriching chat he hands me three packs of pills.

"What are they for? . . . " I began, then added " . . . Don't bother to tell me because I've seen a programme and I now know they're all placebos," I said provoking a reaction.

He went spare. Not at me (?) but at the programme which had berated Homeopathy so thoroughly.

"That programme was shot through with research faults," he thundered.

"I know. Why don't you do something about it?"

He gave me one of his looks.

(*I can't get off lightly all the time.*)

He muttered on for a while about the techniques and questions raised by the programme, then suddenly went quiet.

"There is something hard inside you, which is a recurrent problem—you have to deal with it."

"Do you mean in my boob, or within me?"

He smiled and said nothing.

"I'm dealing with it," I mumbled, not having the faintest idea what he was on about, but knowing that if I questioned him, all I'd receive was another cryptic clue.

It just wasn't worth the hassle, time and energy to try for a direct and helpful statement.

I took my conundrum home and thought about it. Something 'hard' inside me. Anger? Frustration? Fear? Ability to keep meeting strange men?

(*Unchewed food?*)

The list could be endless and he wanted me to choose one?

I had more immediate concerns.

My fingers were becoming more and more numb yet, at the same time, painful if I attempted to use them. Even turning over the pages of a newspaper was becoming an impossible task, and holding a book even worse.

I did manage to reach a page with a headline 'Teetotallers reduce cancer risk by 25%'. The research was carried out in Norway between a group of Good Templars (who pledged to abstain completely) and the rest of the population (who probably tried to make up the shortfall). The risk reduction was not just in areas of the body which would normally take the impact of alcohol but for all cancers. However, it was also pointed out in the article that a small amount of alcohol could protect against heart disease; but there were no statistics to say what happened to the group of non-drinkers.

(*I think this is another case of roundabouts and swings?*)

Three weeks had rushed and crawled by and it was time for my fourth Chemotherapy treatment.

This time I meet the new registrar, who prods and pokes my 'mass' and after measuring with a ruler makes little ticks on a diagram in my notes.

I investigated immediately: '5cm' and a few ticks.

5cm . . . still dangerous, but surely it can't be all cancer? Hope not.

Another long wait for the chemicals to arrive from the pharmacy.

Rebecca has great difficulty in getting the drip needle into the vein in my wrist, so instead goes for a surprise attack on the soft part under the forearm.

I looked away and got ready to scream, when she informed me it was in, and functioning properly.

Sarah took over, leaving Rebecca to move on to other drips. (!)

I mentioned my darkening finger nails and was told that it was one of the effects of a Chemotherapy.

"Will anything else happen?" I casually enquired.

"They may fall off."

"Off?"

"Yes, but they will grow again."

That's a relief. Images of a Potter wearing, or attempting to wear, false nails was not a comforting prospect.

My haemoglobin was also giving some concern. It had sunk to 9.4 and if it went down much further I would need a transfusion.

I can see now why Rebecca was so un-worried about it in January when it had been 12.5. At that time I was positively blooming.

Did the fact that I felt so lousy then imply that I'm not totally aware of how lousy I'm feeling now? I had certainly established 101 ways of feeling tired. Perhaps the brain stops distinguishing awfulness after a certain point, similar to my attitude to money. After a few noughts, it just becomes 'lots'.

Ellis had, once again, offered to accompany me to the hospital AND forgo his Poker game!!!!

I fell asleep by 7 p.m. but not before I'd had several strange conversations with Ellis. I don't actually remember details, but they must have given him an idea of just how 'out of it' someone on Chemotherapy can be.

The vision of my staggering to and from the bathroom must also have penetrated his cast-iron shell security ring for, in the morning, he was delighted that he had been around to help me through the rough night.

Rough night? I thought to myself. This time had been a minor inconvenience compared to the first two sessions, but I let the comment go. He had, after all, made an effort.

The changing of the guards occurred when Ellis had to leave for a business trip. My sister arrived to take control.

He had insisted that I had someone with me!

I'm not sure if it was such a good idea.

I had become so used to being on my own that the constant availability of someone seemed inappropriate, and at times more tiring than trying to do things for myself.

My appetite was nil.

I asked for a plain Matzos for dinner. Wendy thought the large dry biscuit looked like a plate; it tasted like one.

I could face nothing else.

A phone call from my 'Ex' (he who had been 'had' by several of my, so-called female friends) started the re-emergence of horrors I had buried away for years.

A polite enquiry about a recent holiday he'd taken in the USA provoked an outburst laden with avoidance, annoyance and irritation . . .

"It's no Big Deal!!!" he spluttered.

I allowed him to carry on pontificating about freedom, jealousy, envy, privacy and every other outrage dear to his heart, then said . . .

"I only asked if you'd enjoyed America. I would have

227

asked the same thing if I'd learned you had gone to Scarborough and were being secretive about it. You are the one making a Big Deal about it."

The conversation ended and I burst into tears.

He's still doing it to me, I thought. I ask a simple human question and he has the ability to make me feel guilty. The fact that I had a very good idea why he could not tell me about the 'no Big Deal' holiday confirmed in my mind that he was simply continuing his 'hobby', which involved females, preferably attractive and definitely, young.

I felt slapped down, weepy and angry at myself for allowing the continuation of his 'power' to upset me. We had been apart for eight years, but effectively I had taken second, or last place, behind his 'hobbies' for twelve years.

I'd had enough. I was not sure if I wanted to know someone whose attitude to women I didn't respect but, I had known him for over twenty years and with him I'd had the best nine years of my life.

Why did he 'no Big Deal' me now??

Things had to change: I had to make a decision.
(*Was this the 'hard' thing Robert had talked about?*)

Wendy brought me tea at 5.50 a.m!

I try a little breakfast.

Very little.

To be precise, a strawberry.

I had a rare insight into what it must be like to have Anorexia. I could mentally cope with a strawberry, but the

228

thought of eating the proffered plum was nauseating. It was far too much to eat!

My weight of course had plummeted. In January my scales announced that I had reached 10 st 4 lbs. That was way above my normal weight but comfort eating and drinking had altered that. Now, I was mere a 8 st 10 lbs and sinking . . . fast.

But, I still couldn't eat . . . not even the Slippery Elm.

It would improve, it would have to, but at the moment there was nothing I could do about it. I could feel myself panicking that someone would make me eat.

My stomach didn't want to cope with anything. My fingers were making sure they did nothing.

I had already dropped several glasses and while attempting to pick up the pieces found I had pierced my fingers with tiny splinters.

I couldn't feel a thing, so didn't know the pressure I was using. Tiny spurts of blood reminded me that my platelets were also temporarily below par, and would need the assistance of some plasters to stem the flow.

Bother.

This didn't help when I attempted to sign a petition against VAT on books in the local bookshop. One sheet of paper on a hard surface and a scratchy biro made it almost impossible for me to exert enough pressure to make any mark. I had to hold the pen in two hands; it was almost as though I had never used one before. People were looking at me. Did they think I was illiterate and doing a grand job in covering it up?

I explained my predicament and a softer, more yielding, writing instrument was produced. I signed, though I doubt if a graphologist would have accepted it as mine.

But this was me.

I had to accept that.

It was hard.

I was having bad dreams of past and present fears. Of anger seething, eating away, at my vulnerability.

I couldn't cope with them on their own but with my body and brain taking a direct Exocet missile every three weeks I couldn't bear even to think about the problems waiting for me once I was well.

'Once I was well'? That sounded remarkably like a positive statement. But where did it come from?

A letter arrived from the financial adviser who had promised but failed to send me his plan, despite a reminder by me on his answerphone.

"Sorry," he said. "The computer was broken, it completely slipped my mind."

Well it would wouldn't it . . . it's only me, after all, I seethed to myself.

In the meantime I contacted Dominic, another financial adviser, who had been so helpful when I had been made redundant.

He came round immediately.

I had to start making plans for the future in every aspect of my life, which at the moment was a blank sheet of paper.

I was scared to think about it.

Ellis seemed to be improving in his acknowledgement of me as a person in need of help. On Sunday he drove me to Epping Forest, the first of many 'Granny Runs', as I called them.

It was August 1st yet the sun was thin and wintery. I

hadn't minded the lack of summer because I was not allowed to expose my Radiated skin to the sun, but at times the lack of a warmer season mirrored my life. I was in a time warp, every day seemed a bland continuation of the next, only worse.

My haemoglobin had dropped to 9.1. The nurses thought I looked awful.

Cheers.

I waited for over an hour to see a doctor by which time I'd rooted to the spot, with fatigue.

Somehow I got home . . . and crashed out.

I was confused as what to do about Ellis's birthday. Last year he had ignored any form of acknowledgement, let alone a celebration. My presents lay unwrapped, or unused for months.

As a gesture, however, I bought him a pouch of 'chakra pebbles', as he had shown interest in a set I had bought for myself.

The pebbles, or semi-precious gemstones, are linked by their colour to the chakra centres, through which our mental, physical and spiritual energies are focused. The chakras interact to form a single holistic system of balance.

Leaving aside the more esoteric nature of the gemstones/chakras the selection of stones is a pleasing item, and somehow comforting.

He was genuinely delighted by the gift.

His birthday meal was also a success and glimpses of the old Ellis were evident.

What had caused this change in him?

The next day I received a distraught phone call from him. He had been handling the pebbles and found suddenly he couldn't breathe. He had also become very emotional and wanted to talk about 'the future'. He confessed that he'd seen a note by my Wordprocessor about my being abandoned and it had upset him.

"Was I meant to have seen it?" he queried.

"No, not really," I explained.

The scribbled note had been purely as a memory aid and referred to an incident at Easter when he had unconsciously blanked off after socialising with me for five days out of seven.

He was relieved that it had not referred to more recent times, as he felt he was now trying to show me his care and concern.

He was.

The talk continued about my fear of the future and my need to re-establish myself in some form of work, when (and if) I'm cured. We must talk soon, he promised, but for now he had a business meeting to attend and would not be back until midnight.

I was only partially aware of his return to the house, as I had been asleep since 9 p.m. and was feeling especially strange.

I woke to the sound of my name being called.

As I fumbled into some form of consciousness I realised it was Ellis gently knocking on my door.

It was 4.30 a.m.

"What's the matter?" I croaked, reaching for a turban to hide my baldness.

(*Vanity at that hour!*)

He was in the grip of a panic attack, and needed help.

Lots of help.

To calm him I placed my Rose Quartz on his chest. He couldn't believe it when the sensation pounding in his body subsided. He was even more surprised when on temporarily relinquishing the Quartz, the panic returned.

He talked and talked; mainly about his fear of keeping down all the lids he had on his emotions. Last year he had been too afraid to try, but now he was too afraid not to.

I listened and advised, listened and advised for two hours until he calmed sufficiently to return to bed.

I don't remember attempting to sleep, I think I just blanked out with the effort of the whole episode. But what I do remember is feeling happy that at last Ellis wanted to find the root cause of his problems ... and he had come to me.

To me!

I wanted so much to help him.

And us.

(*Oh, Jenny.*)

Our talks continued for days, but he also phoned several Therapists, Counsellors and Healers *and* made appointments!

A letter had arrived from a publisher stating that they were 'impressed' by the first forty pages of my typescript.

(*Cheers.*)

It then continued to find fault with every aspect of the presentation!

(*Hangover.*)

It also suggested that I expanded my description of Ellis.

"Oh dear," said Ellis, as he read the letter. "What sort of things have you said about me?"

I confessed that I was in a difficult position regarding my documentation of him. The book was about my attitude and approach to cancer, but it was all so intertwined with my life, or lack of it, with Ellis, that they were impossible to separate.

He looked stunned when I read out some of the milder extracts.

"Did I do that to you?" he gasped in horror.

He had forgotten most, if not all, of the horror he had caused me, and found it difficult to live with the documented proof.

"I can't believe you're being so supportive, after all I've put you through," he mused.

(*It's called love, Ellis.*)

"I'll make it up to you," he declared.

And I willed myself to believe him . . . I had no choice.

"I do love you, you have to believe me," he insisted.

"I know," I heard myself say.

But, an inner voice knew that there was a long way to go. I had every reason to doubt his stamina.

Paola was worried that I'd taken too much on board and that I may be in danger of over-taxing my strength at a time when I could least afford to.

My feelings were one of relief. I felt as if a large weight had been lifted from my shoulders and put firmly back on Ellis. He was going to take control of the problem . . . or at least try.

It was like living with a heavy drinker, who had finally accepted that he was an alcoholic.

That seemed half the battle.

Paola had to acknowledge that I was 'glowing'.

234

I felt great.

Another friend had given me the name and address of a healer called Mother Meera, who she had heard had produced incredible results with people. One just had to write.

I did.

I wanted Ellis to get well, to resolve his suffering, to be a happier person, to live again.

Please!

For the next few weeks Ellis kept all his appointments with the various Healers and made a huge effort to communicate with me.

"I may have moods," he announced at my bedroom door one day.

"Darling, you've been 'having moods' for the past two years," I quipped.

"Have I?" he replied quietly.

(*He hadn't noticed?*)

He was afraid what might be at the end of the tunnel.

He was afraid of *his* journey.

I used the analogy of my Chemotherapy treatment. I loathed and dreaded it. I had to force myself to go to the hospital every time and offer my body for what I knew was going to be Hell. But, it was for a reason, a purpose.

He also had a reason and purpose to put himself through discomfort, but it would be worth it.

Wouldn't it?

He still could not accept the ease with which I gave my support.

"I can't stop you from finding another man, I have no rights over your time or emotions," he confessed.

I looked at him in amazement.

"Look Ellis, I have only one 'desire' and that is, to be held again by *you*. I can't contemplate the hassle of becoming involved with another man ... and besides ... the Chemotherapy has wiped out *any* thoughts of anything to do with sex."

I should have added that the chances of discovering a man who would be interested in a totally bald (eyebrows, pubes etc had long disappeared) menopausal, emaciated, cancer patient, would be an achievement.

(*Perhaps without the menopause bit, I'd have a chance!*)

My breast had become hot and stingy again.

Should I panic?

I remembered Elizabeth's prediction that in the second week of August I may feel that the cancer was returning, but that I was not to worry.

I did worry, but frequently used the Rose Quartz to cool the area.

It helped.

My fifth Chemotherapy session had arrived.

I was strangely weepy while sitting in the ward waiting for the procedure to commence. I only had two more sessions to go and although the breast had vastly improved on its condition in January there seemed to be an awful long way to go; and it was hot again.

My haemoglobin had actually risen, for the first time since January, but all the nurses agreed that I didn't look in very good shape.

In fact, I looked dreadful.

To add to my list of symptoms I now had great difficulty in getting up from a chair and walking. My joints refused to obey my autonomic nervous system and any progress was slow and sporadic.

The lining of my throat had also become affected by the chemicals and my voice sounded as if it were being relayed through a voice-synthesizer.

My gums were sore and tender and everything tasted of chemicals.

Apart from that, I was fine!

The wait for a doctor to respond to a bleep was exhausting. Eventually I was sent down to another waiting area, where I was assured a doctor could be found.

I sat, and sat, and felt worse, and worse.

A voice filtered through to my woolly brain: Dorothy!

I peered round a corner to see her disappearing into her new office.

I followed.

A comfortable seat and a comfortable person to be with. Just what the doctor ordered, if only one could be found.

Dorothy did her best to phone around to find a stray doctor and informed the Chemotherapy ward of my whereabouts.

"You're doing fine," she repeated to me.

"As well as can be expected under the circumstances," I agreed, but I warned her that should I need an Operation in October then she would really see me in need of counselling.

"I will have to be wooed into the hospital let alone the operating theatre," I confessed.

"Wait and see."

I was finally summoned back to the ward, a doctor did appear, and I was taken away for my consultation and examination.

I was taken off the Vincristine altogether to prevent further neuropathy to my fingers. I was worried that a total cessation of this drug may hinder my recovery, but was assured that continuation was unnecessary, especially as I could no longer use my fingers for anything.

Would there have been permanent damage if it had been prolonged?

Nobody said.

The examination was painful.

"What happens after September?" I boldly asked.

"You'll be given a Mammogram or a biopsy and if there are any cancer cells present then you will be given a Mastectomy.

(*That's what you think, matey; I want a group discussion.*)

I had always found this particular doctor more 'extreme' in her methods. It was she who had put me on the Dexamethasone and the dynamite Co-Danthrusate, and she had wanted me to try another steroid to improve my appetite, so I decided not to accept her version of the future . . . unless I had to.

She did however think I was coping extremely well considering the severity of the Chemotherapy.

Thank you.

Ellis had arrived at the ward and while I had another very recalcitrant needle (flesh?) placed in my arm he took the opportunity to hunt for Dorothy and discuss the Mastectomy issue.

Another Chemotherapy nurse was leaving the hospital in a bid for a more secure job, free from the disruption of merger and reorganisation.

This was the third to my knowledge.

They were all brilliant dedicated and proficient nurses and it's the hospital's loss as well as the patients. Continuity is definitely not the 'in' word within the NHS.

The delivery of chemicals into my blood stream took less time because there was one less syringe to administer, but the whole procedure had still taken over five hours to complete.

Home and bed but it was a completely different sensation. Ellis came into my bedroom to watch television with me and only realised I had gone to sleep when I didn't respond to a question.

Now I'll never know how that episode of 'Nurses' ended.

I woke . . . hungry!

The missing ingredient in yesterday's cocktail of chemicals was the dreaded Vincristine, so that had to be one of the factors preventing me from having any interest in food.

I felt so good it was beyond comparison with the other treatments.

I celebrated with beans on toast; the biggest meal I'd had in weeks.

It was so nice to be slightly more in charge of various parts of my body, and even my fingers had started to come back to life.

So, when Angela suggested going raspberry picking at a local farm, I didn't hesitate.

Was I up to it?

I'd never know unless I tried.

It was one of the very few warm August days and it seemed magical to me to be able to walk among the fruit bushes away from hospitals and bedrooms and feel normal. The fact that every time I crouched down to pick fruit on a lower branch I had to be helped up, was beside the point. My slow-motion speed of picking the few remaining berries would never have earned me any money doing piecework, but I really enjoyed it.

Yet it had all been too much.

I spent the next two days in bed . . . but at least I had the memories to cheer me up; and the raspberries.

Yum.

Trish continued working on my fingers and stomach to accentuate the improvement already produced by weaning me off the Vincristine.

She also had two suggestions: one was that I really should consider consuming high calorie food to boost my weight and energy, as my body was desperately in need of fuel.

"Any suggestions?" I asked, thinking of all the good quality food I had been eating before the Vincristine took hold.

"Choux pastry filled with cream."

"Really?"

"Won't do any harm," she insisted.

"I'll force myself," I said, grinning from food thought to food thought.

Secondly, she suggested that it may be beneficial to try to break down the scar tissue in the breast with the use of a Belladonna Homeopathic remedy.

She had been told of this treatment by a Homeopath and had used it very successfully on her ... greyhound (called Jenny!).

Oh well, if it's good enough for a greyhound it's good enough for me, I barked.

(!)

The pot of tablets duly bought and instructions carefully read, I started the course of Belladonna which, of course, according to the Magic or Medicine programme was all a placebo effect.

Six hours after taking the first tablets I felt nauseous, then disorientated, then my sinuses started to throb, then ... hang on a minute, I feel as if I've just had a dose of Chemotherapy?

Could it be that by breaking down the internal scars stored Chemotherapy was being released?

I stopped taking the tablets and phoned Trish for advice.

The phantom sensations subsided.

Trish was horrified by the reaction caused by the Belladonna and immediately phoned the Homeopath who, by the way, had researched the use of Homeopathy on people having Chemotherapy.

So there.

He confirmed what I had suspected but encouraged me to continue at a lower dosage. It can only do some good.

'Some good' was an understatement. The flashback of Chemotherapy did not recur, but within two weeks the size of the mass had reduced dramatically, and I mean dramatically.

So there. (Mark two)

Trish had also lent me a portable Electro-Crystal Therapy Rod, filled with gems, and a battery.

This was for me to place on my lower back to help stimulate my legs into working order.

(*Walking order?*)

One morning, as I was dressing, from the corner of my eye I could see a small dark mole on my thigh.

A new dark mole.

Horrors.

I tried to move it, but it wouldn't budge.

More horrors.

After a few more minutes of panic the 'mole' removed itself.

I peered at it closely and identified it as one of the little round plastic feet cushioning the Electro-Crystal Unit from delicate surfaces. It had simply transferred itself to another delicate surface and given me a huge fright in the process.

My other Healer, Paola, also continued to be supportive and understanding. She always asked to feel the mass and was continually delighted by the softening up and reduction in volume.

We discussed the 'threat' of a Mastectomy.

I was determined not to have another Operation.

I was positive I was not going to have one.

But what if I had to?

What of my attempts then to assist the cure by my own Complementary methods?

Would it negate and diminish my efforts?

242

No.

The Magic and Medicine programme had warned individuals of having too much false hope in alternatives, as disappointment of failure could have a devastating effect.

My belief is similar to that of my approach to exams and revision. I would never say to a student: 'Don't put any extra effort into your work, because if you fail you will feel it was not worth it.' Giving anything a 100% good shot, and still failing, can never be considered a failure. At least you tried.

Is *not*-trying a healthier option?

A magazine article made the statement that 60% of women with Breast cancer are still alive after five years.

I should hope so.

What is my prognosis for ten, or twenty, years?

It makes you think, unfortunately.

Ellis returned from one of his 'therapy' sessions in which he admitted that his living with me triggered off his 'realisation' that it wouldn't work—but he had wanted me to 'come to prison' with him.

(*Charming!*)

He had always felt that he'd needed me more than I needed him and that my cancer had made him feel wanted.

(*Pleased to be of service.*)

He also confessed that his 'cotton wool' brain had given him an insight into how I must have felt by his rejection . . . and he's devastated about it.

(*Learn from it, then, please.*)

Work on my book had come virtually to a complete standstill. The Wordprocessor's immediate memory could cope only with ten pages, so I saved each chunk and noted the date. The first four chunks were taking approximately six days to complete; the seventh chunk took ten days; but the eighth had already taken four weeks!

I knew I had slowed down but not to that extent. I was shocked.

I was also shocked to hear that twenty-four consultants were to go at UCH/Middlesex.

Good old Virginia seems to think this acceptable because of . . . (suggestions please) . . . but it doesn't make sense to me.

'Wrong diagnosis at NHS hospital' screamed a headline. Reading further it seemed that patients were being told they were clear when in fact they had cancer.

Not a good day for the National Health Service, Local Health Authorities, or Jenny Cole.

Ellis disappeared to the Lakes for a long weekend; with my blessing.

He was willing for me to accompany him (I declined on health grounds) and was worried that I may feel he was running out on me again. I didn't feel that and appreciated that he needed to get away to think about all the changes that were happening in his head.

More horror stories of bungled hospital treatment. This time it seemed that many women had lost the use of their arm or had had it amputated, because of the use of Radiotherapy on their Breast cancer.

Why had I written confidently all those months ago about the modern day use of computers in preventing damage to surrounding tissue?

Interesting reports showed that the approach to Radiation varied enormously not only between the north and south of the country but from hospital to hospital.

Something else for me to worry about, or would I already be feeling the problem by now?

Definitely not a good week to be reading, or watching the news, if undergoing treatment for cancer.

I found I could no longer clip my finger nails, as my hands had no strength. At least, I hope it's because my hands are weak and nothing more sinister?

With cancer, one never knows what exactly is happening . . . until it's happened.

September 1st. My first day as an official Invalid. I was no longer a Teacher/Lecturer and it was very unlikely that I would ever be one again.

Strange feeling.

Frightening.

It was yet another aspect of my life which has disintegrated or disappeared. My school, Garratt Green, had become Burntwood. My art college (Hornsey) had become, the Middlesex Polytechnic. My degree college, the afore-mentioned Polytechnic, had become Middlesex University. I would also have difficulty in obtaining references from my previous employment because all three 'bosses' had since left their establishments and it was debatable if any one else would have accurate information on me.

But then who would employ someone with cancer.

Like that Hotel in Scarborough, which had slowly slipped down the cliff and into the sea, so I felt my past life being washed away.

What else would go?

My final Chemotherapy session had arrived. I had last-day nerves!

Glen was not available to see me; it had been months since I'd last had his opinion on the situation and I felt let down, abandoned and unimportant, although I knew it wasn't his fault.

The 'more severe' doctor did the honours.
(*No boob-side manners?*)
"Everything okay?" she asked.
"Not bad except the night sweats, aching limbs, etc. etc."
"The night sweats and hot flushes are because you are going through the Menopause," she informed me.
"No, no," I corrected. "Glen said that I would need a blood test to ascertain my hormonal level because he didn't think I was Menopausal."

However, it turns out that even if I wasn't Menopausal, I would have to have my ovaries 'turned off' to prevent the release of oestrogen into the body.

"What were your periods like before the start of the Chemotherapy treatment?"
"Periods?"

Initially I didn't understand the question because I assumed everyone would know that I no longer had them. My file was only a few pages thick, after all.

"Periods?" I repeated, looking confused.

Once we had sorted out the relative impossibility of my having periods, she continued: "Don't worry yourself about hormonal levels, rest assured that at your age . . .
(*Scream!*)

" . . . with your gynaecological history, and the severity of the Chemotherapy, your ovaries will have been well and truly turned off. They will never recover."
(*?*)

"So, the hot flushes that I'd put up with thinking they

were a symptom of the Chemotherapy are merely (merely?) Menopausal?"

"Yes."

"Oh well, that's alright then."

But, it wasn't alright. If I'd have known why I was having the sleep preventing symptoms I would have done something to alleviate them, instead of incorporating them into my mental box marked 'temporary throw-away symptoms.'

If the cessation of hormones in a normal Menopause could be likened to a steady drip drip of a tap until the production line ceases, then perhaps my experience can be likened to a burst reservoir. Hopefully it will be over very quickly?

The session was no bother at all, ie, it wasn't painful, but it was a strange, gloomy, end-of-term anti-climax.

There should have been something to celebrate. Not quite sure what but at any rate I had neither the energy, nor inclination, to do anything, especially as I was surrounded by individuals just starting their treatment.

I was given appointments for six weeks and three months.

End of Chemotherapy.

Now, I was free floating.

I was on my own, and it was very very frightening.

Would the treatment be sufficient to prevent my needing an Operation, and would it, in fact, cure me?

Only time would tell.

There was some mail waiting for me when we got home.

I knew I needed to re-train in something and had sent off

for the prospectus of a Flower and Gem Remedies Practitioner's Course at the centre where I saw Robert.

I knew it would be a good quality course because of its pedigree but rang for further information.

"Hallo, could I talk to someone about the Flower and Gem course?"

"Yes, my name's Robert, how can I help you?"

"Hi, Robert, it's Jenny. I'm thinking of applying."

"Are you now?"

"There are a few questions I'd like to ask."

"Ask away."

"Are there any entry requirements?"

"No."

"What sort of assessment will there be . . .

(silence)

. . . or haven't you decided yet?"

"You know me too well."

"Would consideration be given to me if in November I didn't appear to be 'all there' . . . apart from the breast, of course," I added.

(*I'm allowed to be blase*)

"We can accommodate most problems."

All in all the two way conversation gave me the information I needed and within two days I sent in an application form with an accompanying letter explaining that it had been written while under The Influence.

Three days after the Chemotherapy I was smitten by the worst case of nausea and headache since the Cold turkey episode.

Why now?

Perhaps my body was reminding me how awful the whole thing had been and not to feel anti-climactic.

It worked.

It was now time to think of my teeth. They screamed every time something sweet, hot or cold touched them and, although I dreaded more treatment, I knew I had to have them checked out.

I had read somewhere that cancer treatments can affect the health of teeth and that it wasn't unusual for them to need attention.

'Look don't touch' was the order to Peter my Dentist. We (we?) had come through eleven months of gruesome implants and he knew my tolerance to pain, so if I said 'Don't touch', it was serious.

"Perfect," he declared (from the other side of the room).

"Perfect?"

It had been eighteen months since I'd last seen him . . . and nothing needed doing?

It's nice to know one part of me isn't, or hasn't collapsed.

The sensitivity was obviously caused by my over sensitivity and would improve.

If only that improvement could occur throughout my body and mind and not just my teeth.

From Peter, who by forceful means made my smile, smile, to Robert, who by equally but different forceful means would also help to make me smile.

It was only six days after the last Chemotherapy intake and I felt very depleted and shaky, and looked it.

Robert had been on a lecture tour abroad and I remember feeling very worried in case he didn't return.

What would I, and my cancer, do without him? I shuddered to think.

Our volatile mode of communication started even before I had entered the room.

"I see your time abroad hasn't improved your social graces," I finally retorted.

(*Okay, I know that was provocative.*)

"No, I'm an even bigger bastard now," he replied, with a hint of foreboding malice(?)

I started by asking if his trip had been interesting? . . .

(silence)

. . . exhausting? . . .

(silence)

. . . profitable? . . .

(silence.)

"Well, enough of you, and on to me," I said, to stony silence.

(*And stony face.*)

"What have you been up to over the summer then?" he finally asked.

I listed all the positive feelings I had had about my life: the things I'd sorted out, Ellis's willingness to seek help, the dismissal from my life of a draining influence, my plans for the future, my hope for a full recovery . . . my use of the Belladonna . . .

"Never heard about that," he interjected.

I bubbled, I bounced, I wanted him to see that I was on top of the problems.

(Silence)

"Oh go on Robert, say something! It's good isn't it?" I screamed, exasperated by his total lack of response.

(Silence) . . .

"There's something very self-defeating about your attitude to all this, and I can't put my finger on it," he said finally, calmly.

"That's a bit harsh," I managed to squeak.

(*Gutted is the word.*)

"It's how I feel. What do you expect me to do with you now?"

"How should I know . . . you've never told what you are doing, so how can I be expected to carry on."

(Silence)

"I was also hoping that you'd advise me about the Menopausal symptoms I've been having."

"I don't treat the Menopause."

"Okay then, this particular set of symptoms that I'm experiencing, commonly called the Menopause. I've read so many different herbal books and alternative life style books and they all seem to say different things."

"Well I suggest you read one and stick to their advice."

I was getting confused and frightened by his seeming lack of concern.

"Robert, what do you want me to say . . .

(Silence)

. . . I don't want cancer, I want to get better, I don't want an operation, I want to get on with the rest of my life. How much more positive can I be???"

(Silence)

I could feel the panic mounting within me. I felt I was in the middle of a Fellini film.

Suddenly.

"I don't know what to do with you. There is something hard inside you and I don't know what the sucker is."

With that he flung my file down on the table and got up to leave. Almost as an afterthought he said: "I'll have a think about it and may send you some tablets . . . by . . . the . . . start of next week."

"The mood you're in I'll be lucky to get them by the end of the week," I snapped.

Not to be outdone, he growled: "You'll be lucky if you get them by the end of the month!"

I paid my money, fled the building and just dissolved into frightened uncontrollable sobs.

251

This condition continued for six hours and, in the long term, three days.

I rang Ellis, Dorothy, Frances, Anita, John and many more.

I felt devastated by his unprovoked attack ... even if I had been a horrible client I was still his client (with cancer) and he should have been a professional.

That's what I'm paying him for.

During my hysterics I phoned the centre to speak to him and got the answer machine.

"After today's session I thought you'd like to know that I now feel totally defeated. If that's what you wanted, then you've got it."

I screamed.

Neither Robert, nor anyone else from the centre returned my call.

I was demoralised, frightened, disorientated and angry.

I had believed in Robert.

I had delivered myself to yet another man who waited until I was vulnerable before whisking the mat away.

I had a choice.

I had to continue my belief in his ability to heal, or believe in myself.

It took a few days but in the end there was no contest.

I won.

I never went back to him.

I finally regained my equilibrium but the aftermath continued. I cancelled my planned holiday, as I couldn't face being on my own, I was weepy and shocked.

"What he can't deal with is soft-peopley-things," said Charles.

I'll go with that.

Meanwhile, back to the main subject . . . cancer.

Ellis had arranged for me to have a (private) second opinion before I had to return to the Middlesex Hospital for the first opinion.

It required a letter from my GP, which I obtained at a cost of six pounds, and many spelling mistakes.

I also sent Robert a letter.

He never replied to that either.

Give up.

On a brighter note (every dark cloud has a sludge grey lining!) an article in the paper enthused about the antioxidant vitamins, which mop up oxygen molecules, known as free radicals, which can damage tissue. The vitamins E, beta-carotene and the trace element selenium decreased the incident of cancer deaths by 13%.

Although the results were not definitive on their own they added important information to the scientific study of nutritional intervention.

My investigations had led me to the consumption of all the vitamins and minerals mentioned. Perhaps a slight over-kill . . . but preferable to a complete kill?

Friends still continued to rally round and condemned outright Robert's insensitive, unprovoked and unprofessional behaviour. It was suggested that I read Susan Sontag's 'Blame the Victim'.

I also had reasonable proof that our Robert's behaviour to me wasn't out of the ordinary. Many people I encountered who were au fait with Complementary therapists guessed his name immediately as soon as I related the incident.

His fame and infamy go before him.

I was still very unsettled about the future.

I thought constantly about The Operation and the Life After (the operation, that is) the cancer returning, the cancer not going.

Frances was not well. She didn't want to talk about it and I respected her decision.

SOD = Second Opinion Day.

Deep breath.

Ellis's car developed engine problems on the way down to the hospital, which increased my tension dramatically. We had to enter the new security ring around the City, and I (on behalf of He) dreaded the complication of having to abandon the car and inform the powers that be that it was not a bomb (even if it had cost one!).

The car managed to stagger to a car park and we continued by taxi.

We entered the luxurious surrounds of the Private Medical World.

I felt uncomfortable.

(*I know my place!*)

I had purchased as normal a copy of the 'Big Issue' and defiantly read it in the waiting room. I wondered how many people, who graced this inner sanctum of health, had read, or even heard of the big issue . . . or even cared?

Or was my socialist background and foreground making assumptions . . . again?

My name is called.

"Mrs Cole?"

(*Here we go again.*)

As we enter the lift 'Mr Cole' is requested to press a button.

"Er to keep the record straight, I think you need to know that he is *not* Mr Cole," I politely informed the receptionist (who is still probably called a receptionist?)

"Oh, I'm sorry," she said. "I naturally assumed you were married because you seem so relaxed together."

(*Us, relaxed!*)

"Surely that would indicate that we weren't married," I suggested.

"But, you are good friends?" she enquired.

"Well . . . " I started.

"Very good friends," interrupted Ellis.

"Well, not quite . . . " but I fell silent.

I looked at Ellis and tried to imagine how our relationship could be described. It had to be more than just 'good friends', didn't it?

Or was I fooling myself.

There was no time to work out such intricacies.

I was on.

The (Top) Consultant listened to my history, then examined me.

He sat behind a huge desk, which was probably larger than the average National Health examination room, and opened the discussion.

"You have done very well to have reduced the tumour as much as you have."

I smile.

He continued.

"Even though a biopsy may show no sign of cancer, the problem with Inflammatory cancer is that one never knows when it is going to develop again."

My grin froze.

He continued.

"You had an advanced stage three, virulent tumour [I had never heard that before!] and to put you in a 'survival' group I would recommend a radical Mastectomy."
    I knew what that meant. Apart from (in more ways than one) losing the breast, I would also have the underlying muscle and the lymph glands removed. This would most likely cause oedema in my left arm; a build-up of fluid which would give constant bother.

(Bother).

I froze.

"It's called a bad-luck cancer," he continued, as I tried to think of a suitable question.

"Bad luck?" I fed back to him.

"Yes, of all the different types of Breast cancer it really is bad luck to get an Inflammatory tumour."
    (*Are there any 'lucky' ones?*)

"Could you give me your opinion on the suitability of a Lumpectomy, as opposed to a Mastectomy?"

"Well, normally it is something we would always consider, but with an Inflammatory . . . "

I guessed the rest.

"You have a choice," he said gently. "To have as long and healthy life as possible, or to look like Venus de Milo."
  (*But, she didn't have arms!?*)

Even a reconstruction was not advised for several years, until the whole area had settled down, and the need for further (further!) treatment had diminished.
  (*Along with my body, it seems.*)

I somehow kept cool.

This is not what I was expecting to hear, nor had I heard my cancer described in such a negative way.

(*Are there any positive cancers?*)

We left.

(Silence)

We walked over London Bridge.

(Silence)

We drove home.

(Silence)

Ellis had to get his car to the 'doctors', and I assured him I would be alright on my own.

I wanted to be on my own with my silence.

I had said 'yes' to the question on wanting a long and healthy life, or whatever was left of it, but what did I think?

What did I think?

What did I think?

What did I think?

I felt as if I'd reached the end of an interesting journey, only to find that the hotel and resort were not only not what I had in mind, but were totally unacceptable.

(*I demand a refund. Now!*)

What do I think?

I thought of my suicide attempt twenty-five years ago.
    Then, it was not so much that I wanted to die, more a case of not particularly wanting to live.

(*I understand the difference.*)

Now, with this prognosis, I felt it was not so much that I wanted desperately to live, but I didn't feel particularly inclined to die.

What did I think?

The decision to live could be based only on the fact that I was alive and I didn't really have the energy to do anything else.

It was that close.

I could not get enthusiastic about the future, it all seemed too much of an effort.

I had little sleep.

258

The following day Ellis arrived home from Poker, and disappeared immediately on the pretext of work, and more Poker.

(*One must get one's priorities right.*)

I descended into a pathetic state, where I convinced myself that nobody would be bothered if I died.

Nobody needed me.

Nobody relied on me.

I was surplus to requirements.

In an attempt to cheer myself up I purchased fish and chips with a pickled onion, a box of chocolates and a bottle of Lambrusco.

(*Could that be construed as a nutritional death wish?*)

I propped myself up against a heap of pillows and watched Saturday television.

(*An intellectual death wish?*)

The Lambrusco helped.

I woke at 3 a.m. and battled between deep sobs and light relief. The sobs were winning, especially when Waffles showed her concern for my plight.

Not knowing who would take in my precious furry friend, in the event of my demise, was even more distressing than my own mortality.

(*Let not poor Waffles starve.*)

I felt numb.

Ellis arrived home (again) and finding me in a depleted and apathetic state, suggested a walk? a drive? a chat? a cup of tea?

I could not respond.

He insisted that I came for a walk and talked me through all my thoughts and fears and hopelessness.

Would I like a few days away?

He always felt that in moments of inner panic it was advisable to wallow in nature, and hopefully put everything into perspective.

We can but try.

Wales.
   Next Sunday.
   Good.
   Muswell Hill.
   Next Tuesday.
   Bad!

I took Waffles to the vet for her annual booster injection.

"Is she fit?" he enquired.

"Fine . . . except she seems to be sleeping more than usual and needs to chew a piece of Cyperus plant every morning," I casually informed the vet.

A stethoscope was produced and Waffles' underside was listened to.

"She's got a sluggish heart," he announced.

I burst into tears and started mumbling and muttering about how she was all I had and I couldn't have got through the cancer without her . . .

The vet looked up in surprise and while a thankful pussycat sat peacefully thinking she had got away without an injection, he dealt with the human patient.

"It's nothing serious," I heard him say, through my soggy environment.

(*Moggy environment?*)

But I could not be consoled.

Waffles (hissing) had her injection.

I (weeping) had a packet of tiny pills handed to me with instructions to give her one everyday.

What had caused her condition?

Me.

Because of my inactivity and availability she had become a bed-potato.

It was all my fault.

I rang Ellis in tears.

I bought a catnip mouse and started Waffles on an exercise routine. While I threw the mouse up the stairs for her to reclaim, which she dutifully did, she remained quite active. But as soon as I went to sit down so did she. I had to keep peering round the corner at her to see if anything was happening. As soon as she saw me she patted the mouse.

I knew this was a game of cat and mouse but I began to have doubts about who was playing what part.

Ellis arrived home with super de-luxe cat toys.

Trouble was Waffles, being a non executive cat, did not know what to do with them.

She watched as I pretend-played but she walked away with a superior look on her face indicating that I was welcome to them.

She did continue with the mouse though and slowly she came back to life.

That made two of us.

A package arrived from Robert with the 'sort of' promised pills.

There was neither note nor explanation.

So he does know what he's doing with me, I thought. Wish he'd let me know.

I dutifully took my pills, which is more than could be said for Waffles.

Little moo.

Inevitably she ended up with her mouth stained pink from the number of attempts to execute a forced entry of the red tablet. My fingers just weren't strong enough to either hold her, or to be the pill popper. In the end I crushed the pill to powder and mixed it with her food.

She eyed the food suspiciously but if she didn't eat the small amount I put down for her there would be no more.

She ate.

Trish and Edward Cat demonstrated a different method but I stuck to my 'what the eye don't see the cat won't leave' policy.

On the subject of 'seeing' Trish suggested that before I went back to the hospital for the final decision, that I have a Polycontrast Interface Photograph (PIP) scan with Harry Oldfield.

Can't do any harm, I thought, and it will at least show up the extent of the tumour.

Gulp!

Was I ready for this?

Meanwhile Ellis and I went to Wales.

Waffles and pills went to Jo.

I don't know who was more nervous.

The four-hour journey to the Ty Maur hotel locked my joints, and what remained of my muscles, solid.

I could barely walk from the car to the room.

After sleep, food, rest, a bout of choking and more sleep, I woke reasonably refreshed.

We were to drive to Trai-saith, a childhood haunt of mine that I last visited fifteen years ago.

On my last visit I had voiced my surprised to a local, that it had not changed in all that time. It hasn't, in fact, changed in over a hundred years was the reply and I was shown a photograph taken at the end of the last century.

Now, I was to see this special cove again.

We descended along the steep and winding road . . . and . . . where was it?

Disappointment!

The tide was in, covering the vast expanse of sand and giving the whole bay a squalid claustrophobic feeling.

"But the tide was never in when I was a child," I lamented.

Good title for a book, someone remarked much later.

We drove along the coast to Llangrannol. The tide was in here, as well, but it did not disturb my memories.

I insisted that we walked up and along the cliff path.

In for a penny in for a pound-ing of the coastal clay.

Slowly, very slowly, I managed to reach the windy (not winding) top walk way.

"I love the free fresh wind in my wig," I sang to myself, as the cold sensation whistled through the webbing to my scalp.

What was I doing on top of a cliff in a high wind wearing a wig?

I must be crazy.

(*Quiet!*)
But it was fabulous to feel the freshness of non-London air and to look down on the tiny hamlet.

263

I kept a precautionary hold on one synthetic tendril.
I did not want it to turn into a Lemming!
The rain came down and we returned to the hotel.

In the room were copies of up-to-date magazines. One of them had an article on 'Think yourself well'.

(*If only it were that simple!*)

It talked about neuropeptides, which are found in every part of the body, including the immune system. If, as it has been established, these peptides are influenced by the emotional state of the person, then it is easy to understand the link between emotion and diseases.

(*Well, I can see the link!*)

There was a specific section on cancer ... I zoomed in. Lawrence Le Shan, it appears, studied the precursors of cancer and found that the patient usually felt isolated, even abandoned, as a child.

They also find a meaningful relationship in their early adult life and/or a meaningful job, and then lose them. They can then develop a feeling of worthlessness.

Wow! Here was one person who fitted that mould. Even though I was the youngest, and so called favourite, *I* felt completely adrift from my mother from my earliest memories. The sudden cessation of my father's love was viewed as a betrayal. I felt abandoned.

The happiest nine years of my life combined a job I loved, with a man I loved and admired. He let me breathe and grow and feel warm. My feelings of worthlessness, when the relationship ended, sent me headlong into totally destructive encounters with men. I had to almost prove a point.

People with cancer, it said, also have an inability to express anger. As a child I had to walk on egg shells in order not to upset my mother by any display of emotion. On the rare occasion when my childish temperament rose to the surface the price I had to pay was to witness my mother having a medical 'flare-up' and being confined to bed or hospital. It was all my fault. I soon learnt to bury my anger, and continued to do so throughout my adult life. This 'control' aspect was also noticed by other doctors working with cancer patients. They found patients had an unusually stoic attitude to their disease; rather like Glen thinking I was in shock.

However, I am very passionate about 'things' (principles you mean? no, 'things') and injustices drive me insane. If my battles can help others, then watch out, but I have an inability to raise my wrath in front of people, even to this day. I have had to become 'Furious of North London' and many a large organisation has come off worse in my pursuit of justice . . . but ask me to confront someone directly, and I go to pieces.

(*Mostly.*)

One statement in the article with which I entirely agree on, is that companions, whether humans or pets can improve your health. I thought of Waffles and smiled.

The food and ambience at the hotel were wonderful. When I wasn't over indulging in those, I slept.

It was a lovely break and I appreciated the part Ellis played in it. He was attentive and caring and wanted me to be comfortable.

This was more like it.

I began to relax.

The long drive home produced stiffened legs again but I doubled round and went to reclaim Waffles, who was quite capable of putting up stiff legs against my caresses to show her annoyance.

"Oh, she's not here," gasped Jo, as I let myself into her flat.

"What do you mean?"

Apparently Waffles had made a successful escape attempt through a rapidly closing door . . . and had not been seen since.

Oh, never mind, she'll return when she's hungry, I thought as I settled down for a tea and a chat.

After an hour I went home.

And burst into tears.

I couldn't compute the horror of the Little Horror lying somewhere in the rain unable to breathe, having suffered a heart attack.

I returned to the scene of the Break-out.

No Waffles.

"When was it that she disappeared?" I asked out of interest.
"8 a.m."

It was now 6 p.m.

"That's it! I'll never see her again," I declared, trying to be ever-so-brave and failing miserably.

I returned home and dissolved into my second soggy moggy heap in so many weeks.

Ellis was equally upset and zoomed round to Jo's place to instigate house to house enquiries.

(*It's only a cat I hear some of you say? Wrong!*)

Ellis and the friend who had aided, but not abetted, the escape searched surrounding roads.

Jo, searching for something completely unrelated to furry fugitives, looked under her bed and saw two fluorescent flashes of green.

"Waffles!!!!!"

It seems that sometime during the preceding eight hours she

had casually walked back into the flat, under the bed, and gone to sleep oblivious to the chaos she had caused.

I have suspicions about the 'oblivious' bit, but I'll let it pass.

She was back.

I felt exhausted and stretched.
I also felt as if my life was in suspended animation.

I bought a dressing gown, ready for the hospital.
(*Negative?*)

There were some green shoots of recovery, however, in the form of dark grey fuzz all over my head.
(*Grey?*)

Trish drives me to Harry Oldfield's for the PIP scan.
What is a PIP scan?
Well, in lay terms I can only describe it as a psychedelic picture of your insides. A camcorder is aimed at the body, either as a long shot or for a close up of the part which is causing a problem. On screen you can see yourself in glorious moving technicolour with certain areas highlighted in deeper or richer colours. A 'still' button is pressed and the image freezes on the screen. Then a computer printout reproduces the image on to paper.

I had several scans done. One each of the front, back and side of the body, and then a close up of the left breast.

It showed the tumour happily settled in a smallish area well away from the lymph glands. It was a lot smaller than I had ever hoped for. The other scans showed that my liver, gall bladder, thymus and right axillary lymph gland were very 'bothered' (my word) indicating a huge activity to rid my body of the toxins. The back view highlighted the trauma that my body had been through. The left side from shoulder to hip was an angry streak of red and purple, outraged at the attack on it by cancer, Chemotherapy and Radiation.

"Brilliant," both Harry and Trish declared.

Brilliant indeed.

Now I had to decide what to do with the information. Harry and Trish did not try to persuade, or dissuade any decision I may make.

That had to be mine.

Over food for eating and food for thought I outlined my bold, brave or barmy plan to Ellis and asked him for his support at tomorrow's hospital appointment.

My decision had to be based on something other than fear and confusion.

I wanted the best for my body, as I was attached to it in more ways than one.

I was as nervous as if I were sitting an exam, which in a way I was. I had swotted up on the information but would it be enough to pass? As we walked into the department I came face to face with Glen.

Relief flooded my every cell.

(*Every little bit helps*)

"What are you doing here?" said a grinning Glen.

"Professor Taylor . . . decision time!!" I managed to get out.

"May I join you?"

"Oh, yes pleeeaaasssee."

(*More relief flooded, as opposed to flood relief.*)

I was called, quickly.

Both Professor Taylor and Glen had what I call their 'fondle', made positive, amazed noises, then started to be doctors.

268

"Right, you've done amazingly well to reduce the tumour to that size but now we have to decide when to give you a Mastectomy."

I took a deep breath.

"I want you to sit down and listen to me and I don't want you to interrupt until I have finished . . ."
   (*The nurse couldn't believe what she was hearing.*)
   Glen, I believed, obliged, but I can't be sure.

Professor Taylor took it quite well.
   "What I am going to say is not based on fear of a Mastectomy, per se, although I can't imagine any woman willingly skipping into a hospital in order to have one."

(I later heard that this, in fact, did happen! Women with a history of Breast cancer in their family volunteered to undergo a Mastectomy to take away the chance of it happening to them. I'm speechless!)

"I have even bought a new dressing gown in preparation of the possible event," I continued.
   "However, I don't think I'm in a fit state, mentally, emotionally, psychologically, or physically to have an Operation."
   (pause)
"Yesterday I had a PIP scan . . ."
   "A what?" queried Professor Taylor.
   "You can ask questions later . . ."
   (*You're not the only one wearing a white coat.*)
   " . . . I had a PIP scan and it showed me the extent of the 'mass', as I now call it. I call it a mass because if it were all cancerous my lymph glands would be going berserk, and I know that is not the case."
   A nod (ish) from Glen, or did I imagine that (as well)?

269

"I have had every piece of advice that can be given from, *I will die if I* don't have an Operation, to, I will die if I *do* have an Operation and everything in between. I have to go with my gut decision, which is, not to have an Operation unless you can prove to me that my life would be 100% improved."

(*I knew they couldn't, which is why I said it.*)

"Leave me alone to continue with my Complementary treatments and I'll pop back in, say, six to eight weeks for you to have another look."

"Okay," they agreed.

!!!!!!!

I had stoked up my adrenalin ready for a fight and had not been prepared for such an easy battle.

I had come out with all guns blazing to be confronted by the fire brigade.

(*Spoil sports.*)

Professor Taylor left the room, smiling, while Glen did his Question-time slot.

"Night sweats," I fired at Glen.

"Yes?"

"To alleviate the effects of my instant Menopause I have been searching for a natural remedy to take ... trouble is, they tend to use words like 'oestrogen substitute' or 'hormonal boost'. I assume I must never have any product that claims to increase my oestrogen levels?"

"You mustn't have oestrogen whether natural or artificial, ever! You haven't have you?" he implored me.

"No."

"That's a relief."

"It's alright if I have a Homeopathic remedy?"

"Yes, stick to that," he said, relieved.

I'm glad I did my own investigations on the subject because I feel this was another example of my slipping through the various experts. No one had ever told me that I must now avoid the dreaded hormone. What if I'd happily been taking a shop bought product for Menopausal symptoms?

The mind, and breast, boggles.

Glen hurriedly gave me a prescription for the famous Tamoxifen, an insurance treatment, which I would have to take for many years.

The theory and, let's hope, the practice, behind Tamoxifen is that around 40% of Breast cancers are hormone (ie oestrogen) sensitive. If deprived of this hormone they fail to grow.

(*Now I see his panic*)

It has the added bonus that once absorbed it is carried in the bloodstream to all parts of the body, which hopefully will prevent any cells which may have slipped away from the main tumour from growing.

"So this means that I'm unlikely to develop another cancer?"

"No, not exactly," he replied.

It appears I'm less likely to develop a 'second' Breast cancer but have an increased risk of cancer of the womb.

(*I knew there had to be one good reason for having a Hysterectomy!*)

On another plus side there is less chance of my dying of a heart attack, or stroke, and fewer problems with complications due to osteoporosis.

(*Which is why I went on HRT in the first place.*)

Who'd be a female?

Ellis and I left the hospital a bit stunned, amazed, but delighted. It wasn't Champagne time, but it was one small step towards the Off-Licence.

I was exhausted by the effort of not needing to make an effort.

I slept.

Then I booked myself into Tyringham Naturopathic Clinic for a week.

I had to start detoxing my body and preparing it for a life free of everything it had been experiencing this year.

That night I was too tired to celebrate in any way, shape or form but I made up for it the following night when I scraped together enough energy to visit the Wild Track. It was yet another birthday and I was invited to join the party for as long as I could keep awake.

Jimmy summoned me to the telephone.

I knew who it was even before I picked up the receiver.

"Darling, do you mind if I join you? I've finished my meeting and I think I'd like a bite to eat," announced Ellis, who had not been in the Wild Track for over a year.

My rusty brain tried to unscramble what I really thought, but before I was able to do so, my mouth said "not at all."

What did I think?

In the early days of our relationship (when it was a relationship) I had tried to train him into understanding that it was 'my' restaurant and when I wanted to be there on my own he had to appreciate my wishes; just as I would not try to phone him when he was playing Poker.

Over the years we had dined at the Wild Track as a couple, but since 'The Troubles' I had claimed it as my own again. It was, after all, my Bolt Hole; the sponge that mopped up many an emotion.

Now, here he was attempting entry again, and I was confused.

But also, I confess, delighted.
He wanted to be with me, on my territory.
He wanted to be with me.
But?
(*Be quiet!!*)

He didn't play Poker that Friday night, either.
(*Zippadi-dooda Zippadiday . . . or something like that!*)

On Saturday I drove to the Tyringham Naturopathic Clinic.
My initial consultation was a bit strange. I'd filled in a medical record with my application form but it hadn't even been taken out of the envelope and I was asked all the same questions again.

"What do you hope to achieve by coming here?" he fired at me.

"I want to be pampered," I whispered, in a voice that was fading with tiredness.

"Don't come here then," he replied sharply.
(*I see.*)

A long list of activities and treatments for me to choose from, were read out very quickly; too quickly.

How should I know what was best for me? I was getting a little frustrated. Surely he knows what should be done? . . . I hope.

Massage, water aerobics, Yoga and relaxation I knew about, but what was a Scottish douche, a Sitz bath, peat packs and a Constitutional Hydro-Therapy session?

It would be educational at least.

I wish it had only been educational.

Standing naked and having alternate hot and cold water sprayed up your spine is not my idea of fun and relaxation.
(*Now I knew what he meant!*)

The Scottish douche is supposed to improve circulation and boost the immune system, but I crawled into bed and shivered for three hours and felt totally traumatised by the event. Others seemed to like it (?) so I suppose it must be an acquired taste.

The Sitz bath was almost as bad, but not quite. I could tolerate it, which indicates how far down the 'aarrgghh' scale it was.

This torture consisted of a small bath that looked like a double sink unit. In one sink there was hottish water, and in the other, icy cold. By sitting in one, with your feet in the other, and swapping around several times, this too, improved the circulation.

I'm sure it does but I was never sure if I succeeded in drying my bum, because I couldn't feel it . . . for hours.

I believe men found it particularly gruesome, can't think why?

The water aerobics and yoga really gave me a fright. My body refused to cooperate with my brain. Not only was I devoid of energy but there were simple movements my body could no longer attempt, let alone achieve. Here I was, someone who in 1992 had swum 200 lengths for charity (including Macmillan nurses), unable to swish my arms and legs around under water without total exhaustion.

At least the Scottish douche and Sitz bath had prepared me for thetheory of Hydrotheropy.

Onwards and upwards . . . to the Constitutional.

How nice: hot/wet towels were thumped down on my naked torso one after another until I felt like a pressed flower. Then, when another towel was placed on top the whole pile was turned over and thumped down again . . . but this time the towel touching me was cold and wet.

Electrodes were attached to my lower back and liver area and I was then covered with a blanket and told to 'think warm'.

Think warm!! You must be joking.

I imagined my one night in the Sahara desert when I'd felt as if I was roasting alive, and concentrated on that for the duration.

(*Duress-ion*)

The whole process was repeated on my back.

Somehow I managed to increase my temperature by using this mind over matter technique, which is what they were trying to achieve.

Apparently it is an excellent way of boosting the immune system.

(*Well that's alright then.*)

I retired to my (cold) room and had a little whiney weep.

Then the headache started and continued for 36 hours.

I found out later that most people at the clinic developed headaches, possibly because of all the toxins leaping from the body via the brain cells.

And also, perhaps, to do with the small amount of food that was on offer.

I couldn't complain, as I was on the full diet, an amount far in excess of what I had been used to recently, but I didn't dare refuse to eat it, as other mortals desperate for a morsel looked longingly around the tables in search of tit-bits.

The yoga sessions were a problem, partly because of my wig wishing to part company from my head. Tops of cliffs are one thing, upside down yoga positions are another. The tutor slowly talked us through a relaxation technique, which included him asking us to relax from the roots of our hair to the tips; in my case this was not very far! Although, if the wig fell off I could claim a synthetic three feet meditation coup.

My legs and arms and back and neck and everywhere were groaning with outrage at the assault on their weakness. The Peat Packs and Wax baths helped and so did the Massages.

Bliss.

I was lying flat out on my bed wishing I could be warm and cosy and well, when the phone rang.

"Mrs Cole, we've managed to fit you in for an extra massage. Would you like to come down?"

Mrs Cole, quite happily, hobbled down to a much needed back and leg massage.

"Don't take this the wrong way but I could have done with you in my room last night," I gently moaned, through peaceful lips.

"We heard that!" said an assortment of voices.

"Don't care," I purred.

Most evenings I retired to the warmth and comfort of my bed and rested my weary body.

A television programme held my interest but kept me from sleep. It was of course about cancer.

A research team had pinned down a genetic defect, a 'mutation of a control gene' carried in the DNA. One mistake will give a faulty message to divide and then it goes out of control

An antibody had been developed and this had been injected into the cells with good results. A radioactive 'tag' proved that the antibodies had gone straight to the cancer.

(*Mind boggling*)

When the MN23 gene is 'turned off' it allows that gene to metastasise. As 90% of cancers are caused by chance mutation this research may not be universally useful except as another block in the building of a total knowledge of cancer.

I was delighted to hear that scientists regularly exchange information and data between themselves instead of rushing for the victory podium.

I also hope that scientists will understand what I've written, because I barely can.

Saturday arrived quickly, but in some cases, not quickly enough.

One week, in which I had been shown just how depleted my body was and how little I could do with it. But I had to admit that I could do more now than I could at the start of the week, which is why I had chosen to come.

I had, in fact, given my body a jump-start. Now all I had to do was improve my performance and pass the MOT.

Home.
(*I still called it that!*)

Ellis wasn't in.

One irate pussy cat was.

The house had an unlived in feel about it. (?)

The food I had prepared for Ellis had gone untouched.

Where was he?

Strange.

I had not expected him to be standing on the step with a bouquet and arms outstretched, but he knew I would be home in the morning.
(*My ability to both feel and suppress panic came into action.*)

A phone call . . . from Ellis.

He was tired and had pulled into a lay-by to sleep. He would be back within the hour.

Four hours later he entered the house, vaguely aimed his lips at a space two inches away from my cheek, and promptly fell asleep on the couch for three hours.

His proposed trip to Charlie's, our favourite Pasta house, was therefore abandoned and so I started to cook a strange tomato and cheese bake.

(*Why was I remembering such stupid details?*)

Over dinner he announced that as playing Poker was what he enjoyed doing, he was going to make no effort to cut down on this his only relaxation.

"It didn't make sense," he mumbled.

It certainly didn't.

He had been making great efforts to reduce the stress-producing factor of playing all through the night, then going straight to work. A 'relaxation' he indulged in at least three times a week.

So why the U-turn?

Like a wary cat I sat and absorbed the information, but made no move to indicate my feelings.

There was something happening, but I could not work out what it was, least of all how it would affect me.

Time would tell.

He went straight to bed after the meal.

Four hours in a lay-by (he'd said).

Three hours on the couch.

Ten hours in bed.

This was serious avoidance behaviour, even for Ellis.

The next morning I was relieved when he suggested a walk in the park.

I had an appointment at 10 a.m. with Trish, but I was more than happy to accompany him on a gentle stroll that, for me, was the nearest I could get to a walk.

He talked and talked . . . about the work he was doing on rebuilding 'him'. It was beginning to get difficult, but at present he was coping.

His main concern was for my welfare.

(*Really?*)

I suggested that this was one of his externalising cop-outs and that, if he concentrated on getting himself back into some form of equilibrium, then a by-product of this would be my welfare.

We talked of security, and how I didn't have any.

We talked of the future and how (for me) it resembled a thick pea soup.

We talked in a hypothetical way of ifs and buts and maybes and everything else in that mystical land 'the future'.

I expressed my fear of having no income, the dread of having to return to my own house if the worst came to the worst, of my fear of being alone, the whole uncertainty of life.

He commiserated with my predicament and vowed to help me.

I felt so safe with him.

(*Oh, Jenny!*)

The conversation was quiet, rational and unemotional.

I felt good.

(*So why was he looking so serious?*)

"What do *you* want?" he asked gently.

"Me? I just want the old Ellis back."

"Oh, Darling, he never existed."

Never existed?

For some reason I failed to react immediately to that statement; perhaps my post-Tyringham tiredness and euphoria masked the full implication?

(*But perhaps not.*)

It was too late to discuss that now, as I was already late for my appointment with Trish.

I passed a very gloomy Ellis in the hall and gave him a little hug.

"It's going to be alright," I assured him, as he sobbed gently.

The normal trio of Ellis, his mum and I had lunch at one of our many Sunday haunts.

The atmosphere was relaxed and Ellis seemed in good spirits.

He even started to talk about 'love'.

I was all ears.

He said that many years ago he had written a letter to his new born godson, to be opened on his eighteenth birthday. In it lay the pearls of wisdom of that nebulous emotion which he had accumulated throughout his life.

(*Could I have a copy, please?*)

Once again, I failed to react to what he was saying.

I must be more tired than I thought.

On returning to the house I dragged my weary body to bed, and slept and slept and slept.

A few hours later he tapped at my door, cup of tea in hand, and asked if we could continue our conversation.

"Of course," I beamed.

I was delighted that he wanted to continue his personal quest.

He sat at the end of the bed . . . and lobbed a hand grenade into the centre of my all too fragile existence.

"I've put the house on the market and tomorrow I'm going to see an Estate Agent to find myself a flat. I . . . think it would be a good idea if you did the same . . . I've spent enough time on you this year, and it's about time I started to put myself first."

I froze and exploded all at the same time.

"Why are you doing this to me, NOW!!!!????"
　"Why are you doing this to me, NOW!!!!????"
　"Why are you doing this to me, NOW!!!!????" was all I can remember screaming.

(*NO!!!!!!! You Bastard. You cruel, manipulative, unfeeling BASTARD!!*)

"It's for the best," he continued.

"The timing's all WRONG."
　"The timing's all WRONG!!"
　"The timing's all WRONG!!!!" I screamed in absolute panic.

"When would you suggest might be a better time?" he sarcastically enquired.

"How about when I'm 'cured', in remission, dead!"
　(*You BASTARD!!!!*)

By this time I was wailing and crying with such disbelief and anguish, that any further 'conversation' was effectively buried.

I was stunned.

He had not only cut the last remaining thread of our 'relationship' but had sewn in the end, so I could not even reach for it ever again.

He had never been working towards an 'us'. But I had.

You can't say you feel abandoned," he reasoned, "after all, I technically abandoned you two years ago, when we moved to the house."

I clammed up and shut my ears to the wave upon wave of oxymoronic verbalisations.

He was going to help me get a flat because he cared.

(*Fuck off!*)

He escaped to Poker, as soon as he could.

"I suppose you think I'm a coward?" he mused, steadily inching out the door.

"Yes."

In fact he was not dissimilar to a sniper, whose aim is to cause the most chaos and hardship, but does not want to be around to witness the effect of his actions.

"Just go," I pleaded, as I sat crouched over my Word-processor.

"By the way, if the book is published, I think I'd like you to use the name 'Haime' instead of Ellis," said Ellis, alias Haime.

We had discussed the possible embarrassment of his name being used and I had been happy to change it. After all, the book was about my taking control of the cancer and not about losing control of a man called Ellis.

Now, I wasn't so sure.

In most books I have read by someone with cancer, there have always been adoring parents, spouses or children surrounding and supporting them through thick and thin.

With Ellis I felt I had achieved the impossible, despite his appalling track record, and now here he was jeopardising everything for the sake of a few months ... and compassion.

It was also a fact that people who knew him well were aware of his peculiar behaviour and would not be surprised by his actions towards me.

As for the rest of his associates ... I doubt if they ever read books and even if they did, would they care?

I doubt it.

His world appears to be full of insensitive automatons keen only to acquire money and power.

It's so sad ... for them.

Within half an hour of his leaving the house, he phoned, and kept on phoning, to give me another 'thought for today'.

Through tears I begged him to just leave me alone to calm down.

Why keep phoning?

It was bizarre.

Approximately one and a half hours sleep.

But, like all true Ariens I reacted quickly and swiftly to the situation.

I visited every Estate Agent in the area and placed my order.

The menu was sparse.

"Wrong time of the year," they informed me.

How true, I thought to myself, how very true.

My fire and determination to be positive rapidly drained away during the course of the week, as the true horror of what was being proposed took over from my protective shock.

Shock?

Yes. Being told I had cancer galvanised all my inner resources and I knew what I had to do. I also knew what the enemy was and could direct all my energy to its downfall.

I was not in shock.

Being discarded, as I saw it, at a time when I still had cancer, but no job, no money, no energy, and with all the physical and emotional upheaval of a move, was more than my body could take.

This was shock.

Apart from the weight loss, I slept only a few hours a night . . . my nocturnal thoughts galloped away like a herd of wild stallions . . . I couldn't sleep, but boy could I weep . . . my breathing was laboured and it felt as if lemonade was running through my veins.

"I don't know why I bothered to fight the cancer," I spat out to anyone who'd listen.

Lots listened.

Lots rushed around and attempted to pump fresh willpower into my depleted reserves.

Lots got me through the most frightening week of the cancer.

Lots were speechless.

I watched speechless and think-less as a programme on cancer stated that Britain has the worst survival rate of Breast cancer in the world.

(*How come?*)

According to a survey over half of all cancer patients are not referred to a hospital in time.

(*And?*)

Half of all our doctors are general practitioners, but only a very small proportion of their training is directly related to being a GP.

(*So?*)

Only two thirds pass the exam.

(*And the rest?*)

They continue to practise and are GPs for life.

(*Is that a problem?*)

More complaints are levelled at GPs who have not passed the exam.

(*Training?*)

Refresher courses are not mandatory. Cancer courses are rare.

Well, that's cheered me up!

Trish and I went to a lecture by Jan de Vries on Naturopathy. This was one of the events I had been so excited about on my return from Tyringham. Ellis had mistaken my pleasure for recovery.

I was still excited especially after having experienced Naturopathy at first (hot and cold) hand.

Jan de Vries began by saying that Orthodox medicine needs to go back to square one, for without an holistic approach, progress will be minimal. Orthodox medicine is quicker, but the end results are better if you first find the cause instead of attacking the problem. Nowadays there are so many unidentified diseases. This has partly been caused by the indiscriminate use of suppressant drugs, which have made things worse. By suppressing the immune system the body's own resources are knocked out, leaving it vulnerable and unable to fight for itself . . .

(*Don't talk to me about solo fighting!*)

Fleming would be horrified with the use made of antibiotics (anti-life). You should not destroy good when trying to destroy bad . . .

(*World leaders take note.*)

Waste has to be eliminated or the body's chemistry will fail.

Salt, sugar and stress: the three most dangerous enemies of the body.

More cancers are caused by stress than anything else.

(*Tell me about it!*)

I bought two more of his books: 'Menopause' and 'Miracle of Life', since I appeared to be going through both.

After the lecture Trish insisted on luring me back to her place to zap my neck and shoulder, which I'd twisted the previous night.

(*Twisting the night away.*)

She also attempted to calm me and handed me a milky drink to help my sleeplessness.

Don't worry, I informed her, I'm so exhausted I'll sleep for hours.

Home by midnight.

Message from Ellis.

He will not be home.
(*So what's new?*)

I did sleep for hours . . . three to be precise.

At 3 a.m. I gave up all attempts at sleep, or rest, and furiously started chucking out years upon years of accumulated craft items.

Why had I hoarded so much for so long?
In one box I found pottery that I'd made in 1966! I'd never displayed it, as it wasn't particularly good. On the same grounds I would therefore not give it away or attempt to sell it.

"OUT, OUT, OUT," I screamed, exorcising much more stored rubbish than just the pottery.
The pile grew and my anger reduced.
By 8 a.m. I was on my way to the local tip.
As I threw it into the containers I knew I had to learn to throw away much much more before I could truly say that I was cured.

Cured of what?

That would be telling.

Somehow I remained awake, perhaps feeding on the now growing anger that accompanied my fear.
I had my first meeting with Iro an Acupuncturist with many other talents. He was also a Chinese Herbalist.
For many months a friend had been encouraging me to see him. At the time I was seeing Robert on a regular basis, so did not feel the need to encounter yet more opinions and systems.
"But he's 'gorgeous'," my friend insisted.

"That is the least of my requirements," I snapped. "What I want is someone who will work with me to take control of this cancer."

So, I had resisted, that is, until Robert had 'betrayed' me.

I wondered what Iro would be like.

He took my pulses:
"There's a steady bounce, bounce, bounce of a ball, but there are three layers of crinkly paper in between," he announced after gentle pressure on my wrist area. My solar plexus was traumatised.

He listened to my account of 1992 and then delved further and further into my past to build up a picture.
I really must make a tape recording, I thought to myself, as I relayed layer after layer of Operations, traumas, infections, drugs and the throwing down the end of the bed episode.

"Is that enough?" I asked with all my normal bravado.

He looked at me.

"I'm not surprised you have cancer. The onslaught on your body has been overwhelming."

I didn't know whether to thank him, or stay quiet. It was all so familiar to me and if repeated enough times doesn't seem that bad.
I forgot the impact it has on other people.
I started to cry and while comforting me, he took my pulses again.

They were all over the place.

288

He asked about my attitude to the cancer . . .

I bounced, I bubbled, I said what an amazing year it had been for me and how I had enjoyed it.

(*Enjoyed?*)

My pulses had changed, yet again.

He likened my life to a raft on rapids. "Cancer is the ultimate challenge for any individual," he said. "At present you are going over the falls like in 'The Mission'."

He implied that I was destined for higher things, next time.

(*Don't you dare say I'll come back as a man!*)

I have strength but I've allowed people around me to drain me.

(*Now where have I heard that before?*)

He couldn't understand why I worked in prisons with my sensitivity.

(*Delicate little blossom that I am?*)

"Ignatia," he said, suddenly.

"What's that for?"

"Well, rearrange the letters and add a 'd' and you almost have INDIGNATION," he quipped.

Rage, fury and an inability to take anything else was my present state of mental turmoil.

It had to come OUT.

(*Very interesting.*)

He wrote down the 'prescription' which I was to take to Ainsworth the Royal Homeopathic shop. "You need the strongest dose," he added, while informing me of how to take the powders.

The rest of our session was taken up with Astrology, Spirituality, Crystals and everything I'd experienced this year. He had heard of Glen, and his appreciation of Complementary therapies, Harry and his PIP scan, Lily and her colour healing, and Robert. The fact that Iro knew of these individuals indicated to me that I'd used The Best Resources available to tackle the cancer.

I felt safe with Iro.
  (*Now, where have you heard that before?*)

Treatment would start in a few days.

I couldn't wait.

Nina, my friend, eagerly enquired as to how the session had gone with Iro. I prattled on for a while, excited by the range of topics he and I have spoken about, how I felt in good hands, how I appreciated his gentleness (after Robert), how everything was falling into place ... oh, and by the way, I added, he's gorgeous.
  (*Perhaps my hormones are returning?*)

Ellis was at home when I returned.
  We hardly spoke.
  "Did you go to the Acupuncturist?" he finally asked.
  "Yes."
  "What did he say?"
  "Lots of things ... and I have to pick up some Ignatia powder tomorrow."
  "What's that for?"
  "Rage, fury, pain, hurt, refusal to take any more ..."
  "I see," said Ellis sliding out of the room.
  (*Do you?*)
  (*DO YOU??*)

That night I dreamt of a sequence of actions, taught to me by Iro. These actions took the form of breathing exercises and every time I breathed OUT a little more of the cancer left my body.

It was very powerful and I woke at 5.30 a.m. reasonably relaxed.

I heard Ellis leave the house at 6 a.m., and a note informed me he would not be returning that night.

I had left for Tyringham with Ellis acting and behaving like a human being. I returned to someone who was in rapid retreat, closing the doors behind him as fast as he could.

I was powerless, as he rushed away, causing a vacuum in his wake.

A vacuum that couldn't speak.

I took myself off to Ainsworth Homeopathic shop and purchased the 'Indignant' powder. If I had realised the shop was near Harley Street where I would have to come the next day for my interview for the Autogenics course, I could have saved myself a journey. But then again, I was so desperate to take anything that would ease my state of mind I was happy to make a double trip.

Perhaps some people thought I was hell bent on a 'trip', as I fumbled with the thin paper sachet containing the fine white powder. It dissolved on contact with my tongue. No taste, no texture . . . no way this can achieve anything?

I waited.

I returned the next day to Harley Street to be interviewed for the Autogenics course.

'Autogenics: An answer to Stress related Problems' stated

the leaflet. 'A series of easy mental exercises designed to switch off the stress fight or flight system of the body, and switch on the rest, recreation and relaxation system'.

It was also reputed to help boost the immune system.

I'll have some of that.
(*Handy sachets would be nice.*)

"What do you hope to achieve by learning the Autogenics technique?" enquired Dr Curruthers.

I told him all my medical and emotional problems, then listed my requirements and expectations. I rounded it off with the hope that I could be taught how to cope with the mega-stress of Ellis's edict.

"That's a tall order for Autogenics, but we'll have a good attempt to help," he beamed at me.

I seemed to be impressing him by my attitude to the cancer. After a while he looked up from his notes and casually asked if I would be interested in taking part in a BBC documentary on Autogenics . . .

(*Yes*)

It would require a small amount of training with a camera . . .

(*Yes*)

. . . and I would have to take the camera home and . . .

(*Yes, yes, yes*)

"I don't know how you would feel about it or if in fact they would go along with it. They had wanted a stressed businessman," he concluded.

"Yes, I'll do it," I said, trying not to sound too eager.

"Good, then I'll give the producer your phone number, if I may?"

Why was I so keen to be inconvenienced by this request?
Simple.

292

I needed new pursuits and interests ... I'd spent my whole working life teaching people how to do things for themselves ... If Autogenics was as good as it said it was, then I was more than happy to spread the word ... and if anyone wanted a selfish motive then this would be a great opportunity to launch myself into a new career.

The fact that I didn't know what this career would be was beside the point. I was determined to use every conceivable method to publicise 'Me'.

(*Where had I got this confidence from?*)

The producer phoned me that afternoon and we spoke for over an hour. Well actually I spoke for an hour and she managed an occasional 'ooh' or 'aah'. She promised to phone me back within a couple of days.

(*When her ear had recovered?*)

I returned to Iro for my first Acupuncture session (of this illness). I knew what to expect and readily offered my body as a human pin cushion.

The left side of my body responded much more to the needles than the right side, ie, I yelled more.

"Am I being a wimp, or does everyone find this unpleasant?" I gasped between the stabs of pain from the needles.

He reassured me that I was not over-reacting. Apart from the fact that my body was so traumatised by the year's events, he was pushing the needles more deeply into the skin than normal, and then twisting them. I felt like a piano being tuned, as he walked around me tweaking the needles until he got the right note, which was usually me trying to say 'ouch' in order not to swear.

I think a few 'sugars' passed my lips.

He was also fiddling around with the back of my neck, so I indicated that I was willing to take off my wig, as the elastic part was impeding his fiddles.

"Only if you don't mind."

"Not at all," I declared as I threw the wig across the room.

I could not have imagined doing that for Robert.

Now that my scalp, covered in fuzzy dark brown and grey hair, was revealed he took the opportunity to place a needle in the Baihui point, which is the meeting point of all the Meridians, and situated on the top of the head . . . where it is most tender.

It was a strange sensation, especially when the needle was removed; as though energy and tension were trying to rush out through the hole, but were prevented from doing so because Iro had his thumb firmly pressed over the area.

I did feel very light headed.

At the end of the session, he asked if I'd like to try some Chinese Herbs. I imagined tiny sachets of jasmine-type leaves, which I could steep in a delicate china cup. It would, of course, taste delicious.

(*Why not.*)

I had noticed that his walls were stacked with shoe boxes, bearing the name of the contents in both Chinese and English, but I hadn't given them much notice. Now, as he lifted down box after box, he started to prepare three bags of 'things', which to me looked far from herb-ish.

Each polythene bag contained what looked like a piece of polystyrene, some tiddlywinks, bits of wood, a few dehydrated slugs, some sawdust, discarded orange peel, and various other objects that looked as if they had just been swept up off the floor.

While he was preparing the mix, he quietly muttered the harmonic Chinese names to himself.

"Pardon? What are they?" I cautiously enquired.

I need not have asked. He readily launched himself into a description of each shoe box occupant, and the theory behind one of the oldest medical treatments in the world.

It was fascinating.

Forget Adriamycin, Dexamethasone and Ondansetron . . . I entered the world of Bai Hua She She Cao (White patterned snake herb) Xia Ku Cao (Summer dry herb) and Nu Zhen Zi (Female chastity seed).

(*Excuse me. What was that last one?*)

Nu Zhen Zi? This tonifies the Yin. In traditional Chinese medicine the cause of all illness is an imbalance between the Yin and Yang. My dark and passive Yin was obviously in need of a tonic.

Other terminology he used was equally baffling. I knew about Qi (or chi) but, fire poison?

Chinese medicine believes there are four aspects to cancer: Qi deficiency, blood stasis (hard lumps), phlegm accumulation (soft lumps), and fire poison (inflamed and angry area). It sounded as if I were a cauldron of angry hard and soft lumps which, on reflection, didn't seem an unreasonable description.

"In your case," said Iro.

(*I was all (lumps and) ears.*)

"In your case, especially after the amount of Chemotherapy and Radiotherapy you've had, we need to tonify the Qi, eliminate the fire poison and clear heat, but I have also blended in herbs that clear blood stasis and phlegm accumulation."

295

I wondered if the 'phlegm' aspect was the same as the classical medical 'humours'?

When I returned home I hunted through several books until . . . 'Phlegmatic: sluggishness' I read . . .

(*I knew they were slugs!*)

I didn't dare ask about the 'slugs' but enquired about the bits of dried up peel I could see in the mix. It *was* peel! Immature tangerine peel to be precise. Well, let's hope it doesn't mature to 'orange peel' I thought, gloomily. Orange peel is a skin texture, which indicates the presence of cancer in the breast. So far, presumably because of my type of cancer, it had not manifested itself on me.

"Why so many bits and pieces," I wanted to know.

"Well, every Chinese Herb formula has a variety of different tasks to achieve. There are the Emperor Herbs, the Minister, or, Deputy Herbs, the Assistant Herbs and the Messengers."

(*Like it!*)

I had images of thousands of little Chinamen rushing around my body, co-ordinating the cure.

The mix of 'Herbs' looked worse after they had soaked for the required two hours. The hydrated slugs, et al, increased in size and continued to do so when boiled for 40 minutes.

I then had to strain off the thick dark brown liquid and drink it, while retaining the evil looking items for another brew up.

The drink was neither pleasant nor unpleasant . . . just difficult to swallow. It had a strong bitter liquorice flavour and I don't particularly like liquorice. But, having done many horrible things over the year in the name of health, I picked up the mug and glugged it down, pretending it was delicious and knowing it was doing me good.

An added bonus was that it removed a long standing stain in the mug!

(*What on earth was it doing to my stomach?*)

For different reasons Ellis and I avoided each other.

It was easier that way.

We both had things to do which would keep us away from the house. I had booked myself onto an all-day conference: 'Cancer: A Positive Approach' at the Hammersmith Hospital.

The 1½ hour journey was exhausting; and the first thing I asked on arriving at the centre was whether there was anywhere I could lie down.

How would I get through the day if I was this tired before it had started?

The chair (person) who was a female opened the conference by stating that it was okay to cry and feel sad during the course. Counsellors were at hand to deal with any problem.

Immediately I felt weepy.

The morning session consisted of a panel of Oncology specialists. Facts and figures flowed from their speeches. Some I liked, some disturbed.

Eighty-five percent of cancers are curable, or preventable, said a Radiologist, then suggested there were many improvements needed in the NHS especially referral time by GPs.

(*Agreed*).

Why can't they, I thought to myself, set up walk-in clinics along the lines of the euphemistically called Special Clinics. It could certainly work for breasts.

The Chemotherapist confessed that 'Chemotherapy has a bad reputation, which is probably well deserved.' . . .

(*Refreshing!*)

. . . then explained that Chemotherapy can be very mild with a one tablet a day regime, to, taking the person within an inch of their life.

(*Defeating the whole object of saving them?*)

Antibiotics used to be called 'Chemotherapy'.

(*Interesting*)

You can get 10,000 cancer cells on one pin head, which is why one can never declare you are cured. The purpose of Chemotherapy is to wipe out any cells released from the main site, but it also kills off many more fast growing healthy cells.

(*I know!*)

'There is now more consultation between the expert and the patient, which is to be encouraged.' However, if this is attempted in Third World countries the patient panics and thinks the doctor doesn't know what he's doing.

A Community doctor then pleaded for the word cancer to be demystified, as it means nothing on its own. The condition can be either a minor problem or life threatening, so there was a need for more bespoke treatment.

Death is something that this society avoids mentioning but, as it is inevitable, it should be addressed in a sympathetic manner. The Hospice movement is doing just that.

Then, causing some discomfort on the platform, he declared that there was confusion over the use of Complementary therapies but that the confusion usually came from the doctors!

(*Loud cheering and clapping.*)

But he did counsel that there was far too much false 'positivity' and that people with cancer should allow themselves to get angry, to scream, to suffer.

(*Yeh*)

The issue is not whether to use Orthodox or Complementary methods but to understand that they represent the 'masculine' and 'feminine' approach to treatment (Yin and Yang!). Instead of insisting on a separation every effort should be made to keep them together in a useful marriage.

(*Hear! Hear!*)

By now I was becoming extremely tired and fuzzy and having difficulty concentrating and writing at the same time. The Surgeon came and went and a Clinical Oncologist talked about Radiation, Linear Excellerate machines (?), Computers, Complementary therapies and all the other hi-tech equipment now used in treatments.

'Complementary therapies?'

Did I hear correctly?

Yes, the new Hammer Centre will incorporate this dreaded 'feminine' approach.

(*Brill.*)

No so brill was the information that by the end of the century there will be 1,000,000 women with Breast cancer, world wide.

(*How do they know this?*)

It was just as woolly trying to get a definition of 'Cure' from the panel. Some gave a rigid definition: 'If life expectancy is the same as someone who has never had cancer'. Others said that if it hadn't returned within a specific time (usually five years) then the term cured could be used.

(*Five years here I come-ish.*)

'But,' I heard them say 'with Breast cancer one can never say you are cured'.

(*Great*)

But is this just (just?) the Orthodox medical opinion??? As my second-opinion doctor stated, I had to get myself into the group of women who had a far better *chance* of surviving; he said nothing of survival.

(*Shit. I'm too tired to think about this.*)

The Chaplain dragged my mood off the floor by being so alive and sincere.

'You don't need to have a Religion to have Spiritual needs,' he declared.

Everyone needs to have worth and meaning in their lives.
  (*Yes*)

Everyone needs love, support, care and interdependency.
  (*Yes*)

Everyone needs to be an individual and have the freedom to create choice and privacy.
  (*Yes*)

But??
  But, illness threatens these.
  'I am Contingent' (dependent upon an uncertain event or circumstances that may or may not occur).

HELP!!!!

Help, indeed.
  It would have all been so much easier, I silently pondered.
  (*He just wasn't able. That's all there is to it.*)

I was descending into a morose and depleted state simply by being Me. I'd had so much practice this year it was now second nature. After this conference at least I know it's politically correct to 'suffer'.
  (*Have I ever needed an excuse?*)

300

If I was finding it difficult to cope with all the information I'd heard at the conference I certainly couldn't cope with the next item.

A woman and her husband were to talk about the role of the carer and the importance of love and support.

Sorry, this is too close for comfort.

I left.

1½ hours later I entered the house.

Ellis greeted me warmly, as if I'd been away for months.

(. . . *and he'd missed me.*)

"You look tired. Did you have a nice conference? Would you like a cup of tea?"

The warmth and concern accompanying the questions only increased my spiralling emotions.

What was he playing at?

I want you out of the house, but would you like a cup of tea.

It was bizarre.

I couldn't cope.

I went to my room.

The tea arrived.

"I'll be leaving in half an hour to play Poker, is that alright?"

(*Grunt*)

"I've got a feeling you don't like me playing Poker so often?"

(*Grunt*)

"Would you prefer me to stay at home with you?"

"Actually I don't even want to be under the same roof as you, let alone in the same room. Fuck off," I spat, feeling a well of emotion and fear and dread and panic rising to a crescendo as he crept from the room.

The floodgate of misery opened as I heard the front door close, and I started to sob in the manner to which I was becoming accustomed.

Loudly and violently.

For hours.

The next day, Sunday, I had an early appointment with Trish.

She wired me up for a Mega-Calm-Down, then attacked my feet.

The sinus and eye reflex points reacted badly to her gentle (-ish) prods.

I have been crying rather a lot, I reminded her, when she queried the reaction.

I returned to the house to prepare my escape for the rest of the day.

Coward?

Yes.

Me and my emotions had had enough. We wanted a day off.

Too late.

For whatever reason, Ellis had arrived back at the house at least six hours before he normally deigned to appear.

A note on my bed said we had to talk.

(*Oh, no!*)

Before I could escape, he appeared.

"Darling, we must talk."

(*Darling?*)

"There is nothing to say. I'm going out," I said quietly, edging towards the door.

"We must talk. What have I done wrong?" he asked with great sincerity.

"Wrong? Wrong?" I screamed, working my anger into a fire ball which had been smouldering for two years ... and maybe longer?

I ranted, I raged, I voiced my indignation ...

(*Ignatia?*)

... about his treatment, his coldness, his inability to care ...

At first he denied hurting me but, slowly, after I listed the side effects of his actions, he had to admit that he had been a bit hasty.

(*Bit hasty!*)

His explanation was that I had appeared so positive and well on my return from Tyringham that, instead of an inch he had taken a mile.

(*500 miles?*)

Can he put it right, please?

"I won't let you down again," he boldly insisted, where no man, called Ellis, should ever dare to insist.

Too late.

I knew he was intellectually capable of saying things which he and I knew he was incapable of emotionally carrying out.

His two personas, or however many there are, cannot meet.

He accepted my analysis of the situation with reluctant grace, then made me a cup of tea.

He also offered to take the house off the market.

Too late.

I had to get away from him as soon as I could for my

health's sake. But it felt like driving a car over a cliff. For the moment there was momentum, but only just.

I felt a wreck, but I didn't want to become one.

I continued to lose weight.

My breast became hot.

The lymph glands ached.

Now, I was worried.

The producer rang to tell me that the proposed programme on Autogenics was not going to happen. The project had to be finished by the first week in December, giving neither of us a fair hearing as the course continued until late December. However, would I be interested in a programme on my attitudes and approach to cancer?

(*Silly question.*)

YES!

We exchanged phone numbers and agreed to contact each other in January 1994.

Would it happen?

Time would tell, but for the moment I felt 'interesting'; a sensation that had long ago been buried.

The Autogenics evening arrived.

Ten individuals all eying each other across a plush Harley Street sitting room.

Introductions:

"Hi, I'm Jenny. I've got cancer. I can cope with the cancer, it's life that I'm having difficulty with."

Puzzled, or was that embarrassed (?), looks from my fellow Autogenicees indicated to me that they had no real idea of what I was feeling; and why should they?

How would I have reacted to such a statement before I'd lived through the reality of the concept?

No doubt I too would have looked puzzled and embarrassed.

When we finally got down to the training part of the session I felt vaguely conned.

For the best part of a year I had been talking to every part of my body for half an hour a day. So I naturally found it frustrating having to concentrate on saying, 'my right arm is heavy' three times, for the rest of the evening . . . and that some people had difficulty in coping with the task.

For homework we had to attempt this task at least three times a day and write in our little red books what we had experienced whilst doing it.

Bor-ring.

Almost immediately I realised that I was in danger of becoming lopsided, so rushed ahead of the training and proceeded to chant on behalf of both my arms.

I still found it boring and hoped that the sessions would improve, otherwise I could see myself cutting short the course. How Ellis had found the whole procedure interesting was a mystery to me; he was usually totally intolerant to anything approaching hot air. On the contrary, he had so much faith in the technique, that he offered to miss his Poker night in order to be there for me when I returned home. He had, he confessed, felt 'strange' after his first session.

(*How can he tell?*)

All I can assume is that my intensity of personal probing had made me immune to this gentler approach, whereas for someone who kept the lid on his emotions it could be a powerful catalyst. Certainly the reactions within the group surprised me by their diversity.

I would continue even if it was only for the benefit of my immune system.

(*Only?*)

I continued with my house and past clearance campaign. Out went 35-year-old school reports and lesson plans for Psychology and Literature courses I'd taught at Holloway Prison. By now the data would be out of date and besides I couldn't understand most of what I had written all those years ago, so how could I ever attempt to teach it?

What useless rubbish we carry around with us for years and never miss it when it's gone. If only the end of a relationship could be that simple.

But it's not.

"1514"

"Hallo, this is Janet."

"Janet?"

"Ellis's wife."

(*Shit!*)

The shock (mark two) was, why was she ringing me?

The shock (mark one) had been discovering that he still had a wife; that fact only coming to light after we had moved in together.

Back to shock (mark two)

"How are you feeling?" said a concerned voice.

(*Possibly of many years training*)

I promptly burst into tears and allowed her to talk me through the strangeness that is Ellis.

"You must not think it is anything to do with you," she insisted.

(*Blub*)

"He's been like that for at least thirty years."

(*Blub, Blub*)

"You must get out and away from him as quickly as possible, for your own good."

(*Blub, Blub, Blub*)

Relating the various incidents and predilections of his behaviour to each other I realised that they were completely interchangeable. If I started a sentence she could complete it and all of what she had to say could have been scripted by me.

The shock and relief (and anger) that spread through my brain both confused and clarified my situation.

It really hadn't been 'my fault'. I was merely the last (but not least) of a string of humans Ellis had magically empowered with the ability to 'give him peace'. The minute he felt 'not at peace' was the death knell of his gift of empowerment to that individual; and they were to blame, as their unknown magical abilities had failed.

I hadn't stood a chance.

What also didn't stand a chance were my nerves. House hunters trooped through the shell in which I resided and looked at Exhibit A (Waffles) and Exhibit B (Me). Neither of us moved from our bed, and glared in various degrees of pathos at strangers, who had no idea of the behind-the-scenes drama, with a capital D.

Ellis also required me to sign some legal papers relinquishing all rights to the house.

"It appears I'd have had more rights if I'd been your tenant," I icily informed him, when I reappeared from the Dickensian establishment.

He said nothing.

By the time I was next due to visit Iro my liver was unbalanced, indicating anger.

(*No, really?*)

I told him of my outburst after taking the Ignatia powder.

"Good, better to get your sorrow out than to keep it in," he said, quietly, almost starting me off again.

I had been quite dizzy after our first Acupuncture session,

so he decided to work at a much slower pace until my body had regained some of its strength. After a few more weeks of the Herbs, I should be ready for anything.

He massaged my feet and legs along the liver and spleen Meridians, which felt as if they were bruised. Then he prodded needles into a soft bit, just below my knees, and at various other locations lower down the pain threshold.

Then he formed a little cone of moxa, a substance made from dried fibres, on each needle and set light to them.

I'd had moxa used on me before, but it is a little disconcerting to have the Acupuncturist standing, ready with pliers, in case they became too hot.

But, I survived. The needles in my flesh did get hot, but only one gave me any cause to object. The room smelt powerful.

I lay back and thought of pleasant things, which I had to admit was getting more and more difficult as time went by.

Suddenly . . .

"Could this cause me to feel emotional?" I blurted out.

"Yes."

"Good, because I am," I declared, as gentle tears ran slowly down my cheeks and into my ears.

I had not been feeling particularly sad, or fragile, until he made me into a human pin cushion.

Wow, this was powerful.

When I sat up at the end of the session, the tears that had accumulated in my ears, continued their journey and slowly rolled down my neck.

It was just what I needed.

I started to giggle.

November 5th. It's funny how certain dates hold a memory. To me Bonfire Night is a symbol of how my life in the house disintegrated into ashes.

On our first November 5th in the house Ellis was in

America on business. The flat roof of the house gave me a ringside view of the firework display in our local park. It was cold and wearing Ellis's sheepskin coat (wolf's clothing?) I felt the night was magical.

It was all over by the time Ellis returned a week later.

The following year I was rapidly losing my grip on reality, as everything was gathering pace in and around me.

The cancer was eating into me.

By the next year it was all over, but I had doubts if it had ever really started.

*****

I stood in splendour way on high
and gently whispered to the sky,
that flashed and sparked and brightly flared:
"I'm loved"
That inner peace, so rare for me
was now proclaimed for all to see:
He wanted *me*.

I walked in silence looking high
and quietly pleaded with the sky.
Explain to me, please tell me why;
I fear.
The cancerous hurt that grew all year
raged through my hopes; and with a tear
you 'left'.

I lay in torment looking high
and loudly screamed up to the sky
with body crushed by hardened pain:
"Why *me* again?"

So, like your pledge of little worth
these rockets too will crash to earth.

The sky is quiet, and I'm alone.

****

Alone, except when Ellis returned to the house and insisted on making me cups of tea.

This time he brought me a herbal 'natural aid to peaceful relaxation' and a cup of tea, and, he took me shopping.

I found it very difficult to cope with him trying to be helpful. It all seemed so false, yet it probably wasn't.

I felt as if there was double glazing between me and the rest of my life. I could see it unfolding before my eyes, yet I couldn't hear or experience anything.

On my side of the glass I experience everything in glorious technicolour but I am detached from the other side.

Will the two sides meet?

And will they agree?

Partly out of necessity to explore potential earning skills and partly for my own rehabilitation I enrolled in an Australasian Flower Essence course for the weekend.

The original course which had gained my interest, had failed even to begin, so I was determined to at least get a taste of something. I tasted, and entered a world strange even to me after all my 'journeys' over the past year.

I knew there was a good (bad?) possibility that I would bump into Robert, but I was determined that he would neither affect nor inhibit my life any more than he had already.

I saw him before he saw me.

Putting away my coat I silently went through the pyramid procedure that Paola had taught me. I felt like the character in 'Soap', who firmly believed he was invisible after he had performed a series of movements.

It worked.

I stepped into the main room and beamed at Robert, and

continued to be pleasant whenever our energy fields came near to colliding.

I felt powerful and in control.

He could never harm me ever again.

Back to the Workshop.

What is a Flower Essence?

Good question.

I knew of the Bach flower remedies but hadn't paid much attention to them except for the 'Rescue Remedy', which had proved invaluable in times of sudden shock.

I listened to phrases such as Life Force/Vibrational quality of the plant/Core essence/Subtle spirit/the resonating energy of nature, all attempting to describe Flower Essences.

Was this too subtle and ethereal for me?

And the names of the flowers!

No room for daisy or rose or carnation in Australia. The land of the macho man produced plants with names like Cowkicks, Red and Green Kangaroo Paw, Wallflower Donkey Orchid, Cats Paw and Pink Fairy Orchid.

(*Ooh, nice!*)

The theory and practice behind the administration of the Essences is that every flower has its own healing properties. By identifying a person's needs and matching it with one of the flowers, then a much deeper healing can take place.

Deeper healing?

Yes, it is not enough to heal just the physical body, Western minds demand the quick fix, then carry with them the remnants of the original trauma. A whiplash injury once healed, even by Osteopathy, can still leave the individual 'waiting' for the next crunch. The original pain of whiplash was useful but when it becomes 'locked in' the unconscious tension can debilitate the person's life. This unnecessary message can be turned off by a Flower Essence.

(*I think I'm still with the theory?*)

311

At the same time, our bodies have become wrecked by the over-use of orthodox drugs such as antibiotics and inoculations.

(*How many times have I heard that?*)

Life styles, repeated patterns of behaviour, fears and desires can all lead us to develop major illnesses, which would require a deeper understanding of the problem for it to be totally eliminated.

(*This was getting too close.*)

It became clearer (I think) when some of the definitions of the healing properties were put into context.

For example: the Menzies Banksia was 'for someone who has been rejected in a relationship, and who fears being hurt again (*and again and again* ...), but longs for companionship. The symptoms show a fear of repeating the pain, so there is an inability to move on.

(*So why do I leap where others refuse to move?*)

The flower will help them let go of the past pain and allow them to move on with courage.'

(*I think I need an enforcable-cynisism Flower Essence*)

On a physical level it will also relieve built up pain in muscles and soft tissue when applied directly to the area.

Macrozamia: 'For those who attract the wrong sort of person and become sexually abused. This 'freezes' them and damages their feelings of self worth and ability to trust another sexually and emotionally. It is good for all female problems, whether it be childbirth or Menopause, as it aims to balance the Yin/Yang element of the person. It is also beneficial to rape victims, who may either shut down their femininity or over emphasise it.'

I was fast coming to the conclusion that what I really needed in life was to prepare a huge bath of all the Flower Essences and lie in it for a few years. At least I would have little chance of meeting (or choosing) more of these destroyers of my equilibrium.

(*Unless he was a plumber!*)

I was genuinely bowled over by the course; it all seemed to make sense and added another dimension to my ever growing understanding of Me and how I had controlled, or not controlled, elements of my life. I bought the starter pack and raced home to prepare a mix of: Macrozamia (Nuff said), Menzies Banksia (Nuff said-mark two), Brown Boronia: 'For those who have pressing problems but find life holds no immediate solutions.'

Purple Flag Flower: 'For people who are near a nervous breakdown and who feel there's no one around who is really aware of their mental state.'

Cats Paw: 'For people who care about other people only to find that those they give to don't really care for them. Their reaction becomes one of anger and sadness that the one they love cannot give in return.

But, by suppressing their anger it becomes manifested in the physical body, and reappears as an *inflammatory* type disease.'

(*Double Whammy Wow!*)

I started taking the drops, willing myself to believe that something would happen to me . . . that was positive.

I was over-tired and excited by the day and all that I'd heard, and did not manage to sleep until quite late.

Consequently I was drained and exhausted even before I arrived for the second day of the course.

Why had I thought I could last two days when I could hardly concentrate for two hours?

Everything became fuzzy and I was forced to lie down, and then to leave for home before the end of the course; but not before I'd enrolled in a correspondence course.

I still did not know if I believed, or could believe, in these 'Homeopathic' style essences, but it might be fun finding out.

Meanwhile, the Autogenic session warmed up and became almost enjoyable. The amusement was based on the exper-

313

ience related by one of the group when confronted by the family ghost on a dark and windy night, while doing Autogenics. The quick repartee from the group helped to gel us in a way that had not previously been possible. Anger was discussed for the first time. Someone confessed that they frequently felt very angry.

"Do you try to control your anger?" enquired Vera, who was leading the group.

"No, I pour yoghurt over my brother's head at break-fast," was the reasoned reply.

(*Alas poor yoghurt, I knew him well, I thought to myself*)

With five minutes of the official session left it was decided to do some work on Anger.

With panic and anger rising, I suggested that it was perhaps far too important a topic to cram into the final stages of the evening.

"It will only take 5 mins."

(*5 mins for anger!*)

Too late. A document entitled 'Intentional Verbalisation of Anger' was handed out.

The (imaginary) task was to sit someone in a chair and throw every conceivable (real life) abuse at them until all the anger had dissipated.

(*Repeat four times a day until the symptoms desist.*)

I could not get my head around this task as I had no problem at screaming abuse at an empty chair, or even a full one. My problem is that it doesn't achieve anything except make me frazzled.

There had to be another way . . . for me.

But to be fair, the technique can work for those who need it. I had to be aware that I was both in tune with my problems and consumed by them at the same time.

Twenty minutes later! . . . I'm angry.

I left, followed in hot pursuit by a fellow North Londoner, in need of a lift.

For homework I sat a very nice lady in a chair and yelled

at her . . . I just felt guilt, as she really wasn't the cause of my distress.

I had bought a new book I'd read about in a local paper and heard about on the radio: 'Why men hate women' by Adam Jukes. Good title, Good title.

It was too academic for my battered brain cells but some of what I took in was accurate and frightening, especially . . .

' . . . Such men cannot tolerate the risk of getting close— at the first sign of frustration of his fantasy his feelings will die.'

I could not finish the book, as it deepened my despair of man'kind'.

My fantasy-frustrated man returned to the house in time to meet some prospective buyers.

"I know you, didn't you go to Hornsey College of Art in the Sixties?" I blurted out to the male partner of the duo.

"I certainly did."

We talked of the strange old days and how we had diversified our skills over the years.

I'd diversified so much I no longer had any!

I'd also taken some more Ignatia powder and was ready for the fallout.

We had to have another 'chat'. I was finding it difficult to accept Ellis's presence in the house considering he had wanted so urgently to get away from me.

I could no longer risk feeling calm and peaceful in his company, as I had to protect myself.

My rage therefore took a cold and calculating turn, with a touch of contempt. But I didn't scream or lose my temper, I merely told him that it would be easier for me if he actually moved out as he had said he would.

Wasn't this what it was all about?

He had in fact found a flat and promised to be gone by December 4th.

How did I feel about that?

Mixed.

He left for Poker . . . then I felt alone. I carried out every method I could think of to alleviate the pain of isolation and abandonment I was feeling: Visualisation, breathing exercises, vapourisers full of calming essential oils and Autogenics.

The peace I felt whilst doing the Autogenic routine was so strong I suddenly found myself weeping with the experience of feeling so good.

Come on Cole, pull yourself together, you cannot go on like this!

It was true.

I could not remember crying and weeping so much ever before in my whole life. If I'd been a Central Heating System I would have had several plumbers around to investigate the constant leakage.

It was not funny.

It was not even therapeutic.

Or was it?

I knew that something had to happen to alter my approach to all this, or to alter Ellis's approach to me.

I really didn't care which came first.

I needed peace.

Fast.

Meanwhile I had another letter from the 'interested publisher.' He was "impressed", thought the "black humour was attractive" and all in all found the whole script "compelling reading."

Okay, so what does that *mean*?

Action.

"Thank you for your interest and praise. If you want to publish, then great, let me know and re-writes can begin. If you don't want to publish then thank you for your time and effort but please just send back the typescript and I will try elsewhere."

Bold?

No, I just needed to know where I stood. I can take rejection but it's the grey areas I find so hard to tolerate.

Trish and I drove to South Ruislip for my second PIP scan.

The results were incredible!

The tumour had noticeably shrunk in the four weeks since the last scan, and my liver, gall bladder and lymph glands had all calmed down indicating that the toxins were leaving the body.

Everyone was pleased.

I felt great.

Trish felt great.

Wait for it . . .

Trish and I returned to the car.

I put the ignition key in the lock, turned it and was left with the plastic handle part in my hand and the main shaft in the lock.

I knew the day had to have at least one hassle just to keep me on my toes.

(*Or feet, if the car wouldn't start.*)

I rang the AA.
We waited.

It got cold.
We waited.

It got colder.
And dark.

It started snowing.
I rang again.

They had not been able to locate the car at the address I'd given them!

I used the cancer card.

By this time both Trish and I were frozen, as the wintery night worsened. I felt justified in applying a bit of pressure.

"Someone will be with you within the hour; I will make you a priority," I was informed.

I phoned Ellis to let him know what was happening, then retraced my steps to the car.

Trish for some reason wanted to play 'I spy'.

I was not in the mood.

After an hour and a quarter we gave up the frozen wait.

Ellis insisted that we got a taxi and personally set about dealing with the AA.

Brilliant.

Rush hour from Ruislip to Muswell Hill is not funny, especially as I then had to stay awake for the arrival of the AA truck bringing home my car, and then the locksmith sent by the AA.

He arrived at 11 p.m.

Ellis, thankfully, took over when he arrived home a few minutes later.

I crashed out in bed, cold and weary but so grateful that Ellis had been around to take control of the situation.

The relief of having someone else to organise the recovery of my car was superb, the fact that it was Ellis was a poignant reminder that he (once) was a caring man.

However, the fact remained that he could only show his care by dealing with inanimate objects, never humans.

(*Nasty, messy, emotional things!*)

It was all so confusing.

But "Thank you. Thank you. Thank you."

My exhaustion had given me a good night's sleep.

I now had to face Glen and Professor Taylor again, at the UCH.

I had already informed Ellis that I did not want him to accompany me to the hospital because I thought it inappropriate. After yesterday's help I felt somewhat mean, but I stuck to my decision.

Clutching my PIP scans, both past and present, I confidently entered enemy territory.

"Wonderful," they both said on feeling the breast that was softening by the day.

"Ta."

"Now, are you ready for a Mastectomy?"

(*They do keep on!*)

I showed them the PIP scans.

"Very interesting," they said.

(*Yawn, yawn*)

"Are you going to have a Mastectomy?" he repeated.

"I'd prefer it if I didn't . . . no . . . correction I'll be more definite. You are *not* going to give me a Mastectomy!" I said defiantly.

"Then we won't," said Glen.

(*I love you.*)

319

I left relieved, with my breast reprieved, and an appointment for three months time.

Dorothy beamed at me. "You're doing fine."

If only my emotional state was 'doing fine'.

I thought I knew what Ellis and I had agreed regarding my removal to a flat. This belief was based on our conversation in the park and all in all I thought he was being understanding of my vulnerability. As he would be advancing me a fair amount of money I naturally agreed that a legal document be drawn up outlining the proposal. I was even more impressed when he stated that he wanted a solicitor of my choice to view the document, so that I was fully aware of the arrangement. At least he was doing all this for me. I had to be thankful for that.

Peace.

Wait for it . . .

A phone call from a solicitor friend who had been sent the document ended all that.

"Don't sign it!!!!!" she insisted.

"What? Why?" I said, confused.

"I think you need to sit down with Ellis and talk very seriously about this. It's nothing like you imagined it to be," she advised.

"There has to be some mistake, I know what he wants for me," I insisted.

(*Have I ever?*)

Ellis returned to the house and whilst I was preparing some food I opened up the topic of conversation.

"Nina phoned. She's a little bit worried about the wording of the contract. She's advised me not to sign," I blurted out.

"I wasn't particularly happy with it either," he admitted.

(*Whew!*)

320

"Let's discuss what we both think is happening and go from there," he suggested.

(*Great*)

Wait for it . . .

"Well, I thought the arrangement was . . . "

"What made you think I was going to do that?" he spat out.

"In the park you said . . . "

"I don't legally owe you anything," he thundered.

"What about morally?" I managed to say.

"It's not my fault the relationship has ended."

(*What!!!!*)

From then on the conversation slipped into two enemy camps. My side, sickly and ill-equipped, did not stand a chance.

I was being thrown out of his life, but effectively he would have control over mine for ever . . . or until I died.

(*Whichever came sooner!*)

I could not compute the information, but his cold presentation of the facts and his businesslike manner were more than I could take.

For a split second, I think I was quite capable of killing him . . . but my anger went inside, and all *I* wanted to do was die.

I felt so alone.

I was alone.

A new set of conditions are faxed to my solicitor.

It took me two days to steady myself enough to ask Ellis if I could see a copy.

I reasoned with him.

"If I can see something on paper, I'll know what is being offered, and hopefully there won't be any more misunderstandings," I said calmly.

Wait for it . . .

One of the conditions was that if I had a partner then Ellis would have to be reimbursed fully for all his outlay.

"What!!!" I exploded. "How dare you try to control my private life as well as everything else. If I'm crazy enough to want another relationship, then that is nothing to do with you."

I was seething and furious and distraught . . . again.

The breast started to get hot.

Shit.

I wrote a reply to his conditions, putting one or two down for myself.

It was a classic textbook acrimonious war of words.

I hated it.

I had no power.

All I could do was wait and see what would happen.

I'd lost control.

Charles rang. It was an awkward time as I could barely speak without crying and with Ellis in the house I found it impossible to say what I wanted, or needed, to say.

Charles had rung previously to tell me that for personal reasons he had made a pledge not to socialise for three months, but that it did not include me if I was really in need.

I filed the information and forgot it.

He rang several more times to reiterate that if at any time I needed him, he would be available.

I filed the information and forgot it.

Now he was on the phone again.
    "How are things?" he started.
    "Terrible."
    "Do you want to talk about it?"
    "No."
    "There must be something I can do?"
    "Can I see you?" I whispered in a tiny voice, praying that he would not turn me down.
    "Tomorrow, my flat, 4.30 p.m."
    "Thanks. But, if there is something more important that comes up, you can cancel."
    "You are the important issue. I won't cancel," he assured me.

I arrived at his flat, and with no worry of rejection, burst into tears.
    He did his soft-peopley thing on me, and I began to relax.
    I had brought with me my strange paintings and I talked him through the right side of my brain.

We talked for hours.

I relaxed even more.

It felt unfamiliar to be appreciated.

I felt slightly embarrassed.

Back to the House of Ellis.

All was quiet.

He was out.

I had told Ellis about the state of my breast and its surrounds and how both Trish and Iro were working to calm the whole area.

He said he had information stating that Tamixofen can cause the affected cancer area to become agitated ... and ... that it can also cause mood swings.

"It's stress," I mumbled.

"But you've been under terrible stress all year with cancer and look how well you've done," he insisted.

"It's stress."

"I'm being sent the relevant research that will prove to you that it's the drug that is causing you to be unreasonable."

"It's stress."

(*Stale mate—in more ways than one.*)

If he wanted to believe that my bouts of screaming, tears and silence was due to a drug, then let him. But why, I thought to myself, is he the only one I need to be screaming, tearful or silent to?

People still trooped through the house.

As I was talking to one of the Estate Agents upstairs, a terrible commotion could be heard downstairs.

"Good heavens, what's that?" said the startled Estate Agent.

"Sounds to me ... as if someone's trodden in the cat tray ... "

Just then a terrified Waffles, with bushy tail, streaks past us and heads under a bed.

". . . and by the looks of it Waffles was sitting in it at the time!"

True enough, the tray and its contents were all over the room. It took some time to get it back to normal.

It took even longer for Waffles to return to what passes for her as normality.

I think they bought the house.

I hope they give the house the happiness it deserves; but, fingers crossed. I had heard that the road was notorious for its separating couples. Way above the local average!

(*Not an excuse for Ellis, but maybe a contributing factor?*)

Ellis was finally preparing to move out, and as he did so, handed me a list of all the times he would be staying at the house (!).

What?

He wanted me to know that he was available and on hand if I needed him.

I looked at the list.

At first glance it appeared that he would be in the house more often now that he wasn't living there, than when he was.

(*Nowt as queer as folk.*)

Iro hotted up the treatment by plugging me into the mains.

Well, actually he attached electrodes to the needles and then plugged me into something or other.

As the needles, and my flesh, pulsated with the current he left me alone for a while.

(*To stew?*)

To occupy my mind, or to be more precise, to blank out what was being done to me, I started to do some Autogenics.

I kept on doing Autogenics until he returned.

He took my pulses.

"What have you been up to?" he demanded.

"Nothing," I hurriedly and guiltily replied.

I didn't know what I was supposed to have done but in the best South London tradition I denied everything.

(*Denied everything? Now that's an interesting theory.*)

"You've done something to calm your pulses," he insisted.

"Okay, I confess. I've concentrated on Autogenics."

"Fabulous," he said re-checking my pulses. "Fabulous."

I now had concrete proof that this apparently uneventful procedure actually does something.

I also showed him the PIP scans. He was so delighted by the progress shown that he gave me a long hug, professionally of course.

The next day Ellis moved out.

At least I think he did?

Most of his clothes, and all of the boxes he hadn't unpacked when they were brought to the house, remained.

I disappeared to meet two of my northern friends for a lunchtime drink . . . at a pub only a mile away from where Ellis said he would be living.

He never did tell me exactly where he'd moved to, and I couldn't be bothered to ask but suspected that he had merely returned to live with his mother.

I returned to find a letter from the publisher.

Heart pounding I ripped open the envelope.

It was from his secretary informing me that 'boss man' would be contacting me when he returned next week from a conference.

Do I get excited by this?

What did it mean?

If he really had no intention of publishing surely he could have asked his secretary simply to return the typescript?

How do I know how publishers' brains work?

I would just have to wait.

I had booked myself into a Workshop by Matthew Manning at the 'Healing Arts Festival' but before I indulged in the marathon of attempting to keep awake for five hours, I planned to have my Kirlian photograph taken again.

I took with me the Kirlian photograph taken in May, but was not going to produce it until I had heard what they thought about this latest one.

I looked with relief and interest at the new prints: two very black and balanced hands.

(*Well, they were black.*)

The female doing my consultation was intrigued by the print, but kept asking questions to verify her statements.

"Not telling you," I sweetly smiled at her.

"Why not?"

"I'll let you know when I think it's appropriate," I declared.

She sighed.

" . . . Okay, your left hand shows your feminine intuition; there is plenty of potential to develop what you're doing. What are you doing?"

I grin.

" . . . You need to gather your energy together with . . . creativity . . . ? creativity? . . . er . . . writing?"

I grin.

" . . . You have leadership and organisational ability . . . There has been a lot of abuse of my femininity by the masculine . . . I need to let go of my emotions . . . Decisions are needed, but I need to weigh up the pros and cons then go with my intuition . . . Tension in the pelvis area, you need to let go."

"How am I doing so far?" she begged.

I produced the May print from my bag.

"Wow!"

"Quite"

"But your left hand had completely disappeared," she gasped in amazement as she looked from print to print.

The interesting thing for me was that although the left hand had reappeared, two of the fingers on the right hand had vanished. These had indicated my ability to organise myself, so how had they gone? The only reason I could think of was that as it was very soon after the Ellis trauma, when I was still scattered and extremely disorientated.

On to the Matthew Manning Workshop.

Five hours!

He started with a short history of Healing and its legal ramifications. In some Continental countries it is illegal to Heal, as is the case in the States: this is why Healers become attached to a church, and why so many of the more razzamataz American Healers are referred to as 'Reverend'

(*I'd always wondered.*)

There are three important aspects to Healing: intentionality, ie, you must know why you are doing it; motivation in the interest of the client and it is important to have a willingness and an ability to confront yourself.

A negative Aura will 'let in' bad vibes. He demonstrated a similar Affirmation that Jane and Declan had shown me. Asking for a volunteer he got them to think anger/hurt/negativity then gently pushed down their outstretched arm. Think positivity/peace/love he ordered and was unable to shift the outstretched rod of steel.

We should complement each other more: this is Healing.

I remember my mother's edict. "If you can't say something nice about someone, then don't say anything."

(*I'll just throw my manuscript away!*)

Individuals need, he continued, strong support from
friends and lovers, laughter, and positive and negative
strokes.

Positive and negative strokes?

Yes, negative strokes are preferable to nothing, which
explains a Yobbo's need for society's chastisement in
preference to a life of nothingness.

Sounds reasonable to me.

We then had to find a partner, somone we had not come in
with. The group fragmented with some individuals zooming
in on others while others zoomed in on themselves.

Matthew laughed. "You English."

Taking turns to be 'it' one of us had to stand still and
concentrate on either positive or negative thoughts without
informing anyone of their choice. The second person then
had to walk towards them with their eyes closed and hands
held upright in front of them and stop when, and if, they felt
anything preventing their continued progress. The thought
process was then reversed and the observing person had to
repeat the task.

In my partnership we discovered that while either of us
were thinking negative thoughts the other felt a 'wall' a few
feet away from the person, but were on collision course
when the thoughts were positive.

Other couples found the reverse.

"Both are okay," said Matthew.

Onwards and upwards.

A new partner.

329

This time while one remained quiet and listened, the other had to list all their positive attributes.

No problem there.

"Then," said Matthew, "I want you to tell your partner everything that you despise about yourself, your faults, and the worst thing you've ever done. It has to be something that you've never told anyone about before."

He then watched as gasps of horror circulated the hall, and people headed for the door.

"Sorry, what I also meant to tell you is that this time you only THINK these things."

Relief does have a communal atmosphere!

When it was my turn to think all the ugly thoughts I could possibly muster (it wasn't a problem), I had a young French woman holding on to my hands and giving me positive waves of love and encouragement. Halfway through my silent diatribe against Ellis (who else) I stopped suddenly and thought: "Why am I doing this? Why am I feeling like this? It is me that is getting eaten up with rage, nobody else."

There seemed to be no point in prolonging those feelings and I felt myself relax for the first time in months.

The feedback from my partner was that at first she had 'seen' red flowing from me and an extremely strong pressure building up. . . . until . . . it suddenly vanished, and purple and green stripes took over.

(*Purple and green?*)

Matthew then wanted to demonstrate his technique of Healing and asked for a volunteer who had a stiff neck, or creaky knees or something that could be seen to have improved. After various demonstrations by individuals of their unhappy limbs, he came to me. I had already spoken with him privately regarding the cancer, so when I said that

I had difficulty in raising my left arm he needed to know if it was related to the subject we'd discussed.

He thought for a moment, asked a few more people to show the limitation of their bodies, and returned to me.

I sat facing the mass of faces.

"Is there a doctor in the house?" he quizzed.

No, but there was a physiotherapist.

"Why do you think her arm is unable to raise itself above the shoulder line?"

"Oh, permanent damage to the nerves and muscle," came the reply.

(*Cheek!*)

I assured him and her that there had been improvement already on the movement I'd had in September, so as far as I was concerned this was a temporary problem.

(*Grrr*)

I gave a 'before' demonstration of the shoulder's limitation, and waited.

He started his favourite Vangelis track of '1492', and began.

I closed my eyes and he asked everyone to send me positive vibes of healing.

I felt his hands around my shoulder area. No pressure, no manipulation, just the gentle touch of warm hands.

But not for long.

The heat generated by his hands reached deep into the shoulder and it felt as if someone was scraping away built-up deposits from the bone.

This, coupled with the extraordinary sensation of feeling multiple healing coming from all directions, was powerful stuff.

The pain and heat increased to the point where I felt like asking him to stop. Then, cool waves of calm travelled through the area, and the session ended.

Wow!

Before I could say anything Matthew described what he 'saw': red and orange leaves were falling from a tree and as he progressed with the Healing they began to fall more rapidly until the ground was covered with them. Gentle waves slowly washed the leaves away.

He then concentrated on a shore line and cool water until the whole area had become calm.

Wow!

The proof of the pudding etc . . . I raised my arm. It went higher and higher, without pain or restriction.

Wow!

Gasps all round.

Of course, he explained, this does not mean to say that I had been healed completely; normally he would have to see someone for several sessions before it could be called permanent.

If only.

This ended the Workshop and as I gathered my things together to leave many people came up to me to give me their own remedies and suggestions.

I was touched by their concern and I was touched by care; I had been changed by the experience.

The next day I wrote Ellis a long letter apologising for screaming at him, but explaining the fears and worries that had pitched me so high up the panic scale.

It was simple process of cause and effect; the more I screamed the more he froze, the more he froze the more I screamed. One of us had to break the cycle and it might as well be me.

A simple note, left on the stairs, thanked me for my letter; it had helped.

The solar plexus was the centre of our attention this week in Autogenics. At least we were now stringing together all the different bits and could start to see the whole.

(*Very impatient us Ariens.*)

Ellis phoned the next day and, to be helpful, I started to cry immediately! Might as well start as I know I'll end up!

"We must talk," he said.

"I know."

The meeting took place and the storm clouds drifted from their seemingly permanent place above the house. We were not out of the tempest, yet, but at least being on the edge we could see some sun, albeit watery.

(*From my eyes?*)

My breast area was still painful but beginning to calm down. I told Iro that I did not want him to put a needle into the epicentre of the discomfort, as psychologically I could not take it.

No problem. He listens.

Slowly and surely the discomfort in my breast diminishes, proving to me that I was right to let go of the situation.

Matthew had talked about Needs and Wants. I had used up so much energy in trying to hang on to something I wanted, but couldn't have.

I needed my health.

That was more important.

Trish and I attended a Homeopathic evening on 'Remedies for Christmas Ills', and found we were the only two present who weren't Homeopaths!

"What does Christmas mean to you?" we were all asked.

General worries about in-laws and over-indulgence came fast and furious.

I merely hoped there was a Homeopathic tablet marked 'Humbug' as I loathed and hated Christmas with all its falseness.

(*And alone-ness*)

(Silence)

We were told that a cold can be the same cold but it will affect people in different ways depending on their type.

After hearing about Aconite/Bryonia/Gelsemium Types we then found we had questions fired at us.

Questions like: "What type of person is this who . . . has a cold which starts off slowly then gets progressively worse. It doesn't improve with movement but does with pressure. The person is dull faced, has no energy, doesn't want to speak, wants to be left alone, is grumpy etc etc."

(*Sounds like a man to me!*)

"Err. Bryonia?"

Or, another scenario . . .

A child has eaten rich fatty food. It becomes clingy and demands cold drinks even though it is not thirsty. It gets wind, colic, diarrhoea and wants to vomit.

What would you give it?

(*A bucket?*)

"Umm . . . Pulsatilla?"

It was all done in good spirits and despite the poor attendance Trish and I enjoyed ourselves.

I just couldn't take the quick-fire round!

The run up to Christmas was the usual mix of approach/ avoidance. People approached and I avoided.

I couldn't take the frivolity, and even if I'd wanted to, I did not have the energy to participate in groups of drinking, happy people.

I was also finding it difficult to cope with Ellis's Jack-in-the-Box existence.

Now you see him, now you don't.

Despite the list of nights he said he would be staying in the house, I never knew when he would arrive, how long he'd stay or when he'd go.

We still had difficulty in holding a normal conversation and I was finding it very difficult to accept.

My temperature had risen alarmingly and most nights were spent awake or with disturbed dreams.

One day I was so drained I stayed in bed and read a 500 page novel in one go.

I had to slow down.

I realised also that I was beginning to avoid him.

I had to start living life for myself.

(*Thinks?*)

For a start I could pop down to another Greek restaurant. This one I had frequented for nearly ten years ... surely they had missed me?

"Hi, stranger, what's kept you away for so long?" one of the owners warmly enquired, as he allowed me to kiss his cheek.

"Oh, cancer, but I'm fine now," I reassured him.

"I've had a terrible day at work," he mumbled, as he got on with checking the reservations.

"I'm sorry to hear you've had a bad day ..." I started, but he was already heading for the kitchen.

I sat alone for a few more minutes, then left.

Heigh-ho, back to the drawing board.
Thinks!

In October a friend of a friend of an acquaintance (!) had given me his business card at the Wild Track.

"Give me a ring, we could go to a Jazz club in the City," he offered.

Why not, I thought.

I hunted for the card and taking a deep breath, rang.

"Hi, it's Jenny."

"Who?"

(*Good start!*)

I described the restaurant, the company, the card, the birthday boy . . . the cancer.

"Oh right, now I know who you are. Sorry about that."

"That's okay. If you had phoned and just said your name I wouldn't have recognised you either."

"That's a relief."

"Look do you still want that drink? If you don't, now is the time to back out, because I don't think I can face being messed around, especially now."

"No, let's meet next Monday. Can you come down to the City?"

"No problem."

"Right, see you at 6 p.m."

"Okay, and by the way in case you've forgotten what I look like I'll be the one wearing the wig!"

Monday came and I felt terrible. Aching and tired.

Should I cancel?

No, come on Cole, you've got to get out.

It will just be a pleasant interlude.

It took me one and a half hours to reach his office.

I informed the receptionist that I was waiting for Godot

and sat flicking through extremely boring financial magazines.

At 6.15 p.m. she said she would phone through to his office, as he may be on the phone and unaware of the time.

Wait for it . . .

Her body language said it all.
He had taken the day off work.
????? . . . !!!!!
I treated him to a 'Christmas Questionnaire a la Cole' whereby he could score one point for every correct answer and become the Bastard of the Year (runner-up).
I don't think he'd have much difficulty.
I retraced my steps home, surrounded by happy pre-Christmas groups, and collapsed back into my shell.
I won't come out again until all this is over.
I hear Ellis come in very late.
It's apparent to me that he returns to the house when it suits him and not, as suggested, to be of assistance to me.
He hangs around the next morning, then goes off to a meeting in town.
When the door closes I start to cry.

Autogenics for the last time. I have found it useful, despite the preambles at the start of each session. We were asked to choose a phrase that would be positive for us, and us alone. This was to be said at the end of each of our Autogenic Training sessions.
I thankfully replaced the 'I am at peace' phrase, which I'd refused to use under the Trade Description Act, with 'I'm in the process of positive change'.
If I say it often enough perhaps it will come true?

I'll try anything.

Vera wanted us to practice something else: "I want you to look in a mirror and say 'I love you'," she informed the horrified group. Consternation all round.

"You English!" she remarked, to the group which comprised a Jew, an Indian, a Greek, a Welsh (person) and a half Spaniard.

Can't do that!" many said . . . "It's too selfish and vain."

"I can," I suddenly announced. "I have no problem in saying I love you to myself. My problem is getting some other sod to say it, and mean it."

"Aah."

I was reminded of Eric Fromm's book 'Fear of Freedom', which I had read some years ago at one of the many crossroads of my life. In it he postulates that far from loving ourselves too much, we do not love ourselves enough. Why else would we drink too much, eat badly, take drugs, take risks, abuse our minds, gamble, etc, etc? We all devise systems to avoid, or block out, the things we find too hurtful or upsetting.

I rushed to my nearest bookshop and purchased a copy as a Christmas present for Ellis; the dedication hoped that he would eventually discover who he was, and why.

I wonder if he ever read it?

Phone call from Ellis.

"Christmas drink?" he enquired, cheerfully.

I didn't think there was anything to celebrate, and the thought of us (consciously) pretending that everything was alright, filled me with horror.

"Sorry, I'm out tonight."

(*True.*)

338

"That's a pity. I'll see you later on then, or in the morning."

(*Panic.*)

I could not face the prospect of seeing him so near to Christmas; too many tumbled memories would freeze any ability to remain human.

I had to get away.

I bundled Waffles into her basket, and descended on Jo.

"Can we become refugees for the night?" I pleaded.

"Yes. Why?"

"It's me being Me."

I went on my round trip of visits and returned to Jo and Waffs.

Both were amused by the events.

Waffles's brain could not quite understand what was happening. For Waffles, Jo's flat meant being abandoned by me; so what was I doing in the flat as well?

I slid into the spare room and placed a large pebble in the doorway to prevent the door from closing. This allowed easy access for any nocturnal wanderings that Waffles may need. It was rare for her to stray at all during the night, or day, but I wasn't taking any chances.

Little moo!

If she went out once, she went out, and in, twenty times an hour. On each occasion the door rebounded onto the pebble.

Thunk, thunk, thunkthunk . . . thunk.

Waffles!!!!

Another source of amusement, to her, was hurtling up and down Jo's long corridor and making a remarkable attempt at sounding like a herd of elephants.

Waffles!!!

The single bed was not big enough for both of us either, so eventually I gave up any idea of sleep, and went to make a cup of tea.

I must have dozed, for when I woke tired, drained and frazzled, she was peacefully asleep, looking as if butter wouldn't melt on her paw.

I think it would have been less of a problem to have faced Ellis!

I did not return to the house until after lunch time.

As soon as I saw the porch light was still on, I knew he had not in fact returned last night.

My unread note, explaining and apologising at the same time, lay untouched . . . the book lay unwrapped.

A message on the answerphone explained the traffic hold up on the M1 and his consequent absence.

All that hassle for nothing.

Waffles agreed.

What Ellis had managed to do was to have a note delivered wishing me a Happy Christmas, along with a 'present'.

I felt a real cow.

But, I still believe that was preferable to being a shrew.

Waffles remained a pussycat throughout.

Christmas Eve.

Almost over.

I went shopping early and stocked up on provisions for the siege that lay ahead.

Walking back home down the hill, I was trying unsuccessfully to prevent the ever-present emotion from surfacing and rolling down the hill with me.

I liked my own company, I liked being on my own on Christmas day, (honest) so why was I being so Tragic.

The telephone rang. It was Charles.

Due to unforeseen circumstances he was alone over Christmas, so would I like to meet up sometime?

Yeh, nice idea.

"What about coming over to listen to the King's College Choir this afternoon? It starts at 3 p.m."

"Okay."

Well, Waffs, this is a turn up for the book: an invitation!

Actually, in order not to milk the tragic bit, I do and did have invitations. But, my ability to socialise had been so curtailed over the past two years, that I now found it difficult to belong to a group of individuals enjoying themselves.

Charles was a slightly different case.

He was a mate, a buddy-pal, on his own . . . and he didn't mind my ramblings.

For a change I discarded my flowing baggy clothes, which had hidden my scrawny, shuffling body for nearly a year and tried on a skirt that had always been just that little too tight.

It was perfect.

Correction, I had improved.

I had to go out and buy some tights.

Where was my eye-liner?

My heeled shoes needed dusting, not cleaning!

The holes in my ears had closed.

I picked up some perfume, and sniffed.

The realisation was dawning on me that I was not only alive, but getting ready to enjoy myself.

I felt nervous.

Could I cope?

Could Charles?

His eyebrows said it all; I looked great, thin, but great.

I felt fabulous.

After carols and Champagne he suggested a walk to a local restaurant.

"Walk in these things?" I queried, looking at my feminine shoes. He walked, I clattered on my heels.

During the meal a couple of buskers, dressed as Worzel Gummidge characters, put on their show in aid of a children's charity.

They sang: 'The Owl and the Pussycat'.

Japanese tourists in the restaurant looked on in amazement, then started furiously taking pictures.

It was magical.

Back to his flat, tired yet bubbling over experiencing all those experiences, he suddenly asked: "What would you have done if we had not met up today?"

"Don't laugh, I had thought of attending Midnight Mass."

He didn't laugh. Instead, he got the coats out and we clattered and walked our way back whence we came.

We entered Christchurch; I could not remember when I had last been in a church, apart from an occasional wedding.

My guess thirty years.

Everyone seemed to know what to do.

I felt like a visitor from another faith observing Christianity at first hand.

Why had Charles handed me a £1 coin?

(*Oh, the collection!*)

I didn't know Communion was communed in a Protestant church.

(*Pass.*)

Despite my official non-believing stance, I had a feeling of being part of a Community, of being a human being.

I felt alive.

I belted out the carols for all I was worth.

When was the last time I'd sung?

I couldn't remember that either.

I'd also forgotten how high up the scale carols are pitched. As the congregation mumbled into their hymn sheets, I deliberately cleared out at least two years of 'not being heard'.

I was heard!

(*Amen.*)

Home at 1.30 a.m.

(*a.m.!*)

"Happy Christmas, Waffles."

She didn't respond.

I've been enjoying myself, little one, surely you don't mind?" I said to the rigid outline of her back.

I then had the disapproving look, the avoidance, the disinterest, but finally she gave me one of her forgiveness licks, and we sank into a blissful sleep.

To compensate for all the energy I had expended yesterday, I remained in bed until it was time for my rounds.

I had three ports of call.

(*Not three Ports . . . I was driving.*)

343

At Shirley's I watched as three generations ripped open presents to genuine squeals of delight and thanks.

I was presented with an Indian-mantle-type-thing for my new home.

A new start," declared Shirley.

(*It's already begun, I thought.*)

I turned down a request to stay for dinner.

An hour in a family setting, however genial, is my limit; it was not my family.

I have to go.

I want to go.

Where to now? I know, Del had given me an open invitation.

Del's it was.

Del and Father Christmas (alias Stan) greeted me at the door.

The ever-exuberant Del positioned me for a photograph with Father Christmas, handed me a glass and told me to drink, and gave me a Christmas stocking, all at once.

Can I cope with the simple pleasure of all this? I asked myself. The stocking contained tiny parcels containing small gifts.

Small gifts . . . large thoughts . . . huge love.

I was overwhelmed.

"Give the stocking back and it means it will be ready for next year," said Del, already carefully folding it up.

(*Will I be ready for next year?*)

"But don't expect me to be Father Christmas again!" said a voice from the kitchen.

"He always says that, but he always gives in," said the determined Del.

I can imagine!

I turned down another request to stay for dinner at lunch time.

I was going to have Christmas Day Dinner with Waffs, tonight.

My last call was to a Champagne-drinking household.

Presents under a Christmas tree, smoked salmon, nuts, chocolate and good company . . . and Champagne.

I was sinking into a lethargic state compounded by too much enjoyment in such a short space of time.

I had to go.

Home by 6.15 p.m.

I shoved the chicken in the oven and half-heartedly cut up vegetables ready for the steamer.

A message from Charles to phone him.

"Are you coming out to play?" he asked.

"No, I'm too tired to move, and anyway I want to have Christmas night on my own, with Waffs."

"Oh?"

"Oh, really."

"See you tomorrow then?"

"Okay."

By 6.30 p.m. I'd turned off the oven and was asleep.

It had all been too much, but like Oliver I was ready for more.

The chicken had been bitten, chewed, licked and generally mauled about by Waffles during the night. I had not covered it sufficiently.

At the risk of rewarding bad behaviour I cooked it and force-fed Waffles over the next week.

(*Who am I trying to kid?*)

Charles had been invited to a party out of town and asked if I would like to accompany him.

A party!

The host welcomed us at the door then, doing his bit, asked who I'd like to meet.

"An unattached interesting male would be nice."

(*Tall order, I know.*)

"My nephew would be just right for you, you look the musician type. 'Simon'," he called, looking round the room."

"Wrong age," offered Charles.

(*Quiet.*)

The interesting unattached young man was hauled before me.

Very nice, but definitely the wrong generation.

We both queried the host's eyesight or alcohol level, but continued talking way beyond normal social niceties.

I was enjoying myself.

The hostess was involved with NLP and was interested in my approach to (and avoidance of) cancer.

NLP?

The only acronym I could think of was North London Polytechnic, which I knew couldn't be correct.

It wasn't.

Neurolinguistic Programming. A sort of mind-over-matter training for change. Among some of its claims is that it can retrain your immune system to eliminate allergies and deal optimally with cancer, AIDS and other illnesses.

I was lent a book on the subject, adding to an ever increasing mountain of literature 'I really must read'. It has yet to be read in full, but one sentence jumped out at me. "If you believe in the treatment you are taking then there is a greater chance of recovery, than if it were forced on you."

I will store the concept and book for a quieter moment.

The party was becoming anything but quiet.

Who's making all that noise?

Oh, it's me!

Charles was doing his 'Wonderful Jenny' speech and describing all the crazy and amazing things I'd done over the year, when suddenly . . .

"But, your hair is in such good condition," someone remarked.

"This isn't my hair . . . *This* is my hair," I announced whisking off the wig to an astonished audience.

"Gosh, you look ten years younger!"

Charles grinned.

At that moment the host casually walked into the room and, seeing a new guest asked if I wanted a drink.

"I think I've had enough," I suggested.

Far from causing offence, consternation or amusement, my resistance to the piece of hot matting on my head and its removal seemed to be my pièce de résistance.

Slowly I could feel I was shedding the Me that existed in 1993.

(*Slowly?*)

I continued to be, and consume, Bubbly.

I felt as if I'd been to two parties, since various previously-met individuals came and introduced themselves to me (again) on the grounds that I'd only just arrived.

I probably had.

It was cold outside, so placing the curled-up creature which had been sitting on my lap, back on my head, we bid our farewells.

The host, looking from me to his glass, and back again said goodbye to the three of us.

Had Charles regretted taking a Bird from Balham to such a posh do?

Apparently not.

Strange man.

Monday.

Didn't I have something to do on Monday?

My sister was coming for the day, that was it.

I perfected my staying-in-bed technique and awaited the arrival of one of life's natural self-perpetuating dynamos.

My own Duracell batteries were on their last legs, and I hoped she would not be too like Tigger.

We talked, she cooked, we talked, she talked, she talked . . . I could not compute any more information and was in desperate need of quiet.

"Do you want to continue reading my manuscript?"

"Ooh, yes please."

Not a sound for five hours! From either of us.

Bliss.

I had really overdone it.

But like all over excited children I couldn't settle. I tossed and turned and thought and remembered and . . . IRO!

I pounced on my diary; it confirmed that I'd forgotten my appointment that morning.

I never forget appointments!

(*You do if you suddenly come alive!*)

I could not sleep. My over-active conscience composed a grovelling apology. I delivered it to his answer machine the next day.

A quiet, simple meal chez Charles that evening was a welcome breathing space in the richness that had taken over my life.

Wait for it . . .

"We've been invited over to Sheila's place for a drink, later. Is that okay?"

"Fine."

I hesitated.

I had left my wig at home almost to test my need for its protection. I suspected that it had become my 'Linus blanket' and that my new self was not really ready to emerge.

And certainly not in new company . . . sober.

We joined an already lively group, who had just witnessed the cat and mouse games of a real (Oscar) cat and mouse.

Upheaval wasn't the word.

My fabulous, fashionable hairstyle was remarked upon.

Well . . .

The story of my year unfolded.

"Poor Charles, you've heard this so many times over Christmas," I said apologetically.

"I don't mind; you always tell different bits to different people in different ways. I'm not bored."

The other guests were agog at my bubbliness (we were on Champagne again) humour and general attitude.

"Don't let it fool you too much; I do have some terrible moments and I am really afraid of the future. I can't see my way forward," I confessed.

"Nonsense," Sheila suddenly declared, grabbing my hand and dragging me to the top of the house.

(!)

Que pasa?

She stood me in front of a mirror, while she rummaged through a draw in a desperate attempt to find something.

She held up . . . a Magic Wand.

Standing behind me with her arms firmly clutched around my body and the Wand, she started.

"Make three wishes," she demanded, as she jiggled the Wand further up my nose.

(*She is shorter than me.*)

"What sort of wish," I insisted.

"A wish, a wish."

Not being used to making wishes, or having them come true, I cleared my throat and started.

"It would be sort of nice if the book could be published some time this year."

'NO. Try again. That's too wishy-washy."

"I want the book to be published?"

"NO. Try again."

"It's going to be published . . ."

"Again."

". . . in four months."

"Great!!!! Next wish."

I started to giggle. This was unreal. But was it any more unreal than the previous year? No.

"I hope the cancer finally goes this year."

"NO. Again."

"I *want* the cancer to go completely this year."

"NO!"

(*Giggle*)

"The cancer has gone?"

"NO!"

"The cancer *has* gone."

"Great. Next wish."

"I hope that Ellis understand his needs and in turn understands what I need in life . . . sort of thing."

"Too complicated. Again."

I battled with this wish longer than either of the other two.
Why?

Finally.

I hope Ellis and I find peace."

"Great."

The Wand wavered in and around my nose for a few more minutes then I was bundled down stairs to the interested and intrigued assembled throng.

What have you been doing?" whispered a startled Charles.

"Making wishes," I answered casually, as though it were the most normal thing to do in the whole world.

(*For Witches it probably is.*)

If nothing else, I had verbalised my wants and needs.

But actions speak louder than words.

Action.

Another late night.

For the next two days I would be able to relax and stay away from Champagne. With some of Ellis's 'present' I took myself off to Grayshott's Health Resort.

I had been there last year at exactly the same time and knew it to be well heated.

Well heated, I thought to myself and, much to the consternation of a driver coming towards me, I plucked off my wig; and never put it back.

Nobody knows what I should look like, I reasoned.

But people did think they knew who I was.

The resort is a watering hole for many celebrities, and much to my amusement individuals sidled up to me to say . . .

"I know the face, but can't quite remember the name."

(*Hee hee*)

"Jenny. I'm an out-of-work Potter."

They were baffled.

They were sure I had to be in the media to be able to have my hair cut so short; and get away with it.

"It's not a Hair Cut . . . more a Hair Grow," I explained.

I definitely was not the Jenny from 1993.

My medical examination was carried out by the same person who had officiated last year.

"Any problems?" she had asked in 1992.

"Only a tender breast, but I've got an appointment at the UCH in three weeks' time. It seems alright."

"Might be a good idea to get it checked out sooner," she advised.

(*Had she guessed there was something major, wrong?*)

At the time I was not particularly bothered; it was only tender. I spent the time working out in the Gym, Swimming, Yoga, Walking: you name it I did it. But, I did wonder why I was so exhausted by 7 p.m.!

(*Unfortunately, I was soon to find out.*)

This year all she found wrong was low blood pressure, but I confined myself to gentle yoga, relaxation and Tai Chi . . . and food.

All too short a stay . . . I will return when I'm a famous writer!

New Year's Eve.

I had said 'Yes' to an invitation to a local party, but had forewarned my friend that I would not be staying for the Countdown.

It would be too emotional.

I would rather be with Waffles and asleep by 10 p.m.

Wait for it . . .

Charles phoned and asked if there was a possibility of us

meeting up sometime today? . . . late afternoon? . . . early
. . . eer . . . sometime?

"Spit it out Charles," I said grinning to myself.

"Can we see in the New Year together?"

"Yes, but first you have to come to a party with me."

"Okay. What are you going to wear?"

"I'm going to look gorgeous," I declared avoiding the question.

Arriving at Jacquie's party gave two shocks. The first was that I had come with a male-type person and the second that I had discarded my wig.

Wow!

More couples arrived:

As introductions started . . .

You know Jenny don't you?" started Jacquie . . .

. . . "Jacquie you didn't tell me you had an Exotic friend!" they interrupted.

"Exotic friend?" queried Jacquie, with a grin. "That's Jenny."

The thing is, I did feel Exotic! I felt like a rare tropical butterfly that had newly emerged from an ugly cocoon.

Now all I had to do was fly away.

Charles and I flew back to his flat for some quietness and champagne.

What a year it had been, and it was nearly over. All I wanted to do was wrap it up into history and move on . . . but it had been 'My Year'. My Journeys had taken me to places that I could never have thought to visit and I was thankful.

I think.

Charles could see I was deep in thought.

353

"You've had one hell of a year. You must be so proud of yourself."

I thought back over what I had done and was reminded of a ski-ing incident many years back:

Richard my instructor and boyfriend had attempted to teach me 'Parallels', after many years happily poodling around doing 'Stem Christies' and other lesser techniques.

"Now you are ready to try stringing a few Parallels together," he announced one day, so off we went to the top of a mountain in Scotland, to test the theory.

One factor of ski-ing in Scotland is the poor visibility, but you get used to it.

Wait for it . . .

I started . . . I stopped . . . my legs began to feel like jelly. I can't go on I said to myself many times . . . but the next minute I was experiencing such exhilaration and success I continued.

This is horrific!

I've got to stop.

Didn't I do that turn well?

I have no more energy.

Wow that was amazing!

Slowly and not so slowly I twisted and turned and pushed myself to the limit.

When I stopped or fell, Richard lured me down a few more turns; he took my cursing; he praised my fight; he observed my joy.

On and on it went until I felt my body did not belong to me any more.

But.

Suddenly as exhaustion hit me, I was there.

I lay out in the snow hoping that my breathing, muscles, heart rate and, in fact, body would soon return to some form of normality.

Wow!

Richard skied up to me and asked how I felt.

Felt! Felt! I could hardly breath.

I ached all over.

"I don't know how I feel. It's just a ski run isn't it?"

"Look where you've come from," he demanded, gesturing somewhere above my head.

The mist had cleared and I could see before me a long, steep, twisting, bumpy, icy, Scottish piste.

"I did THAT!" I said with some incredulity.

"Yes, didn't you do well. Aren't you proud of yourself?"

"Yes, I'm proud of what I've accomplished. But, DON'T EVER ASK ME TO DO IT AGAIN!!!!!"

Charles laughed and opened another bottle of Champagne.

As the chimes of midnight rang out, an amazing and beautiful fireworks display erupted into the night, and was reflected in the lake below his window.

Magic.

"Happy New Year, Jenny."

"Happy New Year, Charles," I said, trying to cross my fingers and hold a Champagne glass at the same time.

"Happy New Year."

POSTSCRIPT:

"*Miss* Cole, do sit down . . ."
   (*Hurray! . . . but actually it's Ms*)
   . . . "As you know we are very pleased with your progress, but we do feel that blah, blah, blah, blah, blahblah. So you are going to have a Mastectomy now, aren't you?"

"No."

(He sighed).

"I really think you should seriously consider the consequences of not having an Operation."

"I have."

(He sighed again).

"I want to see you again in three months. Please think carefully about what I've said."

"I *have*!"

Clutching yet another appointment card, but this time with a very determined brain, I exited into the Warren Street area and, sod affluence, caught the tube home.
   They've done it again!!! I thought. I arrive at the hospital feeling wonderful and positive, yet within minutes they have successfully undermined all my fighting spirit.

I was at a crossroads.

My scared cry of "I'd rather die than have a Mastectomy" all those months ago was just that, a scared cry of terror and ignorance.

Now, I had gathered together all the information I needed and had come to a decision: I was *not*, under any circumstance, going to have a Mastectomy.

Brave?

Foolish?

Crazy?

Many people thought I was avoiding the issue; did I want to live or did I want to die?

It's not as simple as that, I told them.

I knew I could not allow my body to be 'abused' any more. It had already been taken to the edge of death, by the treatment. If my body could not contain and control the cancer itself, then so be it. But, I also truly believe that for me it would be the worst thing to do.

Firmly believing that the trauma of the operation would release the cancerous cells all over my body, I knew I would be dead within the year.

"Oh come on, aren't you just finding excuses?" I heard time and time again.

"No!"

I remembered (or tried to remember) a piece of research carried out on Chinese people living in America. Traditionally the Chinese believe that you are predetermined to die at a certain time and of a certain illness, depending on one's birth year etc. What the researchers found was that those American-Chinese who still retained the beliefs of their homeland, did die within their 'allotted' span. However, another group of American-Chinese who had largely adopted the American way of life lived longer than their traditional counterparts.

So, if I firmly believe that I will die within a few years of having a Mastectomy, then I will. Apart from that, the type of Mastectomy on offer doesn't bear thinking about. Quality of life is all important to me. I know I would curl up and wither away with (er) the amount of me they would hack off.

My fighting spirit fought back but not until I'd had many a restless night and restless brainstorm.

I know I'm right.
  (*Do you?*)
I've worked it out.
  (*Really?*)
You're just scared.
  (*No, I'm not.*)
Yes you are.
  (*Well, maybe a little.*)

On and on different emotions battled for supremacy. But one thing was certain, I needed a 'second' when attending the Breast clinic.
    Trish volunteered.
    We awaited the onslaught.
    In walked . . . another doctor, Dr Omar.
    "Pleeeaased to meet you," I cooed.
    "Hallo, Miss Cole, and how are you?" he said with a fabulous smile.
    "Great . . . well, that's that formality over and done with," I said, getting off the examination couch and pretending to get dressed.
    "Not *so* fast," he said. (He had no doubt been warned about me?) Like a well trained dog I hopped back on to the couch and played 'dead'.
    (*I hope it is just played.*)

"You won't consider a Mastectomy?" he enquired.

"No."

I gave him my well-worn speech and promised to bring my PIP scans to show him next time; he showed some interest.

Trish and I escaped.

Three months later we returned.

I immediately shoved the PIP scans under the same doctor's nose . . . again he showed interest.

I now know how Waffles feels when taken to the vet. Try *any* tactic (cuteness, big wide eyes, scratching) to avoid the examination.

(*Curses, foiled again.*)

As he examined me he looked sideways at Trish . . .

"Um, Madam, are you aware that you are very yellow," he said with some concern.

Trish and I fell about laughing.

"If you think *that's* yellow, you should have seen her two weeks ago," I replied, realising that I'd devised another diversion. Always take a yellow friend with you.

She explained that her gall bladder was now functioning properly and, although still yellow, she was slowly returning to her natural colour.

He returned to my breast.

"Are you aware that your breast has developed 'piel orange'?" he enquired.

"Piel orange?" . . . I could feel myself freeze.

"Yes, piel orange; orange peel."

I blustered some reply, almost ignoring what he had said.

(I had also been ignoring a heavy 'congested' sensation in my breast.)

"Mastectomy?"

"No."

It took me four weeks to regain my equilibrium.

I booked another PIP scan with Harry. It was exactly a year since the first one. October to October, with a lifetime in between.

Trish came with me as usual. After half an hour of me constantly complaining of feeling sick, she snapped.

"For goodness sake Jenny, the whole of last year when you were barely alive I didn't hear you complain once."

"Sorry."

I suffered in silence.

"You look *so* well," remarked Harry.

"Yes, apart from a feeling of nausea, I feel great, but . . ."

I related the hospital's negativity and how it had left me feeling adrift.

"Let's take a look."

The scans showed, quite clearly, that the tumour/mass had shrunk. It also showed that my colon was inflamed. Later that day my temperature reached 101°F.

I must have gone through some kind of 'healing crisis', as afterwards the heavy, congested feeling in my breast, disappeared.

My original concept of a postscript was to be a few lines up-dating factual events of 1993. Now, looking back on the year 1994, I feel I could write, not only a second book but that most of it would *not* be an up-date of events.

In 1993 I was just a body being saved and somehow I was attached to this body. In fact I felt I was clinging on for dear life. In 1994 I felt the two halves of me slowly merging to produce a complete (ish) human being.

But I did have other issues to face apart from my health: work and money.

In January everything still seemed and was, an effort, but

I realised that re-training was paramount: but what did I want to do?

I had already given advice and care to several individuals with cancer and so it seemed natural to enrol on a Counselling course.

I had no idea what that meant.

I soon found out . . . exhaustion.

The course was only two and a half hours a week, but that was enough to send me scurrying to bed on my return home.

It was both cathartic and distressing to relate my problems to a fellow student, whose turn it was to be the counsellor. I wished, at times, I could invent an in-growing toe nail.

I had thought of nothing else for a year, how did I expect them to know even where to begin?

My vocabulary increased to take in the (jargon) words and phrases associated with counselling: summarising, reflecting back, open questions . . . How many of those have I used in the past and received in return, a closed answer?

It was tough but exhilarating.

During one long day of intensive study we were given, for light-ish relief, some paper and coloured crayons.

"Draw a tree in three minutes," said Stephanie, our tutor.

I was amazed how readily everyone took to the task.

But then came the tricky bit. We had to pair up and talk for ten minutes (?) about the tree as if *we* were the tree.

Very interesting.

Lynette's was a delicate cherry tree in blossom. The blossom never lasted long because it was so delicate, and harsh winds destroyed the beauty of it; already the branches were leaning to one side because of the constant pressure. So, she had to make the most of the time she had looking wonderful. She was a mature tree, whose bark was beginning to gnarl up. Her environment was very pleasant and the only thing she could worry about were the boys who climbed all over her . . .

(*Oooh!*)

. . . and could potentially destroy her branches.

By comparison I was angular and barren, as a tree. I had been planted in very rough surroundings and had had very little care throughout my growing period. I had been badly pruned by amateurs and many little boys had cut into me for no reason at all. Because of my dilapidated state the local council had taken it upon themselves to finish me off with poison.

Not so easy. My species is made of stronger stuff and there was some life left. My purple branches now reached out and ended in spiked 'fingers'. Each finger had a cluster of new green healthy growth. A new tree surgeon had arrived and had made positive moves to help me grow to my full potential. I had heard it all before; maybe I should ask to see his credentials? I had to admit though that already there was a healthy inner strength returning, reaching deep into my roots and out to my barren branches.

(*All that from a three minute sketch!*)

So much for light relief.

I felt very guilty that I had neglected Frances. I had not wanted to burden her unduly with my own personal problems as I knew she was going through a rough time herself.

How rough?

She left a message on my answerphone, thanking me for my Christmas card and best wishes for '94. She said she would contact me when she left the North London Hospice, where she had been spending a few weeks to rest and regain some strength.

Frances did leave, but returned to the Hospice and died there, in February.

Nobody wanted to tell me.

They all hoped someone else would.

I hadn't spoken to her for months ... I hadn't said 'goodbye'.

Richard implied that she had deliberately kept me from knowing how ill she was, as it might affect my ability to fight.

Typical of Frances.

In early March, while on a much needed holiday, I woke with a start. I could not work out if I had been dreaming ... or what. Through the post I had received an invitation to a gathering, at an address I didn't know. I was intrigued. Other people had been invited, but we did not know each other.

We sat and waited.

The door opened and in walked Frances, looking so well and happy.

"Frances," I said, as I rose to embrace her.

"Sorry, Jenny, you won't be able to touch me," she said calmly. "I only came to say 'goodbye' properly, as I didn't have a chance before."

With that, she walked round the room speaking to every one present, then left.

I felt fantastic, even though my waking brain could not clearly get to grips with the clarity, yet dream-like quality, of the encounter. It was only later that I found myself moved to tears by the dream. It had been *so* real.

On 11th February I finished the first draft of the manuscript . . . and burst into tears.

I'd just had a positive reaction from a large literary agency. But they did not want to commit themselves until the book had been completed, so I pounded away on my two fingers until it was. They 'liked my work very much, it made us laugh, it was moving, distressing in parts and made compelling reading.'

. . . "So???" I screamed in frustration.

So, nothing.

They advised that because I wasn't a celebrity (*I'm not yet*) it would be difficult to find a publisher.

The original publisher, who had similarly praised my work, was playing a peculiar game with me. He would apologise for not getting back to me sooner, show interest, make helpful suggestions, then ignore me for months.

"Don't give me abandonitis," I pleaded.

He ignored me for a further four months.

What was even more infuriating were the power games or wind-ups (or downright rudeness) by the video/documentary producers. Time and time again I begged them to feel free to say 'no' if they were not interested anymore in the project they had initiated. I had used the term 'abandonitis' when prompting them for some definitive communication, ex-plaining that it was detrimental to my health to be left up in the air.

(*Hallo, anyone there?*)

Nothing.

I was even fobbed off by the sister of the BBC producer who informed me that she, the producer, was in India for two months maybe three . . . and she'd contact me on her return. So far she's been in India for nearly a year.

(*Lucky woman!*)

Nearer home I was eagerly contacted by another producer who promised faithfully to contact me after she had completed some work. Her idea was to compare and contrast me with a friend, who also had Inflammatory cancer. The common denominator was that we both had fighting spirit, yet our lifestyles and support systems differed dramatically.

"At least you'll get a lovely week in the country out of it" she enthused.

Wow, she sounds genuine and can understand my need to be treated as a human being, I thought.

(*Wrong!*)

I finally sent her one of my slightly sarcastic letters assuming that the deal was off?

(*Me, sarcastic? Never!*)

Why do they do it?

I was reminded of a conversation in Gulliver's travels between a Houyhnhnm and Gulliver when he was trying to explain how he had come from 'over the seas in a hollow vessel made from the bodies of trees'.

The Houyhnhnm replied that Gulliver had 'said the thing which was not', as they had no word in their language to express lying or falsehood.

Many friends tried to calm my ire, explaining that documentary producers are just like that and that even if a contract has been signed it still meant nothing.

(*Hmph!*)

I was reminded of a doctor who longed for a return to the days when on delivering a baby he tells the woman she's been pregnant for nine months. He'd probably make a good producer?

But, joking aside, I could have done without the manipulation and lack of thought, especially as they knew I was ill . . . I had been abandoned far too often to take it lightly.

In March I moved to a flat. Just Waffles and me.
  Bliss.
  Peace?

Confusion.

One morning I heard myself saying . . . "it's nice here but I wonder when I'm going home?" The truth was that the situation appeared on one level to be a continuation of my life with Ellis in the house. I was alone but he rang everyday to see how I was. If he rings, he cares . . . no he doesn't . . . yes he does, no he *doesn't* . . . but he rang?
  I had to escape his influence and my need of him.
  I had to . . . otherwise he would continue to abandon me time and time again.

I snapped.

"You are back where you started, working all hours, playing all-night Poker and living with your mother . . . I wake up every morning and have to say to myself 'I have cancer what am I doing today to control it?' It's very tiring and frightening. You rejected me and rejected my help . . . when you contact me I re-live that feeling of wanting someone who is destroying me. No! you can't do anything for me, except stay away," I thundered.
  I was shaken by my response. Had it only just occurred to me that I had cancer? Yes.
  (*Yes?*)

To add to the many variations of tiredness I had experienced I felt overwhelmed by the responsibility I had towards my body . . . and the local council, North Thames Gas, Eastern Electricity, BT and the numerous other financial demands flooding through my letter box. Now I was totally on my own, the one and only positive way in which Ellis had supported me, was gone.

My immune system reacted violently and I was laid low by a lingering cold and a cold sore. I've never had a cold sore before I raged . . . well you have now. I had visions of my cancer gathering forces for a further attack while I was incapacitated.

(*A bit like the men I meet.*)

A few days later my professional Journal plopped through the door and I flicked over the pages unable to rally any interest in the subject, or myself. My spirits were raised slightly by letters arriving from Aromatherapists thanking me for my article. Article, what article? I vaguely remembered writing something and sending it somewhere but . . . I pounced on the Journal and turning over the page came face to face with 'Aromatherapy and Cancer' by Jenny Cole. Although a first draft, and in need of expanding, somehow it had been included in the Journal in its raw state. Raw state or not, I received many letters and many words of support and care, which were eagerly consumed. I was hungry for contacts which had nothing to do with hospitals, illness or pain. I had to start networking to save my sanity.

(*What sanity?*)

April arrived and with it my birthday.
As a birthday present, Charles sent me to a Psychologist.
(*Pardon?*)
I should explain . . . Charles had met Conrad Kaplan, an Adlerian psychologist who had refined Alfred Adler's

method of interpreting childhood memories; the purpose being to find the one-theme dominant behaviour pattern around which the person has built his or her whole personality. These patterns explain why we constantly find ourselves in the same situation. They answer that nagging question: "Why do we keep making the same mistakes again and again?" Charles had been impressed and thought I might like to explore the method and add it to my 'journeys'.

I was, as usual, game.

Conrad, who looks like the epitome of a Woody Allen psychiatrist, turned out to be calm, approachable, and human. He immediately guessed I was the youngest child in the family, but said he would tell me how he had figured it out at the end of the session.

(*Intrigued*)

Conrad had discovered over the years that so much happens in the sessions that it was impossible to remember everything. As we all have a tendency to ignore what we don't want to hear, and forget what may be of use, Conrad offers the facility of a tape, which may then be listened to at a future date. (It is therefore advisable to keep the cassette away from your music collection!)

To understand the method, he gave me a brief introduction to Adler. Adler, he said, believed that before the age of six every child develops a 'map' of the world based on the child's experiences in the family. But a map which is accurate for a child of four or six may not be so appropriate for an adult (of forty six.) We take with us the child's view of the world and we recreate that world time and time again . . . some of us with disastrous results.

(*I know, I know.*)

The Kaplan method of discovering this theme, or pattern, is to ask seven, simple questions relating to family, memories and decisions.

I must be an interviewer's nightmare because as soon as I'm asked a question about my family or childhood I fire off in all directions at breakneck speed . . . but he quickly got to the hub of the problem. After the questions we started to rummage through the debris.

(The following account has been taken directly from my taped interview so does not contain all the sighs, giggles, gasps and the sound of my voice becoming high and squeaky!)

"I am incredibly independent but there is a little bit of me which says 'why won't anyone look after me?' This is it basically . . . how can someone say they love me yet . . ." I began.

". . . I'll tell you why."

"Go on, go on, tell me . . . I need to know."

(*Giggle*)

"What picture of the world did this little girl have? Oh, and by the way I know I'm not hearing objective truth; the way you perceive the world as a child is how you perceive the world now . . ."

"Okay."

". . . what comes again and again. You move from this lovely house to another house (better to worse) and although you weren't aware of the change you picked up the atmosphere . . . you were, in your own words, 'abandoned in your high chair in an empty room, wondering if anyone was going to pick me up . . . I felt isolated and bored' . . . you had a wonderful time with your father before you went to school then 'he abandoned me, he dumped me at school' . . . many years with this fellow 'he was wonderful, he allowed me space to develop, but he repeatedly abandoned me' . . . the whole situation is going from better to worse and someone has abandoned you; that comes again and again in your life."

"I know that! . . . but why? . . . it's not as if I go after the

369

same kind of man," I insisted . . . "All I want is someone who will not abandon me and all I find is someone who will."

"It's the pattern . . ."

"But I haven't gone out to choose the men; they seemed to have zoomed in on me . . ."

"Uh, Uh, You attracted them . . ."

". . . Okay, I attracted them but . . ."

". . . and they sniff a woman they can abandon in a crisis."

". . . but why do they . . .?"

"They! they! they!" quipped Conrad, as I in exasperation acknowledge my part in the collusion.

(*Bother.*)

"Okay, I stupidly think that each one will be different, yet I give them the opportunity to abandon me?"

"Goooooooood!" exclaimed Conrad, as we both collapsed into laughter.

It's not easy realising that one's own acquiescence has helped produce thirty years of pain.

If life is an ice lolly which has to be divided and shared, my men would have the ice lolly and I would get the stick.

(*With which to beat myself?*)

I thought back on the times when I'd cheerfully allowed my men to 'abandon' me (at Christmas, in hospital, a special occasion), yet I accepted it and welcomed them back as if it were their right. "If there's no pain, then there's no reason to change," Conrad had said. Why should my men change their behaviour when they continue to receive the ice lolly served to them by me? I and I alone had allowed them to treat me this way, yet I raged with hurt and anger at the aloneness of the situation. If I didn't want my theme anymore, and I don't, then *I* have to change.

Watch out men!

A few months later Conrad had reason to ring me . . .
"Charles is sitting here relaxed after a magnificent meal,"
I informed Conrad.
"Hi, Charles."
"Hi, Conrad."
"Oh, by the way Conrad, Charles and I have swopped
tapes . . .
(*Stunned silence*)
. . . and we're doomed"

Charles and I fell about laughing, while Conrad tried to
figure out the ramifications of this action.

Conrad had already told me that my pattern would attract
men with a matching opposite pattern; ie, they see in me a
wonderful dynamic female whom *they can abandon.*
(*Watch this space.*)

My non-abandoned breast continued to improve, or at the
very least, it did not give me cause for concern. True, it felt
heavy at times, but I had to learn that I could not react to
every ache and pain in my breast, or any other part of my
body. Trish advised that if I started to over-react to the
numerous problems of a human body then I could shortly
be attributing even dandruff to the cancer. Be vigilant, take
note, but don't put yourself through torment every day.
I'll try.

Some weeks later I telephoned Trish after having put myself
through torment for a few days.
"Trish, I don't want to panic but the whole of my lymph
area is swollen and I can feel a tight elastic band in my
armpit. What do you think it is?"
(*Panic, panic, panic . . .*)

371

I can't remember what she replied, as by this time I had given myself a few months to live. I was reminded of the character in Dad's Army who rushed around screaming 'nobody panic, nobody panic.' I wanted to, but I simply froze.

"Let's not make any hasty decision until your next PIP scan," she advised calmly.

By luck it was due the following Tuesday. I only had the weekend to get through; only!

I also had an appointment with Iro. When I told him of the rubber band and swelling, his face fell and he looked grim.

"Let's not over-react," he said gently to a frozen under-reacting body. "What else could it be due to?" he continued, carefully feeling the very swollen and painful cavern.

"I don't know," I whispered.

(*Why don't they just tell me it's the cancer?*)

Gently turning over my arm to investigate further he pointed to a mark on the fleshy part of my hand.

"What's that?" he enquired.

"Um? . . . Oh, I know! Waffles!" I exclaimed with joy.

I had forgotten that I had attempted to pick up Waffles when she was very frightened and in her struggle to get away she had gouged my hand with her back claws. I had cleaned the area immediately, so naturally thought it was all okay.

Not so.

In the words of Iro "The army had carted the prisoners off to gaol"; ie, the lymph glands were doing exactly what they should be doing and preventing the infection from spreading around my body.

Whew!

This was confirmed the next day with my PIP scan. I managed to hold up my arm so that a scan could be taken of the inflamed area. An angry red line could be seen linking the hand with the lymph glands . . . but from the lymph glands to the breast everything was calm.

Double whew!

The swelling and rubber band disappeared within the week but I thought to myself, what would have happened if I'd gone straight to the hospital?

I knew what would have happened, and I shuddered.

Everyone breathed a sigh of relief; I just grinned with delight. The cat that initiated the scare peacefully slept . . . and so did I, that night.

In July I attended a whole-day workshop at the Wandsworth Cancer Support Centre. I had no idea that the WCSC, or anything like it, existed in London. How I wished there had been something like this for me last year. It felt great being with other people who not only had cancer but who also shared my energy and determination to live with it. I was in a small group, looking at the role of music and writing in the pursuit of understanding illness.

I think?

It was so different from the average workshop that it was hard to pin down exactly what was being expressed. All I do know is that my excited over-the-top enthusiasm bubbled and bounced its way through the exercises and group discussions. One member of the group, Elizabeth, asked for my phone number and actually made contact the following week. She demanded my manuscript, ploughed through it, and rang at an ungodly hour to rave about it.

"Er, thanks Elizabeth but try phoning in three hours' time when I'm awake . . ." I yawned, but I had to admit that it was helpful to get the reaction of a fellow canceree.

I had to get it published . . . I just had to!

Was I taking on too much?

I was.

So what's new?

I had cancer; therefore I no longer had the resources I was used to, or needed, to hit my head repeatedly against the brick wall of publishing.

I was beginning to spiral . . . and with that in mind I went to see Elizabeth the Astrologer, again. She was amazed when I told her that the three main 'predictions' had been accurate.
  (*Why?*)
She told me what I had already sensed, that it would be another year before I would really be better. I had to take it easy.
  (*Easier said than done, with no income.*)
  It would slowly become clear what my work would be . . . but I mustn't rush it . . . I had to be careful of publishers and not let them drain my energy but also, as I was inept at judging business deals, I had to be extra vigilant.
  I took exception to being told I was not a good judge of business deals . . . I'm a hopeless judge of everything!
  Uranus could either be good or bad. The 9th house indicated long distance travels, in June and December. Any journey undertaken at those times would need to be thought through . . . In October I would have a strong sense of direction in my life (that would be nice), but I would be extra sensitive to others, so once again I had to be on guard . . . I could be in a new home within 18 months (good heavens or, good, heaven?) . . . Relationships are highlighted in a romantic way . . . Ellis and one other man (?) is draining me still . . . I must join more groups, especially

with women . . . something about Ellis is holding me back. (My heart's on a piece of elastic?) . . . My writing will become more and more important to me . . . In July I will have some good news about money (hurray!)

. . . In November and December money and security will be at the forefront of my thoughts . . . think rather than do (but you're talking to an Arien!) . . . mid-40s is a time of change (that's why I've always felt middle aged?) and a new career is on the table . . . Aries signifies enthusiasm and hope . . . Ellis had 'splat' me . . . I get 'lost' when I try to mother other people . . . impulsive . . . do not jump in feet first.

I would wait to see what happened.

What happened was that my (own) house was giving cause for concern. I could not sell it and the tenant was reluctant to part with the rent on time. Then the central heating boiler blew up and my savings went with it . . . it couldn't get worse, could it?

Wait for it.

My tenant announced he could no longer remain in the house and would move out immediately.
 But what about me? I queried.
 (silence)
 My savings gone, no rent coming in, and a house open to squatters and vandals. Great stuff.

In a damage-limitation exercise I persuaded him to stay in the house, rent free, until a new tenant could be found. At least that way I could rule out the last two hassles.
 But I was not happy.
 A cautious letter arrived from Ellis. He had heard on the grapevine that I was having 'problems' . . . could he help? I thankfully handed over the whole mess for him to sort in his

own inimitable style; ie, people do what he asks of them. "It was very bad of Tony to let you down like that, especially when he knows of your illness," he remarked. The strangeness of Ellis repeats and repeats. If asked to deal with an inanimate object, such as a house or money, he behaves like the capable, caring human being I know he can be . . . but, add one female-type human and he's as blind as he needs to be to avoid the issue. My task is to learn to accept that I need help, to be able to accept it from Ellis yet realise that it doesn't mean that he cares (for me).

Strange man.

Talking of strange men I had a phone message from the former colleague, who had offered morale-boosting support when times had been difficult.

"I've got something to tell you Jen," said Charlie.

New job? emigrating? picked to play rugby for Wales? . . . no, a rare cancer which had been slowly, over many years, consuming his insides.

I could sense he was at the stunned disbelief stage so offered him my manuscript. He accepted. During one long hospital wait he and his wife read and read and read. (It was a long wait!)

He was referred to Hammersmith hospital by his local hospital since they had no idea what to do with him. We met one hot summer's day in the hospital canteen and were mutually impressed by how well we both looked. My image of people with cancer had always been negative and bleak yet here we were, looking healthier than when we had last met seven or eight years ago. His eight-hour operation put a (temporary) stop to that . . . a bug nearly put a (full) stop to him . . . but he's coming along nicely now.

When he was due for the mammoth operation I sent a card, but even I had difficulty in working out what to say. In the end, I wrote: "Life is not a bowl of cherries . . . it's a mixed fruit salad with unidentified bits in it." As he pointed out he just wanted the unidentified bits put in a bucket and taken away.

His body coped with the operation and now his spirit is coping with the concept of cancer. "You must get your book published," he insisted.

I know, I know!

During that wonderful hot summer I was asked to give a talk on health to some school children for their end of term project. I had intended to concentrate on massage and Aromatherapy but it soon became clear that many of the children were more interested in the 'mind over matter' aspect to which I kept referring. However, some were even more interested in not being there (!). Eventually their teachers demanded that they all sat in a circle for a quiet hour led by me.

(*Me?*)

I began by telling them about Affirmations and Visualisation but omitted any reference to my cancer, as I was not sure whether some lurking school policy or parent-teacher group would object. But, it soon became obvious that I would have to tell them to put everything in context. After being given the go-ahead from the teachers I did just that.

To hold the attention of 12–14 year old pupils for five minutes might be construed as a success . . . I was elated, and amazed, that they paid absolute attention for nearly an hour. Their grasp of the 'mind over matter' issue was a revelation to me and I continued to expand my examples.

I told them that my tumour was an integral part of me and that I spoke to it everyday.

"You speak to it?" they gasped in amazement.

(*Now, they knew for certain that grown ups were weird.*)

"Yes."

377

"What do you say to it?" they all wanted to know.

"Well, I think of my tumour as a sitting tenant who is refusing to pay rent. If I attempt strong, bully-boy tactics to get it out (surgery) then it could feel angry enough to destroy the whole house. If, however, I accept that it would be safer and more humane to allow it to stay, provided it keeps to the one room and doesn't cause a nuisance, then I had a far better chance to keep the house in one piece. It may even go of its own accord."

"What do you *say* to it?" they insisted.

"Well, things like . . . Hi! lump, I know you're there and I don't mind, providing you don't go walkabout. Keep calm and peaceful and relax."

They were intrigued.

Just then, one of the 'little horrors' of the group put his hand up.

"Miss, if you talk to your tumour every day, what would you talk to if it went?"

I blustered some inadequate reply as I tried desperately to grasp the full implication of his request. I was simply stunned by the question. I still am today.

As I left the group they all called to me and my tumour, wishing us well.

(*Did you hear that, tumour?*)

The summer was magical. Occasionally a memory would jar my peace of mind. Silly things which, taken out of context, would not offend. The African Violet bloomed again, a tape I loved and lost reappeared in a cassette player used, then abandoned, by Ellis.

I started attending Kenwood Open Air Concerts with Charles, with groups, with masses. Music, by various composers and orchestras, good food prepared by me, Champagne, courtesy of 'Champagne Charlie', good humoured people provided by London, fabulous weather by a miracle, and fireworks.

378

Fireworks! They had such an emotional effect on me and represented yet another link with the pain of Ellis. I tried to convince myself that fireworks also heralded in my new year but I was not ready for the overpowering onslaught of the display which accompanied Tchaikovsky's Theme and Variations Suite No 3 in G major Op 55 (I read in the programme!). It epitomised my attempts to regain control of my life, as the music swelled and subsided while another theme worked its way into the equation. In the finale I experienced every emotion that I'd had over the past three years and wept openly with the exhilaration of the moment.

Mind you it could also have been that I'd had too much Champagne!

I searched and searched music shops for the Suite No 3; it was rarely recorded. I was going cross-eyed trying to read the wording on the sides of CDs, and local shops couldn't help. Finally, a very helpful assistant tracked it down in a section unrelated to Tchaikovsky's major works. I am still affected by the music and find tears welling up as the crescendo starts to gather momentum; but the overriding emotion is one of success and winning, not hopelessness. Similarly when I plan Vangelis's '1492' I am transformed back to the workshop with Matthew Manning and the power of hundreds of people wishing me well.

My spirits rose with an amazing 'rejection' from a large publishing company: "Thank you for sending your manuscript. You already know it is unusual and extraordinary. It has left me in a quandary regarding what to suggest. A book for us it is not, since our books fall fairly strictly into the 'practical self-help for everyone' bracket and I would not want to suggest you change what you have written in any way. It has a wonderful lyrical style as well as being a tough, funny and hard-hitting account of enduring the medical process as well as dealing with the question of day-to-day sanity in such circumstances . . . Blah, blah, blah . . . Your writing is streets ahead of other personal stories that have crossed my desk . . . I'm sorry that it is not quite right for our company."

Wow! I had proof, if proof be needed, that I was not imagining the power of my writing nor the sincerity of friends who had said it was brilliant. I immediately rushed to the Writer's Year book and sent off another batch of 'please will you read my manuscript' letters. But, my energy was beginning to surge and wane at an alarming rate; how long could I keep up this enthusiasm?

In September Jenny, Nina, Trish and I travelled down to Winfalcon's new shop/therapy centre in Brighton. Primarily I went to have my Aura photographed again to see if there had been any significant change . . . there wasn't really! What was even more unsettling was that (extremely healthy) Jenny's Aura looked amazingly like mine. Trish explained that it was possible that as both of us were Aromatherapists we had the same type of Aura; all whispy blues and greens with blobs of stress.

(*Mmm?*)

I had also decided to have my palm read, only as an interesting exercise, you understand. I had been introduced to the subject by an extremely entertaining lady at Tyringham Naturopathic centre and I was 'hooked'.

Michael, the resident all-rounder, took my hand and peered at it through his special (rose tinted?) spectacles . . . He began: "Your moon is in Cancer that means you are open to others . . . Your life line has a branch in it which returns to the main line as it gets deeper and deeper . . . at the join is a small triangular island . . . if you allow yourself to be distracted and you don't follow and gain your new heart's desire, then you could get ill."

"How ill?" I queried.

"Oh, nothing serious like cancer," he assured me.

(*That's a relief then!*)

"But I've already got cancer," (*been there*) I beamed.

He peered at me through his strange spectacles and continued . . . "You are in the process of moving (*done that*) and retraining in a different field . . . what you should think of doing is something like counselling (*done that*) . . . I can see you in the media, on television promoting something you believe in and even flying internationally to promote your work (*Written the book . . . oooh!*) . . . Lots of travel . . . Your head line is Simian (ie, it is straight across instead of two separate branches) . . . Wow! what a turbulent and dynamic life you've had . . . don't bother to try to have a relationship, it will never work . . . as your past has already shown . . ."

(*At least he didn't tell me I was to meet a tall dark handsome stranger.*)

. . . "Wow! You have eight lines on your mound of mercury. I've never seen so many . . . 80% of the population don't have them at all because they don't care about anyone . . . You also have humour and creativity . . . someone in your family will have problems with their heart and another will find religion and become infamous . . ."

(*Nothing different there.*)

". . . On your thumb you have a longer 'will' section than 'reason' . . . (!) . . . there are different levels of incarnation, I believe you are on your last trip and you won't be coming back again . . ."

". . . Thank goodness for that; I don't think I can take another life," I said with all the heart-rending emotion I could muster.

He smiled, and gently hugged me.

". . . Your book will have a yellow cover . . ."

(*You're wrong there.*)

For the record, Jenny had five lines on her mound of

381

mercury and Nina had four or five. We were like school kids comparing conkers.

Well! Even if half of that were true it looks as if 1995 is going to be an interesting year; I just *have* to get the book published.

In one of our weekly natter-sessions Trish mentioned a new-to-me technique which I might like to try. I had already made contact with the practitioner on another matter, so rang to find out more about this strange sounding detox method. The leaflet Mark gave me informed me that: "The Bowen technique consists of a very precise sequence of moves at specific points of the patient's body. The therapist gently manoeuvres the muscles or tendons resulting in a general feeling of well-being and pleasant relaxation. But that is only the beginning. The body's natural healing responses are triggered and improvement is usually experienced within a few days." It was a fast and effective treatment also for back problems, hay fever and sports injuries and as Mark had witnessed an impressive improvement on many people after just one session, he was keen to try the technique on me.

Well you know me, I'll try anything once; but I informed Mark I'd try four to six sessions and see how it went.

The procedure is so light and unsubstantial that it is hard to imagine what benefit it could be doing the body, but I persevered. Mark had wanted to attempt some movements on the breast but for the first two sessions I refused . . . then, on the third session, I did allow some gentle pressure which seemed alright. Mmm? Should I be doing this?

As well as the wobbly pressure movements Mark suggested that I might like to do some 'homework'. I've tried many things but this was pushing even my boundaries away. I had to drink 8-10 glasses of distilled water a day, but as it does not hydrate the body I had also to drink my normal amount of ordinary mineral water. I thought that was a bit far-fetched until, after a day of distilled water drinking, I realised I had not needed to urinate. (?) However on drinking a couple of glasses of mineral water I did 'need to go'. My urine was so dark and concentrated that I had to accept that the distilled water did not for some reason hydrate the body and that the detox had already started. Along with these twenty-odd glasses of water I could also take 2-3 baths a week in which I had to put washing soda and bicarbonate of soda. My local chemist must have been wondered about the state of indigestion!

This water and bath detox regime is not actually part and parcel of the Bowen technique, but without making any claims, may well benefit someone with cancer. I was however surprised to hear that it was not a recommended detox system for everyone and does in certain cases have contra-indications, so it is not something to rush out and try without first seeking advice.

On the fourth session with Mark I felt a shoot of pain streak across my breast closely followed by a shoot of panic across my brain.

Enough, enough.

That night I was awake with discomfort and fear as my emotions battled with more 'what ifs' and 'if onlys'. I did return to Mark for one more session but forbade him to go anywhere near my throbbing boob. Whether I was too hasty in withdrawing myself from the sessions is hard to say. My criteria for continuing a therapy is based on my gut reaction and as on this occasion it was churning, there was no question of my continuing.

The heavy congested feeling of pain continued for a few weeks and was joined by nausea and a temperature on the day I went for my PIP scan with Harry in October . . . this 'healing crisis' was followed immediately by a sudden calmness and softening of the breast ... could that have anything to do with the Bowen technique? I believe it did, and although I got cold feet because of my overbearing protection of my breast I think it is a therapy well worth investigating further.

Rejection letters from publishers flooded through my letter box: "it wasn't for us" ... "books on cancer are very difficult to sell" ... "despite the lighter moments it's not easy to read" ...

My exasperation was not improved by an article in a newspaper, stating that the Net Book Agreement was being disbanded. This would mean that the Naomi Campbells of the world would still have 'their' book published but there would be little chance for new writers.

(Seethe, fury, rage!!!)

I had to sit down and talk to myself.

"Why do you want to have your book published?"

(What sort of question is that?)

"Well, why do you?"

(I think it's a worthwhile book.)

"Okay, but do you want it published because of the glory attached to being a published author ... or do you want to offer help to others?"

(To help others.)

"So?"

(So I'm going to publish it myself!)

"What did you say?"

(I'm going ... to publish it ... myself.)

"I'm going to publish it myself."

(There that wasn't to difficult was it?)

"No."

What had I said? What had I let myself in for?

384

When Anita heard of my plan she expressed no surprise at all: "For an Arien, who usually wants everything done yesterday, you have been very calm. As Jenny Cole the Arien I'm surprised you haven't exploded before now. Good on you," she said smugly.

Once I make up my mind, that's it. It wasn't that I'd contacted over 30 agents and publishers that was getting me down, it was more the strangeness of the publishing world. They were all impossible to pin down.

I had various people to contact, including the original publisher who could not say yes or no. I pointed out that as he seemed incapable of reaching a decision, I'd make it for him. Please would he return the script . . . I would refund the postage when it arrived, but not before, as the stamps would probably disappear into the black hole of his office.

He replied.

(*He spoke!*)

"I'll be in touch in earnest when I return from the Frankfurt book fair—honest. With head bowed."

Too late.

I wrote one last good humoured end-of-my-tether exasperated letter to him . . .
   (*Okay, it was sarcastic and blunt.*)
   I concluded . . . "Sorry, I have started on the rocky road of self-publishing . . . but if you have anything positive to offer me, then I'm still open to negotiations. Yours, with head held high."

He never contacted me on his return from Frankfurt and my manuscript still lurks somewhere in his empire.

(*Mind you, he didn't say which Frankfurt book fair!*)

It all became very 'North London'. It seemed that nearly everyone I knew had some knowledge of printing, marketing, ISBNs, copyright, widows, . . .

I soon became surrounded by unfamiliar words and deeds and I was in the middle attempting to juggle them all.

But, I was in charge.
(*Oh yeah?*)

I sent the manuscript to several cancer organisations asking (politely) if they would be prepared to read the work and endorse it in some way. One, simply returned my letter and attached a compliment slip from another organisation. The other two did not even have the grace to say 'no' using the enclosed SAE.

I felt as if I'd been slapped in the face.

My old feeling of worthlessness started to rear its ugly head. Why do individuals ignore me when I've asked for help? . . . why do I always end up doing everything myself?

Is my life theme so deeply ingrained that I ensure that I'm on my own?
(*Probably*)

November 22nd was looming. Hospital time.
I had already prepared a speech for whoever had drawn the short straw to interview me . . . "Examine me, write what you want in my file, but *don't tell me anything!* . . . and I'll see you in six months' time." I could not take any more negativity (or truth?).

With only a week to go to the appointment I woke with a start in the early hours of the morning. I calmly said to myself "Why go at all?" It made sense; I was not going to have an Operation so why put myself through a process which undermines my spirit, and wastes their time? I wrote an explanatory letter to the doctor and reception area and felt fabulously free. My energy returned and it was full steam ahead. Some friends thought I had completely lost my marbles (or lump?) and they may well be right. But as far as the feel good factor went it was the correct thing for me.

I had a further opportunity to investigate my need for 'aloneness' when a letter arrived from Conrad asking if I would be interested in training to be a Kaplan 'Interpreter'.

I telephoned him to ask for more details and was suitably impressed . . . and keen and eager to start (yesterday!).

"Anything else you need to know," enquired Conrad.

"Yes, how did you know I was the youngest in the family?"

"Because of your charm."

(*Me? Charming!*)

"But, I was feeling rattled and tired when we first met, I think I was even a little annoyed, and showed it."

"Yes, but you did it charmingly."

The night before I started the training I thought I would listen again to the tape made at my session with Conrad Kaplan in May.

It was still very powerful . . . too powerful. I'd heard myself relate the events many many times, but to be able to step back and listen as a third person is a strange and powerful catalyst. "Poor little sod," I thought, then realised I'd been talking about myself.

Creepy, but very salutary.

What was even more creepy was that as I drove home after

the first training weekend I remembered that years ago Ellis had told me his earliest memory. I started to analyse it . . .

I froze.

Wow!

I know it's not advisable to start a sentence . . . 'If I knew then what I know now . . .' but, I don't believe I would have hit my head against the brick wall of Ellis's theme for longer than it took to investigate further . . . then run as fast as I could in the other direction.

I didn't need proof that this method was amazing but I was stunned at this insight into Ellis's behaviour. I could almost begin to forgive him all over again.

I was hooked.

I really wanted to practice as much as I could, so scoured the horizon for any friend who hadn't ducked out of sight quickly enough. By this time they were used to me trying out new therapies but this one involved a 'client'. Slowly but surely I ran to ground various friends and 'Kaplanised' them.

They are still my friends!

Charles was delighted at my total absorption of the technique and offered himself as a 'client' for me to practice. "You never know," he said, "my life-theme may have moved on."
      It hadn't.

(*We're still doomed . . . if we're not careful.*)

I was battling with the postscript, which was in danger of becoming another full-length book.

"How is it going to end?" enquired Charles one day.

"It's a smaller version of the main book. It starts with a hospital visit and hopefully will end with us drinking in the New Year. If in reality it doesn't end that way I will just use poetic licence and make it happen," I said, looking at him in an inquisitive manner. "Of course we'll be together New Year's Eve . . .

(*My internal alarm clock relaxed*)

" . . . but I may go to America for Christmas."

(Silence)

(*Really? That's what you think!*)

All I could see was that our themes were on a head-to-head collision course. I could feel the hurt, rage and fury begin to stir in me again, but now I was not prepared to let it smoulder and grow.

I made a decision.

If he went to America at Christmas then I would have no alternative than to end the 'relationship'. A course of action I should have done many many times in the past thirty years but never dared.

Now there was no choice, no dare about it; on behalf of my breast I could not afford to feel dumped, abandoned or unwanted again, even if that was not the intention.

He decided (with no knowledge of my decision) not to go to America.

(*Whew!*)

But I fired a warning shot across his bow, on behalf of my health, and felt good. Now all I had to do was to keep up my resolve. If I didn't *I* was doomed.

The Kaplan training was intensive and exhausting and I readily and hungrily consumed every particle of Conrad's spirit. At the end of each session with our keen and eager volunteers we would turn to him to round it off in his inimitable style. His distinctive husky voice, occasionally erupting into a bronchial cough, graciously acknowledged our insights and interpretations. But then, with great ease and charm (he was also the youngest), he would present a perfect, concise life-theme to the amazed volunteer.

(*Impressed, impressed.*)

As a way of saying thank you to him for giving me so much I presented him with a vapouriser and an essential oil mix for his throaty cough.

"Conrad, you are the only man I've met who has dramatically changed my life . . . and I still *like* you."

He laughed.

We all agreed to meet in January '95. I couldn't wait, but in the meantime I rushed around practising and practising.

This is what I wanted to do.

I felt at home.

I felt part of a group.

I felt needed.

I felt wonderful.

On 12th December Marcus phoned to tell me that Conrad had died that morning.

"It's not fair!!!!!!!!!!!" I wanted to scream.

And scream I did.

I made one important decision: Conrad's method must not be allowed to die with him.

I had even interested Ellis in the method after I had boldly told him that I could have saved both of us a lot of heart ache and bother had I known about our themes.

He asked how he could try the method himself, especially as it was 'user friendly'.

"Sure, but I think you need the full-strength original Kaplan."

(*Sounds like a cigarette!*)

Ellis had made an appointment with Conrad for January but had been informed that it could not now take place. He was referred to Sheila, who had intended to refer him to a Jenny Cole . . . Wow!!

With good grace all round the implications of this incestuous encounter was revealed amidst smiles and horror. In fact I managed to have a very pleasant conversation with Ellis about the Kaplan method, my hopes for the future regarding my work and, although I think he already knew, I told him about the book. He was positive and encouraging yet I could detect some apprehension in his voice.

"By the way . . . I have changed your name as you don't really come out of it at all squeaky-clean."

"That's very good of you."

"Well, after all, it is about my emergence from the depths of life, not the person who helped dig the hole."

"Quite. By the way, may I ask what you have called me in the book?"

"Ellis."

"Mmm, not bad, thanks."

When I put down the phone I realised that I'd become neither emotional nor angry nor stressed talking to this man, who had participated so fully in turning my world upside down. This certainly was progress. After all he had inspired me to find answers to my life and therefore made the whole book possible.

(!)

Christmas whizzed into action.

The local (but brilliant) choir sang carols around the local (but useless) Christmas lights ... I attended a fiftieth birthday party ... and a 50's style 'do' where my wig was once again thrown across the room ... Christmas Eve Charles and I retraced our steps of the previous year and ate at a restaurant before attending Midnight Mass at St Michaels where a small but talented choir sang to perfection ... I visited Del and Stan again (sans Father Christmas outfit), Jeff and Anna and my sister's extended family ... the tiny chicken was eaten this year by human beings, while a small furry cat who had travelled with me through such pain and horror sat watching our every mouthful.

The next day she was bundled into her basket and taken to Jo's, where she immediately scooped open the door of the small bedroom and dived under the bed.

(*Guilt, guilt.*)

Charles was getting worried; he knew that I would love to have a New Year's Eve celebration of Champagne, fireworks and a conversation relating to 1994 but was unsure of how to achieve it.

"What do you want me to say or do?" he enquired urgently earlier in the day.

"Don't worry ... it's normal for people to look back on the year ... just let is happen," I assured him.

It was perfect.

We sat on our balcony sipping Champagne.

"You've had one hell of a year. You must be so proud of yourself," he said.

I thought back over what I had done.

"Yes, I've achieved so much this year *and* I've started a butterfly collection."

"Butterflies?" he queried, being unsure where this conversation was going.

"Yes, butterflies."

Years ago when teaching in Holloway prison one of the more mature students explained the concept of happiness to a group of demanding teenagers. Happiness, she said, is like a butterfly. You cannot tell when one is going to land on you or how long it will stay. But if one does decide to honour you with its presence, appreciate it with all your heart.

Suddenly fireworks erupted into the night and were reflected in the marina beneath our window.

(*Oooh!*)

"Happy New Year, Jenny."

"Happy New Year, Charles," I said slowly uncrossing my fingers.

"Happy New Year."

Too simple.

Life is not like that.

There were no planned firework displays where we were staying and Champagne cost about one week's Invalidity Benefit . . . So New Year's Eve was spent in the company of some charming Irish people in Tunisia . . . and while the band played Beer Barrel Polka and Viva España we drank Sidi Saad, the local red wine.

(*!*)

It 's not what life dishes out to you that is important, it's what you do with it, and we flung ourselves into the exuberance of the moment.

As midnight approached . . . and passed . . . the band played on, while one or two sparklers were defiantly held aloft. Time marches on and doesn't stop for man-made celebrations.

(*How very true.*)

We retired to our room by 1 a.m.

"Hey! That's midnight in the UK," I announced.

Wrapped in a hotel blanket and still wearing my gold party crown, Charles opened the bottle of lukewarm, local 'champagne' we had purchased earlier (Medallion vert vin gazeifie!)

Suddenly a small firework display appeared above the roof tops of the marina but did not reflect in any of the available water.

The 'champagne' was disgusting.

I started to giggle.

At 1 a.m. we toasted the UK New Year with sparkling water.

"Happy New Year, Jenny."

"Happy New Year, Charles," I replied, adding another butterfly to my collection.

"Happy New Year."

BIBLIOGRAPHY

Copyright Acknowledgements.
Grateful acknowledgement is made for permission to reprint from
the following books.

Love, Medicine and Miracles
Bernie Siegal
Arrow.

An Evil Cradling
Brian Keenan
Vintage.

Medicine Cards
Sams and Carson
Bear & Co.

Why Men Hate Women
Adam Jukes
Free Association Books.

Beliefs
Tim Hallbom & Suzi Smith
Metamorphous Press.

Cancer and Leukaemia
Jan de Vries
Mainstream Publishing Co.

Cancer Journals
Audre Lorde
Sheba Feminist Publishing.

A–Z of Aromatherapy
Patricia Davis
CW Daniel.

Guide to self healing
Matthew Manning
Thorsons (HarperCollins).

(The New) Our Bodies, Ourselves
Phillips and Rakusen
Penguin.

Fragrant Pharmacy
Valerie Ann Worwood
Bantam Books.

Marie Claire magazine April 1993
"Can sharks provide a cure?"

Understanding breast cancer
BACUP self publication.

Walkabout Healing Handbook
(Australian Flower Essences)
Drs Vasudeva & Kadambii Barnao.

Other books of interest:

The dark side of the brain
Harry Oldfield and Roger Coghill
Element Books.

Understanding childhood memories
Conrad Kaplan
Oneworld Publications (1995)
distributed by Penguin.

Grace and Grit
Ken & Treya Wilber
Shambhala.

A woman's book of Herbs
A woman's book of shadows
Women Healers through history
Elizabeth Brooke
Women's Press.

Elizabeth Brooke runs seminars in medical astrology and related
topics at the Company of Astrologers:
6 Queens Sq, London WC1
0171 837 4410

Useful addresses and contacts:

Winfalcons
(For purple plates/Aura photos etc)
28/29 Ship St
Brighton, East Sussex
01273 728997

Autogenics
101 Harley St
London W1
0171 935 1811

Tyringham Naturapathic Clinic
Newport Pagnell
Buckinghamshire
MK16 9ER
01908 610450

Bristol Cancer Help Centre
Grove House
Cornwallis Grove
Clifton
Bristol
BS8 4PG
0117 974 3216

Australian Flower Essences
UK distributors:
Suite 1 Castle Farm
Clifton Rd
Deddington
Oxon OX15 0TP
01869 37349

Council for Acupuncture
179 Gloucester Place
London NW1 60X
0171 724 5756

Matthew Manning
P.O. Box 100
Bury St Edmunds
Suffolk IP29 4DE
01284 830222

Homeopathy
British Homeopathic Association
27a Devonshire St
London W1N 1RJ
0171 935 2163

BACUP
3 Bath Place
Rivington St
London EC2A 3JR

Bowen Technique
Mark Lester
Flat 5
Zenith Lodge
Etchingham Park Road
London N3 2DS
0181 349 4730

Julien Baker
01373 461873
Bowen technique UK co-ordinator

Kaplan Consulting Associates
Jenny Cole 0181 340 1514
Marcus Bolt 01923 777750
Ellen Alderton (Brussels) 32 2 648 9398

**International Society of Professional Aromatherapists
(ISPA)**
Hinckley & District Hospital and Health Centre
The Annexe
Mount Road
Hinckley
Leics LE10 1AG